QM Library
KU-334-523
23 1309947 4

The Little Universe of Man

Other works by Professor C. D. Darlington

CHROMOSOMES AND PLANT BREEDING
Macmillan, 1932

RECENT ADVANCES IN CYTOLOGY
Churchill, 1932

THE EVOLUTION OF GENETIC SYSTEMS
Cambridge University Press, 1939
Oliver and Boyd, 1958

THE FACTS OF LIFE
George Allen & Unwin, 1953

CHROMOSOME BOTANY AND THE ORIGINS OF CULTIVATED PLANTS
George Allen & Unwin, 1963

GENETICS AND MAN
George Allen & Unwin, 1964

RECENT ADVANCES IN CYTOLOGY (3RD ED.)
Churchill, 1965

THE CONFLICT OF SCIENCE AND SOCIETY
Watts, 1948

DARWIN'S PLACE IN HISTORY
Blackwell, 1959

THE EVOLUTION OF MAN AND SOCIETY
George Allen & Unwin, 1969

with K. Mather
THE ELEMENTS OF GENETICS
George Allen & Unwin, 1961

GENES, PLANTS AND PEOPLE
George Allen & Unwin, 1959

with E. K. Janaki Ammal
CHROMOSOME ATLAS OF CULTIVATED PLANTS
George Allen & Unwin, 1945

with A. P. Wylie
CHROMOSOME ATLAS OF FLOWERING PLANTS
George Allen & Unwin, 1956

with A. D. Bradshaw (edited)
TEACHING GENETICS
Oliver and Boyd, 1963, 1966

with L. F. La Cour
THE HANDLING OF CHROMOSOMES (6TH ED.)
George Allen & Unwin, 1976

The Little Universe of Man

C. D. Darlington, F.R.S.

London
GEORGE ALLEN & UNWIN
Boston Sydney

First published 1978

ISBN 0 04 570010 9

Printed in Great Britain
in 11 on 13 point Baskerville
at the Alden Press, Oxford

"One of the greatest reasons why so few people understand themselves is that most writers are always teaching men what they should be and hardly ever trouble their heads with telling them what they really are."
Mandeville: *The Fable of the Bees*. 1714

Contents

Figures

Tables and Time Charts

Preface

I address this book to those, mostly young, who are, as I am, dismayed by the present state and future prospects of mankind and the earth we live on. Many have sought for remedies but have been disappointed with what they have been offered. My present object is not to offer remedies, certainly not simple ones with easy labels. It is to explain how we may sort out, from the new knowledge that continually comes to us, what will help us and what may hinder or even destroy us.

In previous books I have tried to explain the biological assumptions we need to make in order to understand men. I have also tried to show how our history, human history, is an evolutionary process, one which continues today, and which we partly and unconsciously control. Now I am showing how the great stream of scientific knowledge, which is sweeping us forward into a dangerous future, is also telling us, if we care to read the evidence, which way we are going and which other ways we might be going.

The evidence that I am offering comes from the union of many sciences and from their applications to our own lives. Agriculture and medicine, education and economics in their connections with one another and with the four great continents Europe and America, Asia and Africa, these are what concern me. To discover and establish such connections demands work and thought from both the writer and the reader. But the reader, although he ought to be aware of them, will not need to have read my earlier works in order to follow what I am saying here. My references will tell him the sources if he wishes to find them.

The lesson I hope he will learn from my account is that a great deal of our immediate future can be foretold. And our remote destiny is also certain. But there is a vast middle area before us, one which concerns us and our children, in which we, by our own knowledge, judgement, and character, have a part to play.

C. D. Darlington
Botany School and
Magdalen College
Oxford

September 1977

Acknowledgements

I am indebted to the University College of Wales in Aberystwyth for the invitation to give the Gregynog Lectures in March 1975 on which this book is based and particularly to the Principal, Sir Goronwy Daniel.

I am also indebted to the Leverhulme Trust for their support of the research needed for this undertaking with the award of an Emeritus Fellowship in August 1975.

Beyond my acknowledgements in the text, I should like to add my thanks to the correspondents in many countries who have helped me in my work. I also owe a debt to certain works whose breadth and depth exclude minute reference: for example the essays of that great medical philosopher Wilfred Trotter (1872–1939). Likewise I owe much to two colleagues who have since died, the late Sir Cyril Burt and Sir Wilfred Le Gros Clark. I may also add that, although I parted company with him over communism, it was in long youthful discussions with the late J. B. S. Haldane, twenty years earlier, that my three books on Man had their roots.

C.D.D.

Chapter 1

The Evolution of Man

I *Our Book of Genesis*

A hundred years ago it became clear that all living creatures sprang by descent from common ancestors. This idea of evolution was irresistible for all organisms except man and great labours were devoted to showing that man also was related to all other animals, by way of the monkeys whose form and behaviour came closest to his own. Now for us the problem is transformed. In the details of the structure of his blood man is seen to be as close to the great apes as they are to one another. Likewise, in his chromosomes, for although man has 23 pairs instead of the ape's 24, the connections between them can be traced equally clearly. Again, thanks to the discoveries of the Leakeys, we can trace back man's ancestors in Africa, where two of the other apes still live, for some 5 million years. And a great variety of human forms have been found in Java up to a million years old overlapping with Aborigines who were still living in Australia only 40,000 years ago.

The questions that we now have to ask are therefore no longer the ones that still puzzled our predecessors thirty years ago. First we want to know why human apes half a million generations ago began to change in the long-term direction of man while their relatives remained apes without any such directed change or sustained trend. So that the chimpanzee and the gorilla today stand where they stood, and do what they did, 5 or more million years ago while man is and does something decidedly new.

The succession of events in human history has come to be understood following the discovery by Raymond Dart, fifty years ago, that the earliest men, having nothing very remarkable in the way of a brain, had lost the great canine teeth of the ground-dwelling apes and baboons and had embarked on a course of making tools which took over the work of those teeth. Did these tools in some sense take control of human evolution and lead to the astonishing development of man's brain?

At that time there were already anatomists, like Elliot Smith, who could say that man's hands taught his eyes and his brain how to do things. But what did they mean by this? Their phrases were formed after the pattern and on the assumptions of Lamarck. The famous founder of evolutionary theory in France believed that the giraffe, having by an effort of will stretched his neck over many generations, had permanently lengthened his neck. The history of man's brain and skull has indeed been shown to follow a direction. His brain during 2 million years has gradually increased in size from one pint to three (Figs. 1.1, 1.2). At the same time it has, of course, changed its internal structure and proportions enormously enlarging the cerebral hemispheres and compacting their convolutions. Now we have no doubt from our knowledge and experiments with the whole range of living things that this is the result, not of an effort of the will, but of the action of natural selection. Bigger and better brains have continually proved to be useful in keeping men and women alive. Before we ask how this has happened, however, let us look at the evidence in more detail.

In the first place notice that the common ancestors of men and apes some 10 million years ago, living their largely vegetarian lives partly in trees and partly on the ground, were all prepared by their character to experiment with new ways of life. Life in trees had given them a co-ordination of hand and eye through the brain which all monkeys show. They had expressive faces and voices; their hoots, grunts, and whimpers could well be the forerunners of human communication. They had a more than incipient ability to walk on their hind legs. They reproduced by single births. There was therefore none of that competition between multiplets which (as Ford has pointed out) in most mammals favours rapid growth at the expense of the slow growth they need for the full development of the brain and its education. In addition to all these, some stocks had developed a continuous sexual life which in gibbons and in men holds couples together in a way unknown to other apes.

When we go further, however, we find that man faced altogether new problems in developing his coordination of hand and eye and speech. All the movements of the two sides of the vertebrate body had been marshalled by the two sides of the cerebrum, the right hemisphere controlling the left side and *vice versa*. All mammals up to the ape had been indifferently skilled with right and left hands; they had been ambidextrous. But man's skill evidently demanded a specialized superiority of one hand. In all races of modern man and presumably therefore in their common ancestors a preference, an hereditary preference, developed for the right hand. This property was connected through the eyes with a sense of space: with a few left-handed exceptions skill became dexterity.

Now we find that not only the right hand but speech also has in man come to be controlled by the left half of the brain. With a few left-handed individuals the control is the other way round. These connections were first inferred by the French neurologist Broca in 1861 from the effects which follow from damage, as from a stroke, to one side of the brain or the other. They show why man's new activities demanded a larger brain and a longer, slower development.

II *Sex*

Comparisons of the mental character of boys and girls lead to a further remarkable conclusion. It is that the development of the individual brain, although of course variable in each sex, follows different lines in the two sexes. The faculty of speaking develops earlier and more strongly in the female; in the male the visual and spatial faculties have the advantage. These differences, foreshadowed in the embryo, persist in maturity. Thus the two sexes evolving in parallel have also diverged. They have become adapted to fill different and complementary roles in the family. The woman through speech is better equipped to communicate and to teach the child and indeed generally to hold society together; the man is better equipped to go out into the world. His longer legs fit him for running and he is adapted to make the rapid movements of throwing and catching, hunting and fighting, which soon became his predominant activities when man and woman together left the trees to live on the ground and to roam the earth.

These differences in activity between the two sexes are the subject of varied evolution in other apes and monkeys. In the gibbon which stuck to the trees the monogamous male and female remained most alike in body and probably in mind. The gorilla which came down to earth diverged into a powerful protective polygamous male and a light little female half his size but still not notably contrasted in mental character. In man the divergence was based both on his brain and his body although to different degrees in different races.

We may ask at this point how the two sexes can evolve by diverging so as to complement one another in many different ways. This complementarity has come to dominate man's social, domestic, and reproductive life. It has arisen by several steps in evolution each of which corresponds to a step in the development of the individual.

The first step was taken at the beginning of sex itself 3000 million years ago. Then the female had to produce eggs large enough to give

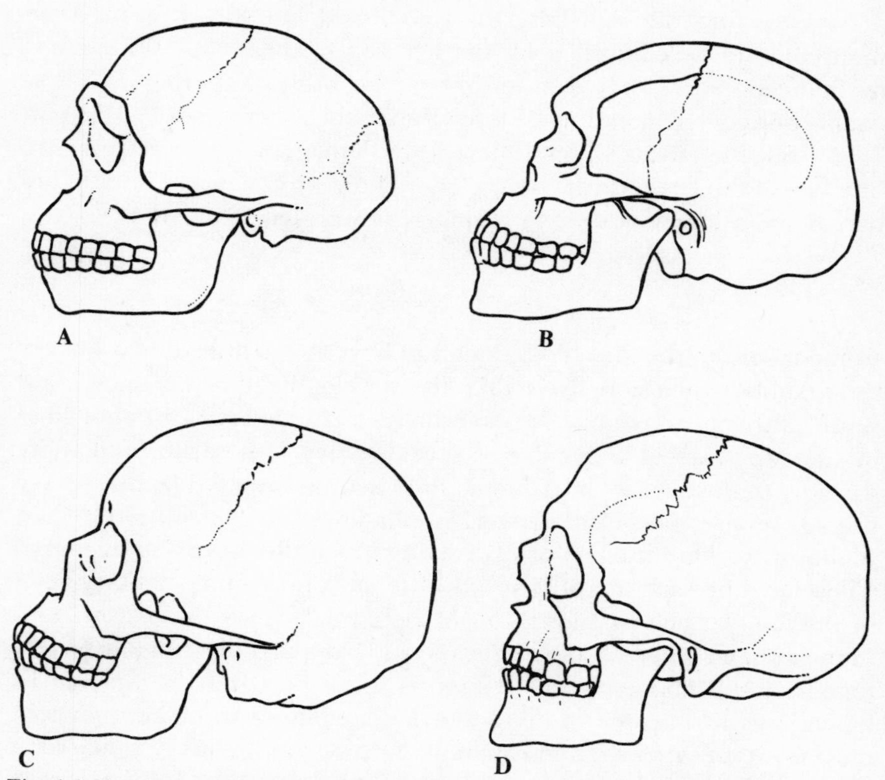

Fig. 1.1 Side views of human skulls: A, Pekin man, *Sinanthropus*, variously dated between half and one and a half million years old: a reconstructed cast from the Oxford University Museum. B, C, and D, modern men, Australian, African, and European from Tylor's *Primitive Culture*, 1871 (drawn by Rosemary Wise)

the embryo a start, eggs which stay put while the male had to produce sperm small enough to get to the eggs. The difference between the two sexes in man we can trace back in evolution to the beginning of the mammals. In the individual it arises at the moment when the sperm enters the egg and fertilizes it. Half these fertilized eggs have two large X chromosomes and grow up as females. The other half have an X and a smaller Y. They grow up as males, the hybrid sex as we may say, producing two kinds of sperm, with X and with Y. This is the second step.

Consider what this means for heredity. Brothers and sisters have the same parents, the same ancestors, but they owe their different character to different chromosomes in visibly different sperm, that is to a different heredity. It is on account of this hereditary difference that the two sexes could be selectively adapted in evolution to take over different and complementary roles in the family and in society.

The third step in the divergent development of the sexes is taken when the Y chromosome causes the young male embryo to develop reproductive organs, the testes, which produce hormones circulating in the blood which in turn modify the structure of the male embryo including (as Jost and Harris have recently shown) the structure of his brain, by a sequence of interactions continuing after birth, indeed up to and beyond sexual maturity.

The fourth step in the divergence or differentiation of the sexes begins to be taken in the first few days after birth when the different structure of the brain interacting with the rest of the body begins to produce male behaviour in the male and female behaviour in the female, a difference soon recognized by the experienced mother.

If we now look at the evolution of man and woman in the light of this new knowledge (the harvest, much of it, of the last ten years), we see that the process as a whole has an interwoven connectedness. At the beginning of the history of man and woman there was the habit of a continuous sexual interest. The gorilla and the chimpanzee have little sense of territory or property and only a priority in their dealings with the opposite sex, little sense indeed of love and hatred. But man and woman were continuously interested in one another and came as individuals to have property in one another. The basis was established for continuous, cooperative activity and complementary evolution. It is indeed probable that monogamy, although rarely absolute, has been the predominant form of sexual relationship, the continuous phase, throughout human evolution and from it all other relations are deviant or derivative. It may well have been so because monogamy is the most advantageous evolutionary relationship, the extreme expression of individual selection.

In taking this view I am returning in one respect to Darwin's approach since his account of the *Descent of Man*, we may recall, was attached to his theory of sexual selection. I am also accepting Haldane's view that the reversal of mating posture to face to face was the basis of the evolution of the surpassing beauty of the female and hence of the human body; and Morris's view that loss of hair was a result of the same selective process. Nor am I forgetting my own argument (foreshadowed by the author of *Fanny Hill*) that pubic hair was developed not only as an ornament but also as a protection in the new circumstances and with the new importance and frequency of human mating.

These, of course, are not facts; they are conjectures, but conjectures like Darwin's and like some others I shall set out, which must be kept in mind unless evidence arises to the contrary.

III *Breeding*

The reader will notice now that this predominantly sexual evolution is something wide apart from the ordinary processes by which organisms adapt themselves to their changing environments. Here the two sexes are adapting themselves to one another. The female is the environment of the male, and *vice versa*. The situation is internal to the species. This is even more evident when we come to one of man's most remarkable discoveries, once thought to be unique among animals, the incest taboo.

The incest taboo is the instinct and custom and moral law which inhibits members of the same family, brought up together, from having sexual intercourse with one another. It involves, together with the principles of instinct and heredity, a third principle discovered in plants. This was the principle of self-sterility to the study of which Darwin devoted three books.

The principle, as we now know it, is that in nearly all plants, from a mildew to the cabbage or the fruit tree which it infests, there is a faculty of disfavouring incest. It is an hereditary faculty due to some well-identified genes which have themselves evolved along with the evolution of all plants. Thus all these species of plants, which are so often hermaphrodite and therefore in danger of self-fertilization, have developed an internal device which inhibits inbreeding. Natural selection, in doing this, has done something to heredity which benefits not the individual but its descendants—in perpetuity. How does this apply to man?

When man had come to have a long-dependent, slow-growing infancy, and hence to have and to understand abiding family relationships, he could not, like a lion or a baboon, allow the family to be broken up to ensure outbreeding. He was therefore in danger (like a plant) of inbreeding. His tribes were in danger of splitting up into numerous family groups which could easily become new, separate, stabilized, inbred species. This is what happens to plants which lose their self-sterility. The cohering family which had been the means of advance for man might have opened the way to a calamity. Indeed this may well have happened in many groups, sporadically, at an early stage of his history, as it has happened in other successful animal species. Failure, due to inbreeding, may well have been responsible for the disappearance of many of those early species of men; whence the gap between man and the apes.

In animals generally an instinctive dispersal of the progeny is the method by which a habit of outbreeding is ensured. Man, preserving his family, could achieve this result only by developing an instinctive revulsion against breeding between kindred who stayed together. Such a revulsion or rejection has been noticed by Konrad Lorenz in geese. Evidently in man such an incest-rejecting instinct could develop by genetic recombination if it were favoured by its selective advantage, the same advantage that Darwin found in hermaphrodite plants.

The descendants of an incest-rejecting tribe would expand and diversify and by outbreeding would build up the variability and adaptability needed to colonize the world as one species. All this great community would be inter-fertile; all individuals would have 46 chromosomes; the whole mass would contain enough variation to make a hundred species of any other ordinary animal. It would, indeed it did, become a *super-species*.

So it is that the rejection of inbreeding has prevented the human species falling apart. Colour and smell mutations might easily have split it. So indeed might exchanges of pieces between chromosomes for these, as we shall see, continually occur in man although they can never establish themselves.

By developing an instinct favouring outbreeding man secured the unity of his species or super-species and its capacity for variation which together enabled him to occupy successively the six continents of the world. But how can natural selection, sexual selection, or any kind of selection favour a property which can show its advantage only in later generations? The answer is that every improvement in the mechanism of heredity, in the organization of breeding, in the system of reproduction, acts only by its effect over long generations in time and over large groups in space. The scent of the moth and the song of the bird, the chromosomes at mitosis and meiosis with their X's and their Y's, just as much as the tribal rites and rituals in man have no meaning for the survival of the individual. They are parts of the coordinated, adjusted, adapted totality of what I call the *genetic system*. And the genetic system of man evolving with man, we shall recognize as the key to the understanding of his past and to the making of his future evolution.

IV *The Brain in Action*

The steps by which the brain has taken over the guidance or direction of evolutionary change may be put in chronological order. There are four of them. The first was clearly indicated by Sherrington already in 1907. Sherrington, contrary to the fashion of his contemporaries, was thinking in strictly Darwinian terms such as require no reservations from us today. A mobile animal must have a long axis with a front end, a back end, a head, and a tail. It must be like a worm rather than a starfish. Its arrangements for communication, its nervous system, must

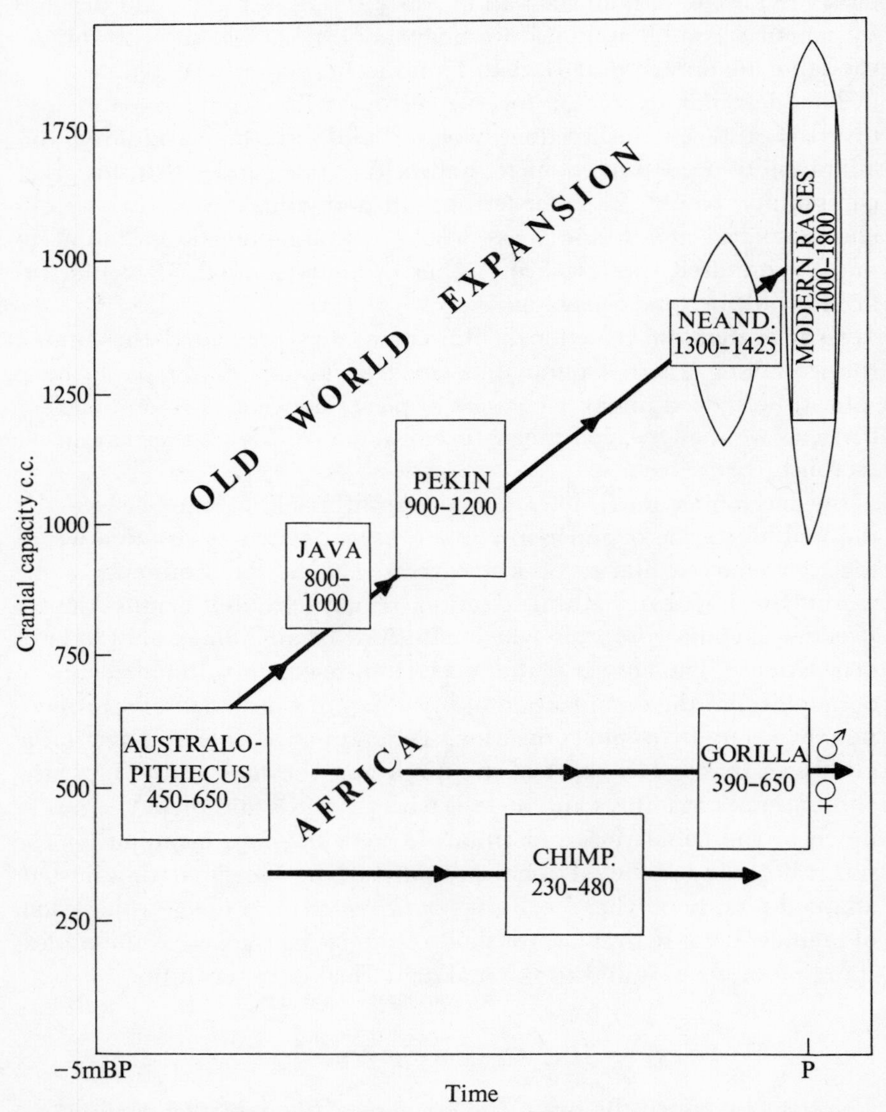

Fig. 1.2 The evolution of increased cranial capacity in man contrasted with its stability in the anthropoid apes (after Holloway, Tobias, Wood-Jones, and others). Note: the difference in cranial capacity between the sexes, as with their total body size, varies among modern races

then be pointed to where it is going, to the front; they must be coordinated in the head where its sensory organs, eyes, ears, and nose must be concentrated. Every evolutionary advance had to come in the head and the sum of these advances was found to constitute a special arrangement of nerves, the brain. Only in this way Sherrington argues later, in 1929, could the individual organism master his environment or increase his mastery of it. He might have added that for movement the brain had to be two-sided, bilateral.

It is not surprising, therefore, that the succession in evolution of fishes, reptiles, and mammals should show a progressive enlargement and differentiation of the brain and the progressive development and bilateralization we have seen in the forepart of the brain where higher and higher possibilities of conditioning, of association, are realized. Finally, in mammals the sight, sound, and smell functions are coordinated in the cerebrum, where a deep differentiation into layers of grey matter or cortex develops, whose arrangement requires a greatly extended and folded surface; hence the walnut-like convolutions which reach their extreme in man. These developments go with an increased but highly variable capacity for learning to which the reflex and instinctive actions of the older parts, the inner and hind parts, of the brain are subordinated.

How then can we see the course of our history? A thousand million years of vertebrate evolution culminated in a second step, the 50 million years of primate evolution, which gave us the apes with their coordination of hand and eye, which in turn laid the foundations for the making of tools but took them, or most of them, no further.

There followed the 5 million years in which many stocks of African apes competed in the arts of tool-making, one of which triumphed over and destroyed the rest. He had to slow down his development to allow for the growth of his brain and in order to do this he had to begin by having only single births. And having done so his two-footed walk and run allowed him to carry his larger brain. A main factor in this success was, we cannot doubt, his having developed the faculty of speech which gave precision and continuity to thought and so brought with it recognition of individuality and kinship, rejection of inbreeding, consciousness of past and future, of life and death, of cause and effect.

Finally, there have been the last 50,000 years, the last 2000 generations, in which we have been able to use these faculties to colonize the world, to transform it, to make it our world.

Evolution, described in this way, appears to have a continuity of principle. The principle is that nervous organization, next to the chromosomes themselves, stands at the centre of organization in the vertebrate. Improvements in nervous organization, that is above all in the brain, have evidently been the driving force in evolutionary change throughout the vertebrates. Of course there have been frequent mistakes and setbacks. Groups of animals, and indeed groups of men, have run and may still be running into blind alleys from which no advance was or will be possible. Obviously the birds could not enlarge their brains if they were to be airborne. Even four-footed mammals were restricted by what they could carry in their heads. A thin skull, as Baker has made clear, was the last improvement to be made in some races of men. Since enlargement in size gives the greatest scope for improvement, as Huxley and Rensch have argued, it is not surprising that our new line had to start from small beginnings.

Ultimately, however, in our particular common ancestors the opportunity came to exploit the full possibilities of the brain and it was taken. Processes of variation and selection were responsible and are still at work among us. The materials on which they were working, the chromosomes of the apes and of men are still there to be seen. The powers of the cerebral cortex are still active in giving us capacities to learn and understand. These capacities vary among individuals. They enable some individuals not only to learn but to invent. Some individuals design new tools, suggest new connections, plan new activities, and foresee new consequences. They can explain, persuade, and teach their fellows and their children some of whom can learn to do these things.

The experience of teachers shows that there are others who cannot learn. The experience of parents suggests that the difference in this capacity to learn, this intelligence, is hereditary. There is indeed no other way in which we can understand either the difference in intelligence between man and the ape or the means by which it arose. Now, if intelligence was useful or advantageous to the individual or the group, and if it was hereditary, it was bound to be favoured by selection. Succeeding generations would then produce more intelligent individuals and more of them. The question then arises; will one increase in intelligence favour, or will it disfavour the occurrence of another? Will the effect of selection *feed back* positively or negatively through heredity? The answer to these questions must decide a great part of our attitude to the past and the future of man.

V *Invention and Feedback*

The idea of feedback was introduced to the study of evolution long before the word itself came into use. It was on an historic occasion which is worth recalling since we shall have to return to the idea in several connections.

It happened when Alfred Russel Wallace was advancing the original argument (in 1858 and in parallel with Darwin) that natural selection could be responsible for the origin of species. 'The action of this principle,' he wrote, 'is exactly like that of the centrifugal governor of the steam engine which checks and corrects any irregularities almost before they become evident.'

By this analogy, however, Wallace was explaining how selection, so far from promoting the change responsible for the origin of new species, could prevent any change occurring at all. The governor of the steam engine acts by negative feedback and its analogy is with what we call stabilizing selection, a process which is continually working to prevent individuals breaking down or species breaking up. But this process was of no interest to Darwin or to Wallace. What they wanted was that selection should reinforce and establish change—by positive rather than negative feedback.

Positive feedback in evolution may be said to occur where the success of one genetic change favours its repetition and so produces a trend, a direction, of evolution in which, disconcertingly, the consequences

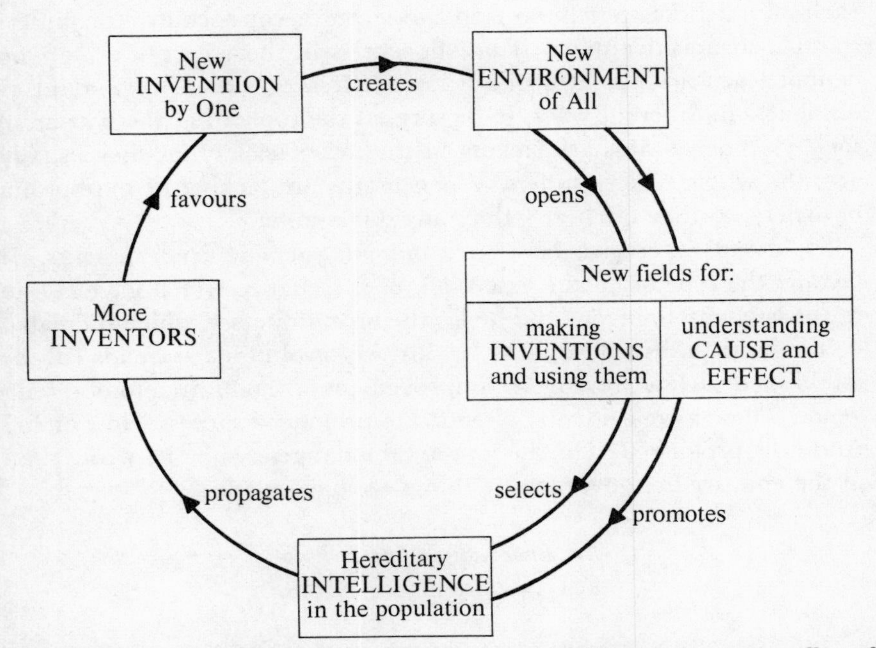

Fig. 1.3 Positive feedback cycle in the evolution of intelligence due to the effect of invention in favouring the inventor and his kindred (after Darlington, 1969)

are assimilated to the causes of change. This is what, we believe, underlies the long trend in the development of the brain of vertebrates, of mammals, of monkeys, and finally of man.

The commonest trends in evolution are those giving increase in size. They yield the easiest advantage, an advantage which, as Rensch has shown, may lead to either success or failure. The success we see in the giraffe's neck and the horse's foot. The failure we see in the huge dinosaurs. They were the ones that took the cash of initial success and let the credit go. In this light we shall have to weigh the prospects for man.

The feedback principle, positive or negative, can be seen to underlie or express almost every kind of human activity and both the processes and the results of all human evolution. We ought therefore to look at it from many points of view. Every useful, workable, or effective human invention from the first bone tool to the last computer, alters the environment of the inventor. Not only this, if it survives, if it can be communicated, it then alters the environments of his children. If they monopolize it, as they so often try to do, it benefits them and their descendants. If they in turn hand it on, it benefits all who can learn it, or copy it and use it. It may do harm but that comes later.

The lesson of history is that there have been a succession of inventions each of which has put those who can learn or copy, control or understand it at an advantage. If intelligence is in short supply those who cannot learn are put at a disadvantage. It makes them redundant or obsolete—in different ways, to be sure, at the top and at the bottom of society. When brains are lacking at the top of society, as they usually are, the whole society suffers. When brains are lacking at the bottom of society, as they often are, the individuals suffer.

So invention creates new environments, genetic environments. It favours the repetition, the extension, of the change which gave rise to it, the capacity to invent and hence the invention itself which it created —it favours positive feedback. In this way evolutionary trends can be established such as have led to improvement of the brain and of intelligence. These have evidently often led to prolonged success. How often? And how prolonged? Goethe foresaw the dangers when he wrote that, in the end, we are governed by things we have made:

Am Ende hängen wir doch ab
Von Creaturen die wir machten.

The same foreboding is seen in Mary Shelley's fable of Frankenstein. There may, to be sure, be neutral situations. The measurement of time, the counting of days and of hours has been indispensable for finely regulating civilization, above all modern industrial civilization. But it demanded the timepiece which from being the servant became the master and controlled the direction in which industrial man was bound to evolve, to be the slave of his own clock.

It is a long way back from these achievements to the improvement of the horse's foot or the human leg. But they also evolved in a directed way. They enlarged the field, the ecological niche, the natural resources, that could be exploited.

So, in the evolution of the vertebrates, the brain coordinates the actions not of one organ but of the whole body. In man it has gone beyond this limited scope to transform his environment, to create a succession of new environments—and almost unawares to destroy many old ones.

VI *The Origin of Man*

Before leaving the beginnings of our history we may properly ask ourselves whether there was any one decisive step to which we can attribute the origin of man. It is a more practical question than might appear. For we can now look at the whole group from which man sprang, the monkeys, the order of Primates, and see what has been happening to them over the last 50 million years or so of their evolution. They consist today of 200 species showing almost the whole range of their own history from the very small, simple, and rapidly developing tree-shrews to our own complicated kindred the great apes, from weighing a few ounces to nearly a quarter of a ton.

The Primates show, more clearly than almost any other animal group, one of the most important evolutionary trends, that towards increase of size. With this trend might have come a change in the proportion of parts of the body—the brain might be taken as an example. But quite another kind of effect is the inevitable lengthening of the life cycle in larger animals carrying with it a restriction of the rate of propagation, a loss of fecundity or of multiplying power.

The effect of this trend is shown by the chromosomes. The small Primates succeed in freely varying their chromosome numbers, creating new numbers and thus reshuffling their genetic materials. This flexibility is to be seen even in different races of the same species (Table 1.1). Such evolutionary experiment may have produced the great apes but in them it has been brought to a standstill. The reason is that it upsets chromosome pairing at germ-cell formation. This is a serious matter during the period when the new chromosome arrangement is

Table 1.1 *Primate evolution: chromosome numbers in the monkey families (after Napier and Napier, 1967; and Chiarelli and Capanna, 1973)*

Groups	*n** 10	..	17	.	19	.	.	22	.	24	.	26	.	28	.	30	.	32	.	34	.	36	...	40
PRO-SIMIANS																								
Tree Shrews, Lemurs, etc.					1	—	—	3	1	2	2	3	1	1	2	3	7	—	2	1	—	—	—	2
29 spp. +2 races																								
NEW WORLD MONKEYS																								
Capuchin group	1	—	5	—	—	—	—	4	4	1	1	3	4	-	-	-	1							
23 spp. +1 race																								
Marmoset group								2	10	—	—													
12 spp.																								
OLD WORLD MONKEYS																								
Macaque group							1	—	—	1	—	—	2	—	1	3	—	1	—	3	—	3		
14 spp.																								
Colobus group								8	-	1	1													
9 spp. +1 race																								
Baboons: 26 spp.							26	—	—	—														
Gibbons: 6 spp.								4	—	—	1	1												
great Apes: 3 spp.								—	—	3	—													
Man (all races)								—	1	—	—													
TOTAL: 124 spp. +4 races	1	—	5	—	1	—	27	21	16	8	5	7	7	1	3	6	8	1	2	4	—	3	—	2

* *n* is the number of chromosome pairs or haploid number.

Notes

1 Three species of the lower groups showed racial differences in chromosome numbers, as follows: Five races of *Lemurus fulvus* had 24, 29, and 30, two races of *Cebus capucinus* had 26 and 27, and two races of *Cercopithecus nictitans* had 33 and 35. For individual variation in number in man, see Chapter 3.

2 The general concentration of numbers in all groups in the range between 21 and 25 (with man in the middle) indicates the continuity, coherence, and stability of the Primate order during the 50 million years' life of man's arboreal ancestors.

establishing itself. For while the two still interbreed the new type must compete with the old. The loss of fertility is something which a slow reproducer cannot bear.

It is, therefore, not surprising that in the course of the last 10 or 20 million years of the ape–man history only one change of chromosome number has succeeded; this was the fusion of two chromosomes so that the haploid set of 24 in the Apes became the 23 of Man. We know how such an event takes place. It has to occur in one cell in the direct germ line, male or female. It is a precise, unique, and unrepeatable change. It must therefore have been the one crucial identifiable event in the origin of man. And the whole of mankind ever since must be descended from that one original cell. Further, since the change was, in its short-term effect on fertility, inevitably disadvantageous, it must have been linked with other genetic changes of long-term advantage, entailing a break with the past. We do not know what those other changes were; whether they were combined changes of structure and behaviour, perhaps connected with man's emergence from the forest, or with his becoming a hunter. The fossil record if it were perfect might indeed appear continuous. Only the chromosome record, if we had it, would show a break. For that break in that cell, we may genuinely say, was the origin of man.

At the opposite pole to the single cell origin is the population question: what was the smallest number of interbreeding individuals who were man's common ancestors before his stock split up into the modern races about a million years ago? It might have been one pair (as Genesis tells us). But probability favours many thousands.

Another large question remains which we cannot yet properly answer. Did the original stock of men break up into species which conflicted and hence extinguished one another without hybridization? Or did man remain a species whose interfertile races conflicted but also merged by hybridization? Or was mankind always, as we are today, precariously balanced between these contrasted alternatives? These are questions we can keep in mind in considering our past and also our future.

Chapter 2

The Making of Society

I *Paleo Climax and Paleo Relics*

When we see man 20,000 years ago, having completed the colonization of the six continents, which he had begun a million years earlier, it is time for us to look back and survey his position. The species was now divided into great races which we can still recognize today because they were so separated in space that hybridization between them was almost excluded. The tropical regions were cut off from one another also by their relations with their own special human diseases. They were all undergoing evolution.

We can, however, make a number of useful generalizations about the species as it then existed, and about the people of that time. Always they made their living by hunting, fishing, and collecting; always they divided their pursuits variously between the sexes. They had domesticated dogs and could often weave fibres and grind grain. They undoubtedly lived in tribal breeding groups which were organized universally, but with vast diversity of detail, by mythical beliefs and magical or religious rituals. Such beliefs and rituals held the tribe together, morally, economically, and genetically, by explaining their unified ancestral origins, and sustaining them against their fear of the unpredictable forces of the external world, their fear of nature, of other men, and of the dead. In developing these rituals and beliefs, strangers with magical powers sometimes were able to break through the tribal boundaries. And, as it still does in New Guinea, trade by barter often brought neighbouring tribes peaceably together.

How did these people think? There is no doubt that they had certain advantages over civilized and even over agricultural man. Those on the advancing frontier of human settlement must have been endowed with that boundless causal curiosity, childish curiosity as Lorenz has put it, which enabled them to master new environments, to observe (artistically), to know (scientifically) and to exploit (managerially) new plants, animals, and minerals. But almost universally they must still have had the primitive mind which Lévy-Bruhl has described; the pre-logical or semi-rational mind which fails to separate the individual from the group and which, pursuing causes with misguided zeal, argues *post hoc ergo propter hoc*.

There are several qualifications we must make in using this notion of the primitive mind. One is that some men must often then as now have seen further into the connections of cause and effect. The witch-doctor, medicine man, or shaman (according to the continent) who was also the first priest and the first politician must always have kept one step ahead of his client if he was to maintain his authority.

Another is that our civilized societies have never excluded the primitive mind. There is a proportion of people in all societies, differing as between the sexes and as between races or classes, who see no sense in the definitions, connections, and inferences which their teachers hold to be self-evident. Indeed in all societies there is more pre-logical thinking than we like to admit. Civilization, we may say, has advanced only at the cost of a struggle between science and superstition working on the intelligence of the participants, a struggle of whose progress the legal status of torture and the social status of astrology might serve as indicators. Advanced societies, therefore, are those so stratified as to keep the primitive mind in a subordinate position. In this way individual responsibility and the rules of evidence allow with fluctuating success the development of law and the organization of knowledge, and all that follows from these practices.

II *The Root Growers*

Just as Paleolithic history or evolution, with its already quite varied human activity and knowledge, was reaching its climax a crisis occurred in the climatic history of our planet. Between 14,000 and 8000 B.C. the ice cap which covered northern Asia, Europe, and America began to melt uncovering vast new areas which were occupied year after year by northward migrating peoples. It is one of the few undisputed facts about the origin of agriculture that men began to form permanent settlements depending on their cultivation or at least utilization of plants for food at about this time, a time which can now be approximately dated by radiocarbon testing of organic remains. Where did this happen?

Paleolithic people evidently discovered the conditions of settlement in many different parts of the world. The origins and natures, durations and consequences, of their first settlements are uncertain. What concern us, however, are the independence of the origins and the continuity of the results.

Take three cases of uncertainty. West Africa has been suggested as a place of origin of agriculture on the grounds that plants exist there that could have supported sedentary people. But there is no evidence that they did so. Again, the Nootka Indians of British Columbia discovered by Captain Cook (and by John Jewitt who was captured by them in 1802) were entirely independent of agriculture being supported by whaling and fishing and so well supported that they could even enslave their neighbours. They showed no trace of diffusion from centres of civilization. But there is no probability that, if left to themselves for another few thousand years, they would ever themselves have generated civilization.

A third example depends on the discovery of pottery with a characteristic corded pattern of decoration extending from Thailand through South China to Taiwan and Japan, where it is known as Jomon. It is believed to go back as far as 10,000 B.C. being sometimes associated with remains of roots and fruits in caves. These finds are of interest because they are older than any useful pottery from any other parts of the world, perhaps older even than the earliest European cult figures. But again they have led to no succession, no elaboration, no buildings, no villages. It seems that the gathering of yams did not stimulate anything but the pottery and the pottery did not stimulate anything but the gathering of yams. The two of them together did not give rise to the cultivation of grain which was first seen in the north of China and began five or ten thousand years later.

Did these people in South-East Asia die out and leave no trace? As we shall see they produced not civilization but navigation.

A region of interest of a different kind is the New World. When Columbus arrived in Cuba in 1493 he found the Arawak people growing crops that were entirely new to him. Some of these were roots, manioc (or cassava) and sweet potatoes. But in addition there were seed crops notably maize (its Arawak name) and beans. When the Spaniards went further to Mexico and Peru other new crops appeared, gourds and chillis, our ordinary potatoes and tobacco. None of them had ever been known in the Old World. They were in fact all derived from American wild plants. Evidently agriculture had been developed in America entirely on its own.

During the last fifty years we have learned how this happened. The ancestor of maize is a weedy grass which grows wild in Guatemala and is still known by its Aztec name of *teosinte*. The steps by which the trembling flower-spikes of this grass were transformed into the massive ears of modern maize have been found on ancient sites in Central America and Peru covering a period of 7000 years. When the Europeans explored America they found that the new crop had been carried by largely vegetarian farmers from its place of origin across North America to the Atlantic coast, down into South America, far into Chile.

In this way we see two kinds of evolutionary continuity. There is a continuity in geography of colonizing farmers diffusing from a centre over America. And there is also a continuity in history between the origins of this farming and the villages, cities, and finally empires of the Maya, the Toltecs, the Aztecs, and the Incas.

It is these continuities we must examine in the Old World as well as the New if we are to understand the history of man.

III *The Grain Growers*

The map of the Old World shows us a region where, as in the birthplace of agriculture in the New World, the great continental masses have a narrow junction. Where the three continents of Europe, Asia, and Africa meet there are pathways where men, animals, and plants moving from one continent to another are bound to pass. At the northern point of Syria there was bound to be the greatest movement as the ice caps in the tenth millennium B.C. began to melt and the climate began to get drier and warmer.

It is here that a great mound, Tell Mureybit, has revealed one of the first village settlements in the Old World. The deposits, 4 metres thick, must have been many centuries accumulating. The plants which remain in the deposits, beginning at about 9000 B.C., are the seeds of wild plants of species still growing in the neighbourhood today. They are nearly all the kindred of cultivated crops of today; they are prototypes or ancestors of the wheat and barley, lentils and vetches, that are now being grown by peasants nearby. Only one plant that they used copiously, a knot grass, *Polygonum*, is a weed which has failed to pass into modern cultivation.

From this Nuclear Zone of ancient and incipient cultivation three arms stretch out to the corners of a triangle east, west, and south along the edges of mountain ranges. On these arms are found the earliest settlements of true grain cultivators over the period of the next 2000 years (Table 2.1). These settlements all contain the remains of the same plants. Evidently they had all been in communication with one another at an earlier stage in the tenth millennium. To this store new arrivals were slowly added, notably peas, linseed, pistachio nuts and later the vine and the olive, and on the southern arms the date and the fig. A few of these plants can now be described as crops. This is the Nuclear Zone from which Old World agriculture came.

Fig. 2.1 Map of the Nuclear Zone showing the sites of plant remains from the earliest agriculture assigned to the eighth and seventh millennia B.C. (after Zohary, 1973)

This evidence allows us to ask and answer a series of questions. First, by what steps and why did the wild plant change when it came into the hands of the farmer and was cultivated? Secondly, how did the cultivated plant then move or migrate? Thirdly, what do the answers to these two questions tell us about the work, life, and movements of the farmer?

Today we can say a great deal under these headings. For we can identify remains of plants by their seeds, we can date them by radiocarbon tests, and we can distinguish their living representatives and ancestors by their chromosome numbers and by their experimental hybrids. Also, owing to their immense economic importance today, we know by genetic evidence from a few basic grain crops, what changes can arise by selection under cultivation. By using these methods in concert we can establish a basis for historical inference.

What had happened in the first few millennia of cultivation was that the ears of the wheat and barley (like those of maize) were now held

Table 2.1 *The supplanting of wild by crop plant remains in early Nuclear Zone settlements (after Helbaek, 1966, 1970, 1972; Harlan and Zohary, 1966; Mellaart, 1967; Hopf, 1967; Zohary, 1973, 1974; Darlington, 1973)*

Site	*Region*	*Date*[1]	*Wild Plants*[2]	*Crop Plants*
1. Tell Mureybit	N. Syria	8300 *b.c.*	W, 2x, B, L, V	—
		9000 B.C.		
2. Ali Kosh (Luran)	S.W. Iran	7500 *b.c.*	L, F etc. (90%)	W, B (10%)
		8200 B.C.		
3. Chatal Hüyük[3]	Anatolia	7000 *b.c.*	—	W 2x, 4x, 6x?
		7650 B.C.		B, P, L
4. Jericho	Palestine	7000 *b.c.*	Fig (*Ficus*)	W 4x, B
		7650 B.C.		(L, later)
5. Argissa	Thessaly	6000 *b.c.*	—	W 2x, 4x
		6560 B.C.		B, P, L
6. Choga Mami[3]	N.E. Iraq	5500 *b.c.*	weeds of threshed	W 2x, 4x, 6x?
		6000 B.C.	grain	B, O, P, L

1 ^{14}C dates corrected between 1000 and 9000 *b.c.* by addition of 7 per cent to earlier estimates (Libby, 1970).

2 W, wheat, *Triticum* (2x, diploid, einkorn; 4x tetraploid, emmer; 6x hexaploid, bread wheat); B, barley, *Hordeum spontaneum→vulgare*; O, oats, *Avena* spp.; P, pea, *Pisum sativum*; L, lentil, *Lens esculentum*; V, vetch, *Vicia sativa*; F, flax, *Linum usitatissimum*.

3 irrigated 5900 B.C.

Note: Deposit at Site 1 is 4m. thick, at Site 3, 21·5m. thick.

together by stiff central stalks which did not break or shatter when they were threshed. They were losing the brittleness which wild grasses need if they are to scatter their seed and propagate themselves. They were being preserved, not by their own natural devices but by human harvesting. The change was a gradual one. Only after several millennia do grains appear which drop naked from the chaff in threshing.

How did this change come about? The first crops comprised a mixture of many grains and many useless plants, the weeds of the future. The original wild species, such as Emmer wheat, must have been, as it still is in primitive cultivation, a mixed natural population ripening, as a wild plant should ripen, over several weeks. The first quarter of the crop, it has been said, would be eaten by birds and the last quarter by mice. The middle half would be harvested by the farmer, a part to feed his family or his animals, and a part to be seed for the next year's sowing. So, inevitably he was selecting the middle of the crop each year. He was breeding for a uniformity in germination, in growth, and in ripening every year of his life.

The farmer, in this way, was producing his own stock, a land-race; not pure but serviceable; not free from weeds but with weeds which ripened along with the crop. In this way in every crop he was selecting also for a non-shattering ear or capsule that would hold its seed till he threshed it. So it was that wheat, barley, and rice, flax, cabbage, and poppy, evolved in ancient agriculture. This *unconscious* selection set the pattern for a large part of the domestication on which man's new means of livelihood was to be built. For each of the other crops was being selected at the same time for ability, first, to hold its seed until it was threshed and, second, to produce more seed than its ancestors would when grown on soil that had been tilled and manured.

Among these improved grains along the northern arms of our triangle were some of a new kind of wheat which excites our particular interest. For it is a new species, *Triticum aestivum*. It is the ancestor of our bread wheat: it can be baked. The earlier wheats, Einkorn and Emmer, had different numbers of chromosomes: they were diploid and tetraploid (2x and 4x). Bread wheat is hexaploid (6x). It does not exist wild, it is the result of a cross between Emmer and a wild diploid relative, a goat-grass. Such is the rigour of botanical arithmetic, we know that it must have begun as a sterile triploid (3x) hybrid. Like many cultivated plants it has become fertile by doubling its chromosomes. This new crop plant with a larger yield probably arose many times in the sixth and fifth millennia B.C. before it began to be swept into the farmer's bin or basket to be propagated by his sowing. And it may still be arising anew today as such new species often do.

The origin of bread wheat has often been demonstrated experimentally—for the first time by Kihara in Japan. But its history has recently been explained in detail by Zohary in Israel. His interpretation is as follows. The cultivation of the wild Emmer, *Triticum dicoccoides*, a tetraploid, began in Syria and Palestine (probably in the eighth millennium B.C.). Farmers slowly carried it northwards and on arriving in northern Persia it met the wild goat-grass, *Aegilops squarrosa*, a diploid which had been entirely separated from it. The two crossed to give the hexaploid bread wheat *T. aestivum*.

While Emmer wheat spread southwards without such hybridization, forming the basis of agriculture for the next seven millennia in Egypt, in Ethiopia, and even in southern Europe, bread wheat found the way open for migration into the colder climates of Europe and Central Asia. So it entered into northern India and last of all, only in the second millennium B.C., into northern China. But, though it came late, its chromosomes (Riley has found) show that it was an early primitive form of bread wheat that reached China. By the second millennium B.C. bread wheat had reached the Atlantic in the west and the Pacific in the east: carried of course always by farmers, as it has been until that memorable day in the world's agricultural history when the Mennonites brought their Odessa wheat to Dakota in 1873.

Into this main web of our story a few significant threads have to be woven. When wheat arrived at the furthest point of its journey it was often found to have been preceded by other crops. How did this happen?

In primitive agriculture, as we saw, the farmer sows and reaps a mixed crop. It is a natural population of one or more species infested with weeds. This sort of crop was evidently raised at Choga Mami in Iraq before 6000 B.C. As the cultivators spread from the centre entering new climatic zones these weeds sometimes displaced the crop itself. Wheat and barley were displaced by oats in the north and west and by millets in the south and east: it was with these millets that the first farmers arrived in China about 4000 B.C. In this way new crops forced their way into the unconscious hands of the farmer. And in the north of India, in the Kulu Valley of Himachal Pradesh where rice and wheat still grow side by side, it may well be that rice was first harvested as a weed of wheat 4000 years ago.

Most of these new crops have been picked up in the outward expansion of agriculture. But one of them has a special history. Rye is the only staple crop in Europe which did not come from the Ancient East. It was (according to Helbaek) gathered in on the route to China, partly in Central Asia, as a brittle-eared weed about 4000 B.C. Thence it made its way back in the second millennium B.C. to become an important crop on the northern frontier of the Roman Empire whence it has been carried everywhere in the world to the northern limits of agriculture. It did not reach the Nuclear Zone itself until the Turks invaded Anatolia in the tenth century A.D. By no accident at all, however, also entering Europe from the East, new cultivated plants, not staple crops but notable auxiliaries, hemp and the peach, came from China itself in Roman times. Thus after four millennia the original movement of agriculture was reversed.

IV *The Beginning of a City*

In the ninth millenium B.C. some early grain farmers on the southern slopes of the Taurus Mountains, leaving behind the fig and the olive, moved north into the Konya plain, 1000 metres above sea level, lightly wooded with walnuts, almonds, and other fruit trees. Here they met a drier climate, new people and new animals, new soils and new minerals. They found herds and flocks of ox and ass, boar and deer, goats and sheep which had attracted archaic paleo-minded hunters. It seems that the wealth and security of agriculture drew in and domesticated both the insecure hunters and their prey for soon there appeared a people of mixed character, farmers and herdsmen whose habits gradually changed in the settlement of unknown name which, following Mellaart, we now speak of in the Turkish tongue as Chatal Hüyük.

The new settlers slowly converted their houses from the wood of the forests to the brick of the plain. They discovered, or more probably accepted from their neighbours or guests, the art of baking pottery. Their women on whom they now partly relied for the work of tillage improved in status and the improvement was reflected as elsewhere in the rise of the earth goddess.

Another 1000 years passed and a separate caste of priests had taken their place in the maturing society. They presided over domestic shrines with wall paintings, reliefs of bulls and goats, and cult statues of clay and stone. Attached to these shrines they had bakeries and workshops for leather and woollen work. The priests might seem to have been a leisured class purveying myths and rituals to appease the forces of nature in exchange for the work of craftsmen living in another quarter of the town. But at this time the crops began to be irrigated and here we have an indication of what the priests were doing. It seems likely that they had discovered how to make themselves useful or even indispensable and therefore socially important in society: were they beginning to supervise not only the building of their own shrines but also the operations of agriculture, the fixing of the calendar, the prognostication of the weather, the maintenance of the law? They were indeed probably beginning to do what their successors did in Egypt or Sumeria 4000 years later.

We can see the evidence that some men and women must have hoed the land, sowed and reaped the grain, spun and dyed the wool or mohair, woven the cloth, carpets, and baskets; others must have fashioned the tools, weapons, and ornaments of wood, bone, flint, obsidian and alabaster, all to be found nearby, like the copper and lead which were later to be smelted. But the working people all lived elsewhere, away from the priestly quarter. Elsewhere too were the markets where these things and their raw materials were bartered: obsidian to Jericho and also, in exchange for copper, to Cyprus. Crops and stock were common to all these places of settlement and minerals were exchanged between them. Together they give us the clue to the trade which united the Nuclear Zone from the Persian Gulf and the Red Sea to the Highlands of Anatolia in an interdependent society.

It is a paradox that not far from Chatal Hüyük we still see kelim carpets woven to the same patterns that were used in Chatal Hüyük; and that villages, in my opinion, more primitive may still be seen scattered over the mountains of Kurdistan. Yet from this central zone diffused the movement of people, of talents, of invention which have ultimately spread to the ends of the earth leaving its quiet centre in undisturbed stagnation. The reason is twofold. First, the climate of the Nuclear Zone became drier as the ice receded. Secondly, the farmers used up the resources of their original territory even before they spread into new territory. Wherever they spread they encountered new resources and also new people with whom they mixed and profited from the mixing. After 3000 years of trial and error in their sedentary beginnings they began to expand and expansion brought a prize in the shape of an experienced agriculture. Their expansions, their migrations, are the basis of the resulting diffusion of culture of which archaeologists speak. But of course the migration is never without hybridization, and in consequence the diffusion is never without a creation of new culture.

V *Stratified Society*

The consequences of settled cultivation were such as we could partly foresee. The cultivators between the Salt Lakes of Anatolia, the Zagros Mountains, and the Rift Valley of the Jordan expanded their numbers and multiplied their settlements. The crops and stock they raised had a common range which was bound to be maintained by the trade in minerals and animal products. This trading activity was inevitably provided by their nomadic Paleolithic neighbours attracted by the unprecedented advantage which the farmers' necessary habit of storing grain offered for the whole society.

Wool and leather, copper and gold, obsidian and lapis lazuli were worth carrying in exchange for bread and wine, and were the means of holding together the whole of the Nuclear Zone in a common but stratified society. Amicable trade was the basis then of a society divided into cooperating classes of farmers, craftsmen, and miners, traders and priests.

The evidence of the Ancient World is that in stable societies classes also were stable. Those who worked together bred together; those who worked apart bred apart. But the success of agriculture impaired its stability. It brought increase of numbers, expansion, and migration. From migration there would always be hybridization and innovation. The results, of course, differed according to the peoples involved. Some new peoples were kept apart by differences of colour as in Egypt and India. Others, being less easily distinguishable, merged. Some new peoples were conquered or subdued so as to be serfs or slaves. In general these were the peasants, the cultivators, while the conquerors, the governing class of warriors, were herdsmen or horsemen. The skill of the craftsmen often enabled them to maintain their separate and also their mobile character.

Out of every mixture these peoples made new recombinations, genetic recombinations, which survived like those of their crops and stock by their usefulness to society, and by their capacity to adapt their character to new situations. What were these new situations? Geographically and also chronologically they were first Europe, then Egypt, India, China, and Ethiopia.

These are broad and easy distinctions. More difficult are the finer distinctions between the modes of entry into each of these new continental areas. The Egyptian dynastic governing class of kings, warriors, and priests came into Egypt from the East about 3500 B.C. They probably brought a Semitic language with them which they superimposed on the established Hamitic. Within a few centuries buildings began to appear in Crete and giant temples in Malta. All of these things in Egypt, Crete, and Malta rested on a basis of an assured food supply, a common agriculture, and a kindred expanding peasantry. But how were they connected with one another?

After another few centuries cities began to be built in the Indus valley, cities supplied by the same crops as those of the Nuclear Zone and also some new ones. Did the founders come through Afghanistan or overseas by way of Dilmun? Probably by both routes. Later, farmers arrived in the land of Aksum, in what the Muslims were later to call Abyssinia and the Christians Ethiopia, bringing the same barley, wheat, and pulses, and on the nourishment, the energy of those crops a kingdom was founded. But when they arrived and by what route, through the Yemen or through Nubia or more probably by both ways, we do not know.

What we do know, however, is that grain-growing agriculture created a society continuing in time and continuous in space, communicating by trade long before it communicated by writing, and through this communication the craftsman as well as the trader was able to move, carrying his abilities to the places where the men and materials were available to employ and feed him. Grain-growing agriculture set in motion many chronological successions of development but the primary line we are always bound to find is:

FARMERS→FOOD→TRADERS/CRAFTSMEN→PRIESTS→TEMPLES

Settled agriculture everywhere provided the infrastructure of civilization. The succession holds true equally for Malta or Angkor Wat in the Old World and for Chichén Itzá or the Golden Temple of Cuzco in the New. Though of course, where neighbours were nearer and more pressing, warriors and city walls took the priority over priests and temples (Table 2.2).

VI *Agricultural Feedback*

What was it that switched the course of human activity from the unstable, unbalanced, insecure, specialized rewards of Paleolithic hunting and gathering to the stable, varied, secure, balanced subsistence provided by agriculture? The Paleolithic trappers in Europe and America might multiply their numbers by the destruction of mammoths and horses, the fishers on the Mekong Delta could prosper immensely. The whalers on the Nootka Sound might capture and keep slaves. The diggers of manioc and collectors of cocoa beans on the Orinoco and the Amazon might trade and travel. The yam and the banana along the rivers of Thailand might feed men and women who could bake pottery. And for many millennia men might harvest grass seed along the Nile. But these were not the foundations of a world-wide movement. Their promise was unfulfilled; they attained only stagnation. One achievement does not always feed back positively to produce another.

Table 2.2 *Chronology of innovation and diffusion in the Old World*

E and S ← *movement* → *W and N*

Group	*China*	*India*	*Egypt*	*Innovation*	*Nuclear Zone*[1]	*Crete and Malta*	*Mid. Danube*	*N.W. Europe*
A *Settlement*	4000 B.C.[2]	4000 B.C.[3]	6000 B.C.	Agric: grain	8000 B.C. }	5000 B.C.	5000 B.C.	4500 B.C.[4]
	5000 B.C.			pottery	7000 B.C. }			
				Chambered tombs	—	—	—	3000 B.C.[5]
	1600 B.C.	2500 B.C.	3100 B.C.	Buildings, temples	6000 B.C.	3000 B.C.[5]	2100 B.C.	2100 B.C.
	1600 B.C.[7]	2500 B.C.	3000 B.C.	Cities/writing[6]	3500 B.C.	2200 B.C.	—	A.D. 0
B *Metals*	—	—	3500 B.C.	Cu smelting	7000 B.C.	—	6000 B.C.	—
				Cu forging	4000 B.C.	2500 B.C.	—	—
	1500 B.C.[8]	2200 B.C.	2000 B.C.	Bronze	3500 B.C.[9]	2000 B.C.	2500 B.C.	1800 B.C.
	300 B.C.	700 B.C.	900 B.C.	Iron forged	1500 B.C.	—	—	800 B.C.
	700 B.C.[7]	—	—	cast	—	—	—	A.D. 1500
C *Stock*	—	—	—	Sheep	7000 B.C.	—	—	? 2500 B.C.
	—	3500 B.C.[7]	4000 B.C.	Cattle[10]	5000 B.C.	—	—	? 2500 B.C.
	1500 B.C.	—	1600 B.C.	Horse[10]	2100 B.C.	—	—	800 B.C.
	—	—	2500 B.C.	Ox plough	2500 B.C.	—	—	? 800 B.C.

Notes

1 S. Anatolia, Syria, Palestine, Kurdistan to Elam.
2 with jade from the Urals and Baikalia.
3 with one African crop, sesame, followed by two native crops, cotton and rice.
4 with passage graves and long barrows.
5 independent invention according to Renfrew, 1973.
6 cf. Darlington 1969, Table 4 (Genealogy of Alphabets).
7 wholly independent of diffusion from the Nuclear Zone.
8 Shang dynasty bringing wheat, barley, horses, chariots and bronze monopoly.
9 1000 years of uncertain recognition of alloys; *cf.* Gimbutas 1973.
10 *cf.* Darlington 1969, Table 1 (Domesticated Mammals).

General (i) The sequences of innovation and diffusion are chronologically parallel in the New World if we allow for (i) the secondary separation of the two centres in Mexico and Peru (like that between China and the West), (ii) the absence of herding and smelting in Mexico, and (iii) the absence of writing in Peru.

(ii) Detailed problems of early agriculture are considered by Hutchinson *et al.* (1976, *Phil. Trans. R.S.* (*B*) **275**: 1–213). The evolutionary connections are explained together with necessary references in my *Chromosome Botany* (1973).

What switched the course of human activity is shown us by the Old–New World comparison. Grain-growing (probably on poor hillsides) was the necessary beginning of the agricultural revolution in both worlds. It provided the fuel for the sequence of improvements, expansions, migrations, and hybridizations which has lasted for some 10,000 years. This was a short period on the biological scale which preceded it, but it was a long period on the historical scale which was to follow it. Agriculture was thus speeding up the evolutionary processes of men and of the animals and plants with which they had to deal. If this was another invention promoting intelligence how did it take effect?

In the first place why did grain-growing do the trick? Why did roots and fruits in themselves lead nowhere? The reason is that the cereals and pulses are annual outbred crops. They produce every year a harvest of seed giving a variable crop. This crop is always capable of being selected, unconsciously at first and later consciously as well. The processes of selection continue year after year wherever and however cultivation takes them.

The root and fruit crops can also be selected. But they can be selected only consciously and only occasionally for they are always propagated vegetatively by invariable unimprovable cuttings. For this reason seedless bananas and yams that were taken overseas from Indonesia can still be recognized thousands of years later and thousands of miles away. They happen to have often been triploid so that they were utterly sterile; and also utterly stable like the societies that have fed on them. The feedback they induce is negative stabilizing feedback.

All cross-fertilized seed crops, on the other hand, are automatically self-adapting to new conditions, whether these conditions are changed by nature or by man. That is how seed plants could be transformed by unconscious selection: they become adapted, not only to sowing by man and harvesting by man, but also to migrating with man, to growing on new soils, better or worse soils, and in new climates, better or worse climates, to which man has taken them. They are unconsciously selected by and for their new way of life.

The second reason for the pre-eminence of grain-growing as the engine of human evolution is that where grain-crops exist in great variety, including cereals and pulses, they can together provide a great reward, the complete high-protein vegetable food on which (when olives, figs, and grapes were added, as Zohary has shown) civilization as well as agriculture could rest. A third reason is that obtaining this great reward made great and increasing demands for industry and skill. Sowing, tillage, harvesting, and storage could all be done badly or well. The one factor, that there was hardly any limit to the reward, discovered or exposed the other factor, that there was hardly any limit to the industry and the skill required to win that reward. The competitive machinery was adjusted to secure almost unlimited evolutionary and historical improvement.

For these reasons there is indeed much virtue in the biblical legend. Picking fruit in the garden was too easy for man or woman. It was for the good of their bodies and their souls that they forfeited this temptation and were condemned for all future time to earn their bread by the sweat of their brows. Of course we must add that it was on Cain the tiller rather than on Abel the herdsman that this fate was inflicted.

The other side of the evolutionary picture and of its feedback mechanisms is presented by man himself. The plainest way of putting it is to admit that man had been creating a new environment, several new environments, for himself by the radical innovation he had made in his way of life. From a dependence on his abilities in hunting, and his wife's abilities in collecting, they had together by stages come to depend on abilities of different kinds. Tilling the soil, tending the crops, feeding and breeding their livestock, were what now made their lives and their living. These demanded different physical and mental faculties and a different cooperation between the sexes in using those faculties. The position of the woman was probably enhanced by her new activities. But the pressure of population was not removed by the new security; it merely re-opened the road of escape by migration.

In their survival man and his domesticated crops and stock now constituted one symbiotic system like the alga and the fungus in a lichen. Each part of the system was automatically, inherently, selecting the other parts of the system just as, in my view of the genetic system, all the genes, all the chromosomes, and all the members of the population select one another in the course of evolution. And just as the effects of selection on man have been feeding back over the millennia, promoting the inventions which have altered the conditions of his survival with relentlessly increasing speed.

Thus, for 10,000 years the land, the crops, and the animals have been turning the hunters and collectors willy nilly into farmers, stockbreeders, and craftsmen; into something more and more different (as the Epic of Gilgamesh already makes clear) from the wild men they still saw around them, men whom they no longer recognized as their equals or kinsmen, men who seemed now to be of a different race, men to whom they gave the names of heathen and pagan, barbarian and savage.

The diversification which followed after a hundred generations was a diversification and divergence of new peoples, farming peoples with various types of farming, settled farmers, slash-and-burn farmers,

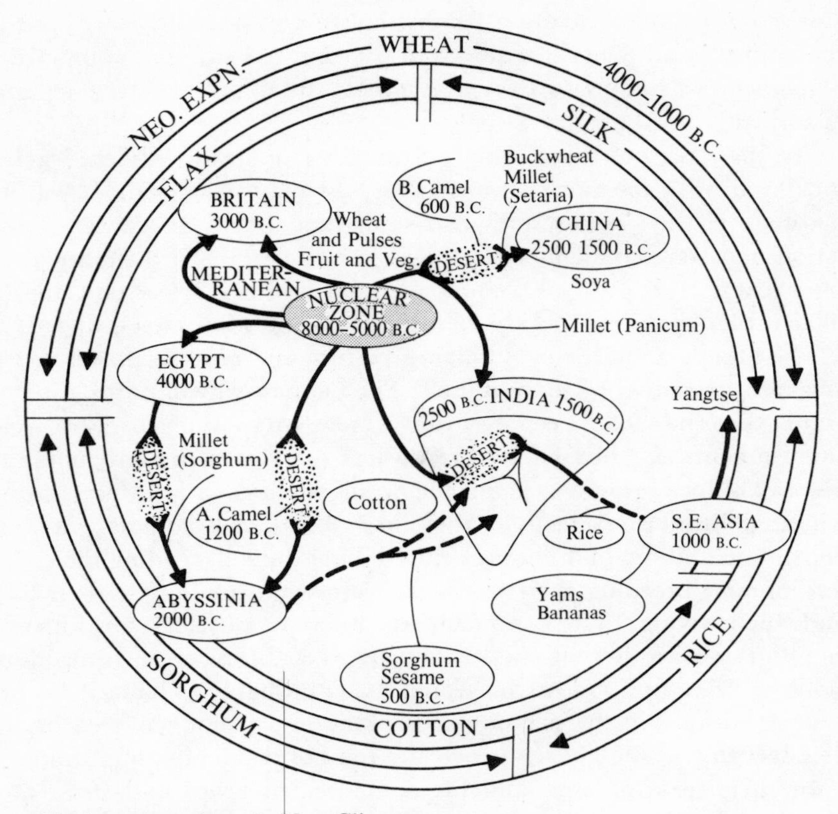

Weeds replace Crops in New Climates
Deserts replace Grass and Trees with Grazing, Felling

Fig. 2.2 The Old World in the Bronze Age showing the distribution of crops following the expansion of cultivators from the Nuclear Zone with the creation of deserts by pastoralists and their extension by the camel after 1200 B.C. in Africa, Arabia, India, and China (from Darlington, 1973)

mixed farmers. It led to a separation, often a separation of brothers as the Book of Genesis puts it, between the tillers of the soil and the herders of animals, sometimes with sheep or asses or cattle or all three, as we may see them today on the edge of the Persian, Arabian or African deserts. Some were living on milk, or milk with blood, or meat without blood. For some were starved of salt, as in Africa, while others were soaked in salt, as in Anatolia or Palestine.

So man became attached to different kinds of animals. Since man domesticated the horse 4000 years ago certain men have been selecting the horse for their purposes. But these men have for all this time been selected for their abilities in managing the horse—the horse has been selecting them, the horsemen. Many books have been written to describe the character of this interaction and the historical, racial, and social variety of its results, especially what has been done by the men who worshipped the horse; men like Attila or William the Conqueror, Saladin or Ghenghiz Khan, who believed in power and knew they could rely on the movement of the horse to gain their ends, to enlarge an empire for both the horse and for themselves.

These new varieties of people living in different ways and in different places derived their differences originally from the Paleolithic peoples to whom they had been frequently back-crossed, a process on the lines practised by all experimental breeders. This back-crossing enabled them to survive on roads so long, reaching climates so diverse as those of China, India, Ethiopia, and Britain. But their new climates were not the only unaccustomed environments to which they had to adapt themselves. When the wheat farmers of 6000 years ago descended into the valley of the Indus they picked up a new kind of humped cattle. When 1000 years later they crossed the watershed into the valley of the Ganges (as so many later invaders would do) they found rice growing among their wheat. Here again they had created a new environment for themselves. It was an environment which absorbed or subdued both them and their successors of different colours in creating Indian society, a society dedicated by its religion to preserving those differences of colour, race, and caste to which it owes its origin.

At the centre of this Indian society, still feeding it after 5000 years, is the Indian peasant, with a certain character which he shares with the grain-growing, earth-turning, increasingly vegetarian peasants who have patiently and prudently earned their living all over the world in continuous succession since Chatal Hüyük or (if you prefer it) since Adam.

Who were the successive races of invaders who swept into India and subdued it? Some were pastoralists. Others were stratified peoples themselves subdued by pastoralists. Last of all were the horsemen, who became their governing class. To know how this happened we have to turn back to Europe.

VII *The Metal Industry*

Like the invention of the bow and the domestication of the dog, the use of drugs and poisons and the smelting of copper and gold, all belonged to Paleolithic man. They came before agriculture. For copper and gold were found native and a good fire would melt them. But after wheat followed an inevitable sequence of discoveries: bread and ovens for baking it, kilns for firing pottery and soon furnaces. A fire fed by a forced draught was bound to reveal the presence of copper in its ores which in turn meant, for those who could travel and knew the value of rocks, apparently unlimited new sources of metal. Soon, before 6000 B.C., the products of casting copper appear at Chatal Hüyük. Within 500 years they were to be found in the Balkans.

These advances no doubt led to mining, for which flint and obsidian already provided the examples, and to the discovery of ores from which, not only copper but also tin, arsenic, lead, silver, antimony and mercury, could be extracted to yield the range of metals known to the Ancient World. Among these were the natural and later the artificial blends or alloys including the bronzes whose strength or hardness set their discoverers and mankind in Europe and Asia (as well as in Peru) on a new course. The discoverers were of course miners, smiths, and traders, at first all in one. They carried their materials, their equipment, their product, and their skill with them as was true later in India, Arabia, and Africa and most recently with the Gypsies in Persia and Europe. But these craftsmen relied on husbandmen or herdsmen to feed them. They were the moving parts of an articulated, stratified society.

The first bronze smiths according to Mariya Gimbutas, were not working near the earliest settlements on the southern side of Anatolia but on its north-western edge in the Kuro-Araxes Basin. Here about 3500 B.C. invading nomad Kurgan herdsmen, passing round the east end of the Caucasus picked up some of the bronze workers, no doubt the young and adventurous, and carried them and their trade in a sweep of 1000 miles and 1000 years round the north of the Black Sea and into the Danube Basin where a chemically less advanced mining and metal-working industry was already established.

Such was one of the means, perhaps the chief means, of expansion or diffusion of the new and inevitably somewhat secret invention of bronze. But it was the means of something much more than the development of a metal-working monopoly. For armed with bronze and equipped with cattle and a little later with horses, the pastoral people, the barbarians of the great northern river basins from the Danube to the Volga had created a society of a new kind with an unprecedented power. These pastoral people, the original Aryans, were prepared to attack and were able to subdue, as a governing class, the settled tribes of all the older farming peoples to the south of them. Reversing the movement outwards from the Nuclear Zone they turned inwards and repeated what Arabian herdsmen had done a millennium earlier to Sumeria and Egypt. They successively invaded in the period from

2500 to 1500 B.C. the settled farming lands of Italy, Greece, Anatolia, Persia, India, and China. Into the first five of these they brought their bronze craftsmen, their horses and carts, their priests and their gods, their shaft graves and citadels, and probably their bards and their music. From beyond the Tarim Basin, disguised or transformed as the Shang, and travelling more quickly than the first peasants who, as the end of their tedious migration had brought only millet, they brought bronze, jade, and bread wheat into China.

The conquerors provided kings and priests wherever they went. Except after their longest journeys to China, which they entered by way of Kansu, and to Java, they superseded the native languages with their common Aryan speech. They preserved their class character—indeed they were preserved by it. But their numbers were small and their racial features were continually and slightly shifted by hybridization, by back-crossing. Their Aryan languages were also continually shifted by the inflexional phonetic and grammatical preferences of their racially diverse subject populations. They founded no empires since this was before wealth established the communications that empires demand; but they founded the kingdoms from which empires later rose.

Particularly the Aryan rulers of India moved on a millennium later to found Buddhist–Hindu kingdoms in Burma, Thailand, Cambodia, Java and—their furthest destination—the small island of Bali. Thus the diffusion of Aryan culture and the Aryan race, both successively diluted, stretched from the Atlantic to the Pacific shores, leaving different marks on every intervening people, each step showing kinship with the next, but at the two extremes showing no recognizable kinship beyond the crops they grew and the weapons they bore. The roots of their language were buried deep.

VIII *What happened in S.E. Asia*

A little later than the development of bronze in Europe or of cities in the Indus Valley, and much further east, we can trace the circumstances of a different kind of revolution. Out of S.E. Asia, to be precise, out of the islands of Indonesia, in the second millennium B.C. issued forth a race of people whose achievements are easy to decipher and have never been paralleled anywhere else in the world. They were navigators and the outrigger canoes they built and sailed in the next three millennia traversed a vast expanse of sea; indeed they explored the greater part of the Pacific and Indian Oceans. They went so far that it is easiest to say where they did not go—for this was presumably only where they did not want to go.

They evidently did not want to go far outside the tropics. They also did not want to land on coasts that were already occupied. They fought shy of the mainlands of China and Africa, America and Australia; also New Guinea and most of the islands of Melanesia, whose shores were generally and actively defended by cannibals. But from Madagascar to New Zealand whatever land was uninhabited they discovered and colonized before any European arrived on the scene.

We know the course of their travels by the character of the Indonesian canoes they sailed, the Indonesian language they spoke, the Indonesian root and fruit crops they carried everywhere with them for food and for future cultivation. And we know them of course by their Indonesian bodies and minds, and blood groups, which they also inevitably carried with them. Theirs was therefore a diffusion of race and culture, an oceanic diffusion which stands in elegant and (may we say?) experimental contrast with the great land-bound diffusion of Aryans which was going on at the same time on the continent from which they had emerged. So far as it was a colonization of uninhabited islands, it entailed, indeed it allowed, no hybridization, only differentiation. Also like the Amerindians before them they hardly ever turned back or even needed to turn back. Like the Amerindians in America, they in the Pacific became purer and purer: they became Polynesians. They even lost some of their blood group differences, and for this reason like the Amerindians became vulnerable to strange diseases—which, of course, they never encountered until the Europeans arrived in the Pacific. But so long as they sailed their canoes they never lost the skill, knowledge, and prowess as ship builders and navigators, the excellence for which their success in exploration perpetually selected them.

The crops they carried with them were the root and fruit crops of their homeland propagated without seeds. Their yams and bananas, sugar cane and bread fruit, they took all over the Pacific, gaining in addition one American recruit, the sweet potato or kumara from Peru, which they in turn took to Hawaii and New Zealand.

The Indonesian yams and bananas they also took to Madagascar whence these crops, being vegetatively propagated, betray with botanical accuracy, the fact that the descendants of the colonists passed them on to tropical Africa. Here in the first millennium A.D. they provoked a second revolution of quite a different kind from that in Polynesia. Arriving in the Congo Basin they may be said to have fuelled the expansion of the Bantu people who spread from there in all directions. The Buganda and Kikuyu who entered the Lake region of East Africa in the eighteenth century, and the Xhosa and Zulus who entered South Africa in the nineteenth century, seem to have been equally indebted to the Indonesian voyagers for yams just as they are to the Portuguese for maize and manioc.

The expansion of the Indonesians was therefore unmistakable in its effects. But for its causes we have to look to indirect evidence. The whole of S.E. Asia had been in the cultural stagnation we expect of root growers for five or ten thousand years. Beyond their vegetative crops and their pottery they had picked up nothing but pigs and fowls, the art of the bow and of building canoes for fishing in the sea, all of them Paleolithic inventions diffused in S.E. Asia. Were they aware of the consequences that grain-growing had had in S.W. Asia or was beginning to have in the Indus Valley in their time? Was it possible that movements from the west and new inventions from the west had disturbed them and had opened up to a few enterprising Indonesians the possibilities of migration?

Such connections seem likely. For we know that one wave of migration after another struck Indonesia from the west during the next three millennia. Across the Bay of Bengal came rice-growing itself. Then there were the Hindu–Buddhist, the Muslim, and finally the European invasions and conquests. And at the intellectual level those travellers between Euphrates and the Indus who used Dilmun in the Persian Gulf as their trading post in the third millennium B.C. may well have voyaged beyond their first marketing destination carrying some knowledge of astronomy, mathematics, and navigation with them. For either they or Hellenistic explorers, two millennia later, seem to have carried the Babylonian science of numbers with its 60-system beyond India until it reached even the shores of New Guinea, where it is said to survive today.

IX *The Colonization of Europe*

The map of the world whatever projection we may use shows that Europe, the smallest of the continents, has a configuration all its own: not solid but loose, not a lump so much as a labyrinth. The complexity of the coastline and the river and mountain systems, would be bound to enforce diversity on the peoples who occupied it, a diversity itself which would be bound to crack and tear with every change of climate, every invasion or expansion of peoples. When we look further into the content of those mountains we find the variety and proximity of their mineral resources. When we consider the human history of the continent we recall that by entering it man had escaped from his ancestral tropical habitats and from the human diseases endemic in them. Hence it is not surprising that agricultural peoples dispersing from the Nuclear Zone should find their most immediately profitable and diverse opportunities in Europe.

What does the world's archaeological record tell us? We need not of course take it as final or representative; Asia may have much more to show us than yet appears. But the evidence of the artistic achievements of the late Paleolithic hunters in France and Spain so far suggests that these were some of the most advanced observers not only of their time, but of any time, for as animal draughtsmen they have never been surpassed. It is, however, after the coming of the agriculturists out of Asia in the sixth millennium B.C. that the peculiar originality of the Europeans had the opportunity to make itself felt. Now at least there was a sufficient security in the food supply to allow the building of chambered tombs, of passage graves, of the great temples of Malta, and of the oriented astronomical observatories of France and Britain culminating in Carnac, Avebury, and Stonehenge.

Much of the technical skill and all of the manpower behind these achievements (18 million man hours it is reckoned on Silbury Hill) were no doubt native. The particular astronomical calculations must, however, be connected with those which were being developed by the priest–astronomer–engineers whose forbears we saw at Chatal Hüyük and whose successors supervised the even greater works of Egypt and Babylonia.

Another line of evidence on the early European development is offered us by the rock drawings of the Val Camonica. This Italian valley, 30 miles long, runs down into the Lake of Iseo and lies to one side of the route by which amber was carried through the Alps from Jutland to the Adriatic ports on its way to Mycenae and Knossos. Miners and smiths evidently sought it out for its copper, silver, and later its iron ores and in the Iron Age its population rose to about 6000. Here in the last two millennia B.C. pictures were engraved on the rocks, about 20,000 of them, representing in a sequence unparalleled outside Egypt, the changing aspects of the lives of the people; it is a sequence bridging the period from the Neolithic to the Roman occupation.

Here, as described by Anati, we can see, not only the traps, dogs, and stags of the hunters, but also the men and women of the valley themselves. We can see their cattle and horses, their tools and weapons, their huts and boats, their maps and their number symbols; we can see their priests and warriors, their ancestors, their gods and devils; their phallic symbols and their sexual perversions. At work in his smithy we can see the smith in his ritual head-dress. Most telling of all, dated about 1600 B.C. we can see their daggers which come straight from

Mycenae and, now at the centre of their funeral processions, their wheeled ox-carts which had taken 1000 years to travel from Sumer. And above is the Tonale Pass reminding us of the God Thor and the route taken by Germanic tribes descending from the northern forests into Italy.

These things represent in part the primitive ritualized ideas of man's relation with society and with his gods. But their discoverer persuades us that they also represent a rejection of these ideas. They show us European people acquiring civilization on their own terms, with each man in charge of his own destiny. They have lost the artistic merit of the animal artists of the Paleolithic; but they have acquired a human character with a new idea which was to dominate the development of Europe. In this respect they are the counterpart of the Homeric epics and the Icelandic sagas.

In order to understand how this happened we need to study carefully the conflict in Europe which was to last the whole of the 4000 years since these inscriptions were first made, the conflict between the peripheral barbarians and the civilized central peoples, the northern and southern peoples, or the pagan and Christian peoples, who, with their contrasted abilities and opposed attitudes to life, penetrated and in doing so stratified one another's societies. For it is this penetration, this combination, which has come to impress its consequences on all the other habitable continents.

We are inclined to assume that this sort of thing could happen anywhere; that since the advance of human intelligence and its product, civilization has never been entirely stopped in the Western world during the last 10,000 years, nothing could ever be expected to arrest such an advance in future in the world as a whole, or even in any part of it. This is a question we must bear in mind as we move into the other continents.

Chapter 3

Heredity and Genetics

I *The Meaning of the Problem*

If we ask ultimate questions about man's past and future we have to look searchingly at ideas and assumptions that we may have taken for granted. Our science gives us axioms but they are not infallible and not eternal. Rather, from time to time, we have to pause on our journey to reconsider our beliefs and the words with which we try to define them.

Formerly, people spoke of the living connections between parents and offspring by analogy with blood or with property. These seemed to account for their likenesses, unlikenesses being seen as merely accidental. Herbert Spencer took us a stage further by speaking of the living principle as *heredity*. Now, by experiment and microscopy, we have moved on to think of heredity as made up of two somewhat contrasted processes. We have come to think of the individual as having his own character differing from all others, a character which he owes to his origin from the material of a unique body, the fertilized egg, and its development by somewhat predictable processes. But we have also come to think of the great diversity of individuals arising from parents by processes which are evidently more uncertain, less predictable. To nail down the predictable and the unpredictable parts of heredity is the crux of our problem.

We study this problem in the first place by comparing parents and offspring. The variety of such comparisons is of course infinite but they all depend on differences and fortunately (both for the processes of evolution and for our own instruction) it is the business of heredity to separate these differences. In this way we have been enabled to sort out the materials and the processes responsible for heredity and variation. All the processes of pulling to pieces, of putting together and of getting to work, and all the materials concerned, we speak of as *genetic*.

Formerly, people spoke of the distinction or opposition between the influences that come through and from the fertilized egg and the influences from outside it. They spoke of nature and nurture. Now we may speak of heredity and environment. Or, as we shall see later, even more exactly, of what effects are genetic and what are environmental in origin. We must look at this distinction again and again.

II *Heredity and Environment*

It is not too difficult to separate the effects of heredity and environment by experiment especially with plants. You take seed of two stocks or races of plant which you know to breed true, that is constantly maintaining their different hereditary characters. You sow them in two kinds of soil which you know to be of different physical and chemical character. You compare the growth of the plants that results in the four situations you have created. You can see that differences in either heredity or environment or both have affected these results. And, if you could see the differences between the parents, you would be able to see the differences between the classes of offspring.

In nature, however, such an experiment does not offer itself to us ready made. We have to look suspiciously at what nature does offer. The first thing we notice is that animals in nature are not usually planted. They move about as they choose, often choosing different places to live, different environments, those which suit best the character, the genetic character, of the individual who chooses them.

This choice of the environment means that differences in hereditary character lead to differences in the environment. Inevitably they do so more and more as the infant offspring of an animal or man move away from their parents. And they do so in proportion as the offspring genetically differ from those parents. If we are not to be deceived, therefore, we must remember that in nature or in human society there is always an element of heredity included in what we think of as the environment.

There is another way in which the observer may be deceived. He may assume, as educationists and others with a mathematical bent often do, that it is possible to measure the relative importance of heredity and environment in producing differences between groups of human beings. Such a measurement is however a little fallacious and the word 'heritability' used in this connection is quite fallacious. If we compare a cat and a dog, or a man and a monkey, we don't need to ask whether they were raised together or raised apart. The environment will hardly matter. Similarly, if we can compare the two sexes, as sexes. But if we compare two brothers, who through adoption are brought up apart from one another, then the environment may well matter although not, of course, equally in all respects.

What we can measure from them is not a grand principle of heredity against environment but the relative importance of differences in heredity and differences in the environment in the actual situation studied. These actual situations need to be carefully examined. Both the hereditary and the environmental side can lay a trap for the unwary statistician.

One example of this trap is of practical and historical interest. Darwin supposed that twins were more like one another than ordinary sibs because they had shared the same environment, the same womb, together. Galton pointed out however (in 1875) that twins were of two kinds. Some were like ordinary sibs from two different eggs. Others came from the splitting of one egg and were therefore, he suggested, identical in heredity.

As we all know, such twins are indeed often miraculously close to identity in form and behaviour. They show how accurately heredity can act in controlling the activity of thousands of millions of cells even during two whole separated lifetimes.

Galton's distinction was evidently right and no one has ever seriously questioned it in principle. Statistical psychologists take it for granted. But, as we shall see, it needs modifying in one detail. The splitting of a human egg is not quite so simple as the splitting of a potato. In a proportion of one-egg twins, perhaps about 20 per cent among Europeans, errors of splitting occur which cause differences between the twins in the development of their bodily and mental character. Are such differences due to the environment as Galton supposed? By no means. The cause is internal to the one original egg. It is external to the two daughter eggs. It is inherent in the process of splitting. So that the one circumstance which was supposed to separate heredity and environment in fact has been misinterpreted by Galton and his successors in favour of the environment.

As we proceed with our study we shall see that simple rules which would make everything easier for us need to be corrected by reference to such imponderable effects; to what happens, not just to whole organisms, but to single cells, to little bits of cells, and to little things inside them. We shall meet paradoxes as well as rules, paradoxes which will deepen our knowledge of nature and of human beings.

III *Mendel's Paradoxes*

The basis or beginning of our understanding of genetics is the type of experiment which Mendel invented some years, it would seem, before he could have read Darwin's *Origin of Species*. The experiments he made have implications which are being so continually extended that they mean something fresh for every generation.

Mendel began work with peas because they were inbred. They were regularly self-fertilized and therefore, unlike most wild plants or animals or man, they produced pure lines. These pure lines have the same uniformity that makes a million ears in a field of wheat or barley all shoot on the same day. Varieties of peas evidently, Mendel thought, breed true. But they had not always done so since Mendel had, and we have, varieties differing sharply from one another in shape, size, and colour. These must have arisen from one another, or from the wild ancestors first grown, and still growing, in Syria. They must have arisen by changes in heredity, by mutations.

Mendel crossed these parental varieties (P generation) together and found that they gave uniform progenies which resembled one parent or the other in respect of each difference. He then self-fertilized plants of this first filial or F_1 generation. They evidently produced germ cells with the contrasted parent characters represented in equal numbers. To do this the germ cells must have contained a single representation of characters and the plants themselves must have contained a double representation. The proportions of types he found in this next F_2 generation proved this as you can see.

Thus consider one difference of character as *A*—*a*. Then $AA \times aa$ gave an F_1 *Aa* with germ cells *A* and *a*. These freely mixing and mating would give an F_2 in the proportions 1 *AA*: 2 *Aa*: 1 *aa*. To be sure Nature can, and Mendel could, grow only a sample of the progeny so the proportions were not exact. Mendel was thus compelled to plunge into algebra and also into statistics. This was bound to disturb his audience at Brünn in 1864. He emerged from the numbers and symbols to propose that *A* and *a* were *elements*, carried double in all the body cells of the plants and single in all their germ cells. His audience must have gasped at the audacity of the man in using such simple methods to arrive at such far-reaching generalizations.

As for his readers, obviously, when they came to the suggestion of 'elements' as responsible for all heredity they evidently read no further. For elements meant material particles, chemical entities, what we now glibly, a little too glibly, call genes. They meant a new and strange philosophy of life, a philosophy of determinism, of reductionism. It was a heresy which the Mendelians when they rediscovered Mendel tried to forget and most of mankind today still shrinks from admitting.

Mendel's rediscoverers (in 1900) rejected his elements. But they were excited beyond measure by what they at once called his laws, the principles that the elements separated when germ cells were formed and reunited when germ cells reunited on fertilization to give Mendel's ratios. They hastened to demonstrate that these ratios were universal. And in principle they succeeded. All heredity was Mendelian and what was not Mendelian was not heredity. But the rediscoverers overlooked the fact that Mendel had made a third kind of discovery even less acceptable than his philosophy or his laws. He had discovered a number of paradoxes.

The first paradox that comes out of Mendel's experiment is that in any outbred community, that is any human community not a pea community, where all the parents and grandparents are genetically different, the children also will be different. Brothers who by definition have the same *ancestry* will always have a different *heredity*. If it isn't *A* and *a* that are sorting out it will be *B* and *b* or *C* and *c*.

In making this discovery Mendel had also discovered a dangerous flaw in the popular view of heredity. Differences between brother and brother had always been attributed to the environment or the order of birth or mere accident. But they were in fact part of the normal and strictly regulated and utterly indispensable mechanism of heredity. Heredity was responsible for differences between brother and brother or father and son as well as for their likenesses. This is a principle that has not yet got into our dictionaries or our schools. It is not yet part of our culture.

The mechanism of heredity which has governed evolution, as we now know, for 3000 million years, may thus be said to conceal its operation. It does so in a most misleading way. Its combination of certainty and uncertainty puts us off the scent. This is even more strikingly shown by the differences between the sexes. For brothers and sisters have the same ancestry. And the difference between them, the difference of sex, is also due to heredity. As we have seen, it is due to their chromosomes.

In these Mendelian situations Nature is, we now know, paradoxically attempting, and indeed succeeding, in doing several apparently incompatible jobs at once. If *A* is dominant and *a* is recessive she can be displaying some characters while concealing others to be passed on to later generations where they may be exposed and even destroyed. Every new human individual is therefore a Mendelian experiment multiplied in the range of its consequences a thousandfold.

What Nature displays and what she conceals, what she keeps and what she throws away, all depend not only on the heredity of the individual but on whether the group is inbreeding or outbreeding, whether we are dealing with a P generation or an F_1, or an F_2. When, as in all human populations, we have a mixture of all these situations, we are in possession of yet another means of testing the action of heredity. For if we (or Nature) select from any mixed population or community types that we prefer, and the cause of their differences is genetic or hereditary, we can change the character of the strain or stock or race by favouring *A* or *a* or even their combination *Aa*. It is in this way that selection has, among other things, increased the yield of wheat, the speed of race horses, and the intelligence of sheepdogs during the last 200 years, and the intelligence of man during the last 2 million years. Without Darwin ever hearing about it, Mendel had shown how Darwin's selection worked.

IV *The Chromosomes*

The idea that the chromosomes were responsible for heredity had been mooted twenty five years before the rediscovery of Mendel. But as soon as people who had seen chromosomes heard about his experiments they saw that the pairing and separation of the chromosomes and the halving of their numbers at germ-cell formation, at *meiosis*, and their meeting and the doubling of their numbers when the sperm nucleus fused with the egg nucleus at fertilization, all these now made sense. These events corresponded with what Mendel's theory required. They also saw that the chromosomes suggested other unexpected principles that Mendel's experimental breeding had not yet revealed.

Before 1900 observers had noticed that several male insects had one chromosome unpaired at meiosis which passed to only half the sperm. One observer, looking at a grasshopper in 1902, suggested that this odd chromosome was a 'sex-determinant' deciding, as we saw, whether the egg which the sperm fertilized would produce a male or a female embryo. He was right. Ten years earlier it had been noticed that the paired chromosomes at meiosis coiled round one another and seemed to exchange parts. This idea was revived and became, in the hands of men breeding the fly *Drosophila*, the theory of crossing-over which in due course showed them how to map the position of hereditary elements or genes in a row, in a linear order on each of the chromosomes.

Since 1900 there has been a great movement of knowledge and ideas on these questions. Some people were looking at chromosomes. Others were breeding flies, or examining the pedigrees of human abnormalities, or studying animal behaviour, or latterly transforming bacteria and viruses, or working out the chemical connections between all these. This movement has given a connectedness of fact and theory to genetics. From being the study of heredity it has become the framework for understanding the connections between all the properties of life. The *properties*, it turns out, are all fundamentally chemical. But the *connections* are all extended in time and space in the senses we call evolutionary.

Now the genes had been mapped in the chromosomes of *Drosophila* by 1920. But it was not until 1930 that we knew, from looking at chromosomes in plants and animals generally, that crossing-over was built in to all sexual heredity. It had been supposed to occur between paired chromosomes in *Drosophila* at meiosis; it was now demonstrable in all sexually reproducing plants and animals and above all in man. The points of crossing-over could be recognized several hours later at 'chiasmata' in the cells that were going to produce sperm or eggs. So, without any experimental breeding of man, we knew from looking at the chiasmata in his chromosomes how they were actually being rearranged; we knew how his genes, or rather his parents' genes, were being systematically recombined in heredity between every generation and the next. That is one side of the picture we get of chromosomes and breeding. The other side is that it has also shown us how each method taken by itself has limitations which we need to keep always in mind when we tackle the most difficult problems of all, those of human heredity and human evolution.

These problems require time and effort to resolve. No less so now that we know more about chromosomes and heredity in man than in any other animal or plant. Probably a million human beings have had their chromosomes examined. Usually the object has been to ascertain the cause of some abnormality, some defect, of body or mind. Millions more will be examined, since we are still only at the beginning of our exploration. This is true because man is far and away the most diverse, most complicated, and also most important of all living organisms. He is a world in himself.

What have we found? Every human being, with some interesting exceptions to which we shall return, has 23 pairs of chromosomes, one of each pair from each parent. The different pairs are all distinguishable by their size and shape and also by the patterns of banding they show when they are suitably stained. Any abnormal chromosome indeed can be traced from one generation to the next by its pattern. Every chromosome carries its pedigree on its back. That is true whether it is in man himself or in the crops and stock he breeds and feeds. Not only this but the chromosomes from opposite parents, which generally correspond, often slightly differ. In our heterogeneous outbred populations most of us have such visible differences between one or two pairs. A time will come when, as in some plants, every individual will be recognizable by his or her chromosomes. We have not yet reached this finger-print stage. But we are already, as we may say, recognizably *hybrid* in the structure of our chromosomes and hence evidently in the content of our genes. Of course we have long known that this was so in a general sense so far as the genes were concerned. The diversity of our brothers, sisters, and children told us that. But the sources of most such variation have been too small to be seen in the chromosomes. Now they show us that they vary in size and arrangement beyond anything we might expect from our knowledge of breeding experiments with other animals.

What is this extra variation, this unaccountable variation, doing? We know a reason for it. In plants and animals generally, pieces of chromosome, apart from regular crossing-over, are often turned round or moved from one chromosome to another or doubled or lost altogether. Often if they are small, they have only minute effects. These changes of minute effect, which Mather has called *polygenic*, are not the kind the experimenter likes when he is pulling heredity (or chromosomes) to pieces. But they are probably just the things that nature finds most useful in putting heredity (and chromosomes) together. In making plants and animals grow bigger or faster, for example. They are just what is wanted, for example, to promote the evolution of maize from teosinte.

V *Sex and Mutation*

The new knowledge of chromosomes made it possible to look at many kinds of serious defects of unknown origin, both in the new-born and in embryos which had been lost by abortion. It then became clear that in our outbred societies more than 1 per cent of all human embryos at conception had visibly abnormal shapes and numbers of chromosomes. Most of these were lost during pregnancy, the remainder were born to show varying degrees of physical and mental abnormality.

It was then found that these errors were about equally divided between the sex chromosomes and the rest, the 22 pairs of so-called autosomes. The smallest pair of autosomes (No. 22) often fails to pair and separate regularly at the special egg formation process, at meiosis, in older women. Eggs are formed with two of this smallest chromosome; fertilized by normal sperm they give embryos with three of them. These 'trisomic' embryos (which also occur in the chimpanzee) develop into the characteristic Mongolian idiot; they have slow and defective growth of the brain and of intelligence; they also have low resistance to throat and lung infections.

Before the introduction of antibiotics these 'Mongols' nearly always died young. Darwin's tenth child, born when his wife was forty-eight, and dying at the age of five, was evidently of this type. Now these children may well survive with a declining mental age to a physical age of sixty or seventy. Mongol women have also been known to breed; half their children are then Mongols. Rarely children are born having the reciprocal defect, only one instead of three of the Mongol chromosomes. They have an opposite physical form known as Anti-Mongol. They die very young.

Of all the chromosomes in man as well as in other animals the most interesting are, and always will be, the sex chromosomes, the 23rd pair, the large X and the small Y. Women, as we saw, are XX and men are XY. Men, like other male mammals, produce sperm of two kinds, with X or with Y while women's eggs all have X. The effect is that of a Mendelian cross, more precisely a 'back-cross', $aa \times Aa$, the large X chromosome being the recessive *a* and the little Y the dominant *A*. The result is that nearly equal numbers of boys and girls are conceived and born: the one-to-one ratio we expect from a backcross.

The difference between a boy and a girl, is of course the most important genetic difference in our species or indeed in any other species with separate sexes. Throughout history it has baffled men and women, philosophers and theologians alike. But now I shall use it to illuminate other differences. Its basis is what we call a super-gene for it separates what are profoundly different types of organism, mutually adapted of course to live together, to breed together producing fertile offspring, and in so doing to love one another; but in all other respects the two sexes differ in mind and body like two distinct species. And, as with the differences between the cat and the dog, the environment as a rule plays no part in it.

The sex difference entails, as we have seen, a regulated series of consequences. The X and Y chromosomes pair at meiosis in the formation of sperm whether in a man or a monkey or a rat. We then find that they pair in a short segment in which the two chromosomes agree and correspond. In this 'pairing segment' they cross over and form chiasmata which hold them together. But in addition each chromosome has a non-pairing or, as we call it, a 'differential segment'. There is a short one in Y a long one in X. This is responsible for their different sizes. It is also responsible, evidently, for their different actions since they differ in appearance at cell division as well as in behaviour in the nucleus of the resting cell (Fig. 3.1).

What these different actions mean becomes clear when the two chromosomes occasionally fail to cross over. They then fail to hold together and are unable to pass into opposite germ cells. Then sperm

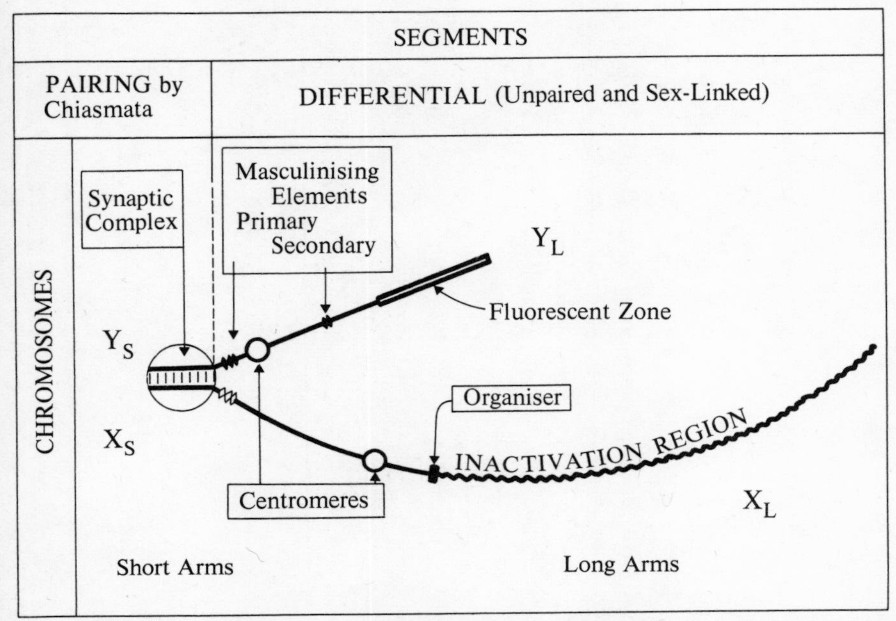

Fig. 3.1 The male sex chromosome complement as paired in germ cell formation in man. Note centromeres; segment of X inactivated in females; fluorescent segment and masculinizing elements in Y; pairing segments; differential segments. (After Darlington, 1976)

can be formed with both X and Y, with two X's or two Y's, and also without either of them. When these fertilize eggs with their regular single X four abnormal kinds of embryo commonly arise and develop (Table 3.1).

Most of the abnormal embryos conceived are lost as abortions during pregnancy or as stillbirths so that less than one in a hundred of total live births is abnormal. Fewer still grow up to be adult people and nearly all of these are deformed, defective and sterile or infertile. The severely abnormal survive at the cost of much suffering to themselves, to their parents, and to the community at large. But from them we have learned lessons of immeasurable value about heredity and variation in man and also about the mental and sexual behaviour of ordinary men and women.

We need to ask first a very general question. How are we to fit these people, these occurrences, these mutations, into our scheme of things? Are their abnormalities environmental or hereditary? Evidently they are neither. Nothing in the environment can affect their particular

Table 3.1 *Common types of normal and deviant sex determination, their causes and consequences (after Polani, 1970)*

Egg	*Sperm*	*Embryo*	*Sex*	*Fertility*	*Name*	*Character*	*Range of Intelligence*	*Per thousand*
X	X	XX	female	+	–	–	normal	495
X	Y	XY	male	+	–	–	normal	500
X	O*	XO	female	sterile	Turner	short	low	0·4
X	XX	XXX	female	infertile	–	–	low	0·8
X	XY	XXY	male	sub-sterile	Klinefelter	feminine	low	2·5
X	YY	XYY	male	sub-sterile	–	tall	low	1·5

* no sex chromosome

character except by killing them. They do not inherit their properties from any ancestor who had those properties. And, since they are mostly sterile, they cannot pass on their properties to any descendants. These properties of body and mind are however certainly innate, certainly genetic. They are certainly due to their chromosomes, to the whole set of 45, 46, or 47 of them.

They are variable properties owing to the variations in all these chromosomes. The XYY men show a violence, for example, which appears only in a small proportion, apparently at the lower end of the range of intelligence and social class where behaviour is less well controlled. We can say therefore that these are chromosome mutations. They are like big gene mutations affecting many parts of the body including the brain and a wide range of form and behaviour.

Chromosome mutations affect especially the sex chromosomes and the shortest (No. 22) of the ordinary chromosomes. Why is this? It is because pairing and the crossing-over, the chiasmata, which hold partner chromosomes together, sometimes fail and, where the pairing segment as in X and Y and No. 22 is shortest, it fails most often.

The second question we have already asked is what these abnormalities tell us about normal sex determination. The answer is that the initial step is one which decides whether the embryo develops testes and not ovaries. This step is evidently determined by the presence of the differential segment of the Y chromosome. The testes then secrete hormones which set in motion a sequence of reactions in the embryonic brain and in behaviour which, as we saw, continue until sexual maturity and beyond.

We can now go further. The effective piece of the Y chromosome, the determining group of genes, seems to lie next to the pairing segment. Apparently it can cross over to the X and give an X chromosome which is male determining, but not quite successfully so. It is probably from such occasional accidents that individuals arise whose structure is of one sex while their temperament is of the other. They have, it is said, the wrong 'gender'. They may or may not be homosexual. They may or may not be fertile. But it is certain that they cannot be expected to behave like sexually normal people without doing harm to themselves. Formerly society (following scripture) made rules for them, or rather against them. Now we have learned to help them to discover the rules their chromosomes are making for themselves.

What then makes heredity? It lies entirely or almost entirely in the chromosomes. It is divisible into small pieces arranged in a thread. It is composed of parts, the genes, recognized by Mendelian inheritance, and by recombination through crossing-over. But many of the parts, the polygenes, are too small, their actions too minute, to be recognized in this way. There are also larger units, segments of chromosomes like the differential segments of X and Y, which we may trace right back through the primates and the mammals and which we describe as super-genes. And all the chromosomes can break the rules of heredity from time to time making rules of their own.

VI *Populations*

The principle that the chromosomes carry heredity and that differences between chromosomes are responsible for differences in heredity—for almost all variation, and particularly all Mendelian differences—means that we can describe all these things in two ways: first, in terms of the similarities of kindred, parents and offspring or brothers and sisters, and second in terms of the chromosomes we can see in their cells, body cells and germ cells. The father who has two corresponding genes *A* and *a* produces equal numbers of germ cells *A* and *a* and equal numbers of children carrying his *A* and his *a* whatever the child may get from the mother. His 46 chromosomes pair and separate in germ-cell formation so that each germ cell has half of his chromosomes, he will therefore pass on each of them to half his children. And in those children they will meet corresponding chromosomes from their mother.

The consequences of these rules are well known in Mendelian experiments where (as we saw) $Aa \times Aa$ gives proportions of 1 *AA* : 2 *Aa* : 1 *aa* in the progeny. This is the rule which shows us what has (as we also saw) baffled the man in the street: namely that what we call heredity is responsible, not only for sibs being like their parents and like one another, but also for their being unlike. Indeed the more unlike the ancestors were the more unlike will be their descendants.

This is the *family* side of heredity. But in all human societies wider relationships are important. The prohibition or taboo on mating or marrying within the family, to which I shall return more than once, means that every family is part of a larger breeding community. Its outbreeding links it by heredity with all the members of this community. For example, all people with any English (or Welsh) ancestry are cousins, near or remote. They have ancestors 10, 20 or 30 generations back in common with one another. They do not have chromosomes in common because the chromosomes are broken up by crossing-over in every germ-cell formation. But they have parts of their chromosomes, their genes or super-genes in common.

How are these genes and chromosomes related? This is the *population* side of heredity. Every outbreeding community may be thought of as having a pool of genes and chromosomes from which its individual members are taken. At random? Not quite at random but for many purposes and if the parents were not close kindred, nearly so. Two interesting consequences follow from this conclusion.

First, if a particular gene has dominant and recessive alternatives it will exist in the population in three forms *AA*, *Aa*, and *aa*, with the first two looking alike. *Aa* will be concealed. How common then will it be? The answer is that if the frequencies of the genes *A* and *a* are p and q, the sperm and eggs will be in those frequencies and the three classes of organisms, of men or women, will be in the proportions of $p^2 : 2pq : q^2$.

This principle, which as schoolboys we learnt at the age of nine, is known as the Hardy–Weinberg Law (so that we have a law at last). It came to light when Archibald Garrod in 1902 discovered among his patients a darkening of urine, an abnormality known as aklaptonuria. He found that it occurred in Britain in about one person in a million. We might infer from this that a recessive gene is responsible; that about one gene in a thousand in the whole population is the defective recessive; and hence that about one person in five hundred is hybrid for the gene. But, as always happens in the study of populations, we have to make a correction. About 1 per cent of all marriages are, or used to be, between first cousins. And, through having the gene in common, they produce one-third of all the alkaptonurics. So the frequency of the gene, as we suppose, is not one in a million but a little less.

For most of its life the rare recessive gene is floating unseen, although not always without any effect, in the population; waiting as it were to pick up its identical mate, waiting particularly for the chance of a first cousin marriage which may never come its way before by chance it is ultimately extinguished.

The unlucky appearance of such defects in the progeny of cousin marriages seems to justify the condemnation of inbreeding. But the defects are the result of the rarity of inbreeding in large modern populations. As I have found from separate family studies, they are the consequence rather than the cause of the incest taboo.

VII *Kinship and Correlation*

Our second population puzzle concerns just this question of how many genes first cousins have in common. To be sure most members of our species probably have most of their genes in common. After all we know that some of them are held in common with apes and monkeys. But here we are interested to know what proportion of their genes close kindred in an ordinary outbred population have in common *by virtue of their kinship*; that means what proportion of the variable ones. The answer is that every child has half its genes or chromosomes in common with each parent, and *vice versa*. Moreover, since each sib gets two randomly different halves, different sibs on the average have half their genes in common. Each remove in kinship, each intervening meiosis with chromosome halving, indeed halves the common share in genes. Grandparents and grandchildren, or uncles and nephews have a quarter in common. First cousins an eighth, second cousins a sixteenth and so on. Hence the high frequency of alkaptonurics from marriages between kindred.

Before Mendel had been rediscovered or the chromosomes were known, Francis Galton had invented a method for measuring the resemblances of relatives as compared with the largely 'unrelated' members of a population. It was the method of what he called correlation. This method can be applied, for example, to measure the similarity in fertility between mothers and daughters or in height between fathers and sons. It shows them to have a correlation of one half, or as we may say, half way between identity and complete randomness. So it is, in general, with all corresponding measurements of fathers and sons. For first cousins or second cousins, as we expect, the correlation is of the order of $\frac{1}{8}$ or $\frac{1}{16}$. This principle was pointed out by Udny Yule in 1906 and in 1918 R. A. Fisher showed that correlations, for example, for height agreed with 'the supposition of Mendelian inheritance' provided that a large number of differences were responsible and were being inherited.

Evidently therefore there are large numbers of gene differences affecting measurable and, as we say, continuous variations in plants, animals, and man, variations which have small effects and are inherited in a Mendelian way. These are Mather's polygenic differences.

These correlations have a wide significance but in making use of them we must always make corrections to allow for what we know of systems of breeding and kinship. Inbred communities are small communities and the genes in common, as I said by virtue of kinship, become too close to unity to be argued about. Assortative mating of parents who choose one another for their resemblance again reduces all genetic divergences in the progeny. And one final reservation: one-egg twins should have (as we saw) all their genes in common but (as we shall see), they are not always genetically identical.

Our experience guided by these rules tells us about what we can expect, what heredity can teach us, when we look at human populations. But it also tells us something of what human populations can teach us about heredity. It works both ways.

VIII *Professions and Pedigrees*

In human societies, in populations of men and women, we have peculiarly human opportunities of exploring the action of heredity. In all animals similar types live together and breed together. As we say, birds of a feather flock together. Their sexual lives are a continuation, a concentration, if you like, of their social lives. But human societies are divided into groups which differ, as we have seen, in their following a host of different ways of making their living. They have different aptitudes and skills of hand and eye, of speech and mind, and therefore preferences for different activities, different trades, professions, and recreations. If they do anything well, they choose for occupations what they do best and find easiest. These lead to the mating and marriage of men and women within groups of similar likes and dislikes, aptitudes, and interests. Whether the marriage is chosen by the spouses or arranged by their parents, or fixed in kinship by the customs of society, the result is always, as we say, *assortative*. If there is a genetic element in the assortment then we are bound to get the same kind of result as the breeder of horses or dogs gets when by selective mating he produces a breed with the characteristics he wants.

The common result of this effect of assortative mating is the formation of professional castes in all ancient and most modern societies. From these castes, in India especially, ever finer sub-castes are derived which govern the life of the country so that family interest smothers the merits and opinions of individuals. But in advanced Western societies these processes of breeding are more diverse and we can follow through the pedigrees of families whose activities are documented and open to detailed comparison. These pedigrees show us that assortative mating is often favoured by social conditions. This is the case at both ends of the social spectrum. At the bottom combinations of low intelligence, disturbed personality, and addiction to violence give us the characteristic family patterns of the criminal class to which I shall return later. At the top, in the educated class or rising into it, we find that ability is inherited. Moreover, specific abilities of different kinds can be combined. They can be brought together and they can be separated.

Here there are many notable contrasts. The Dutch painters over several centuries worked in guilds and married in guilds and begot painting families. But the English painters who have never worked in guilds are nearly all individual and unrelated. There are hardly any painting families. In music and in the theatre, on the other hand, where men and women equally take part, marriage and breeding are everywhere for this reason favoured within the profession. The English

Who's Who in the Theatre consequently is able to publish 80 pages of English theatrical pedigrees covering 300 years which for interpretation deserve a book to themselves.

These examples of hereditary achievement concern what Galton 100 years ago called 'Hereditary Genius'. They represent the steps by which the abilities of individuals have contributed to the building of civilization. For the understanding of heredity, however, disabilities and failures, which are what we now have to consider, are equally important.

IX *Chemical Heredity: Disease and Diet*

Many genetic differences exist in man which can be identified when they have chemical effects which are immediate and consequently exact. Nothing in nature can then intervene between the gene and its product. They are at the opposite pole from those minute polygenic differences which can be traced only by their remote effects on variable measurements of size, number, and rates of development. Often, indeed usually, they are recognizable by their existing together with their alternatives in stable proportions in a population. These 'balanced polymorphisms' occur in all species of plants and animals and were first defined by E. B. Ford. They maintain themselves frequently because they give us, or any other animal or plant, several lines of defence against unforeseen dangers, notably those of infectious disease. Sometimes *A* gives more resistance than *a* and sometimes *Aa* gives more than either.

Our blood groups are the best-known balanced polymorphisms in man and their proportions are often so constant that they enable us to distinguish one race from another like the Gypsies from the Gorgios in Europe, after many centuries of contact. Or Jews returning to Israel from different countries after many centuries of separation. Other polymorphisms by their chemical effects enable us to see how and why peoples have moved in the past, what diseases have attacked them, what foods they have eaten, and what evolutionary processes have enabled them to survive (Table 3.2).

Genetic resistance to disease in principle was probably recognized in ancient times but its scientific importance was first brought to light by a certain Dr. W. C. Wells in 1813 in a lecture in London later published by the Royal Society. He pointed out that Europeans were excluded from West Africa by their susceptibility to diseases to which Negroes were resistant. He argued that the differences between races had arisen as a result of this kind of action which Darwin later called

Table 3.2 *How blood group polymorphism frequencies can be used to establish origin by race and also hybridization between races* (*after Race & Sanger, 1975*)

		Negroes				*White*
Critical Polymorphism		*W. African*	*S. African*		*American*	
body-type	Duffy	90%	—		68%*	0·0%
antigen	V(Rhesus)	40%	33%		27%*	0·2%*
		Mongolian				*Eskimo and White*
		Carib	*Chippewa*	*Japanese*	*Chinese*	
antigen	Diego	36%	11%	8–12%	2·5%	0·0%
		New Guinea, Sepik			*Negro, European, Mongolian*	
antigen	Gerbich	64%			0·0%	

* from race mixture

Note: These are differences which have probably arisen by recent mutation. Others found in the ancient ABO series seem to have arisen by loss in peripheral races during man's paleolithic expansion (see *The Evolution of Man & Society*: America, ch. 25; Oceania, ch. 27). The Duffy blood group is one of the Negro methods of providing resistance to malaria.

natural selection. In this way opinions about human heredity and disease lay at the root of the modern theory of evolution.

The most important of these diseases was malaria. Many forms of malaria exist and are due to different species of parasites (*Plasmodium*) carried by different species of mosquito (*Anopheles*). This knowledge makes it possible to control the disease in certain regions, but the control has not remedied the grave evolutionary effects which the disease has inflicted, by way of natural selection, on peoples, chiefly black peoples, inhabiting the tropics of the Old World.

The world-wide medical studies of the last twenty years have made it clear that the *Plasmodium* parasites, the mosquito carriers, and the human species, have evolved together for millions of years. They have all been continually improving their methods by genetic change; for the parasites they are methods of attack, for man methods of defence, and for the mosquito methods of partnership. What man has done (as we have learned following Allison's discovery in 1954) is to produce by gene mutation hundreds of chemical variants of his blood pigment, the haemoglobin on which both the mosquito and the parasite feed. These were less digestible for the parasite (and perhaps for the mosquito) and thus enabled the human victim to resist infection and to survive. But all these variants were deleterious to the health and fertility of the resistant human beings. The result was to favour a balance in the proportions of the genes responsible for normal and for one or other resistant form of haemoglobin.

One after another these variants have been tested by natural selection and superimposed on one another in the long struggle between man and malaria. The most recent to be discovered was in isolated groups of Bedouins in many Arabian oases. They had a resistant but highly deleterious 'sickle cell' haemoglobin. By selection they had developed the faculty of continuing as adults the production of yet a third type of haemoglobin, that which is usually confined to the foetus and the newborn child but is fortunately resistant to the malarial parasite. In other words a new genetic mutation in the people of these oases had maintained an infantile condition in maturity. It had been favoured by selection because it had partly corrected the character of the blood so as to give resistance to infection.

Such genetic situations illustrate the succession of crises which different races of men have had to meet. Above all they concern peoples living in marshy surroundings, or in the tropics, or crowded in cities. They have continually operated to protect the tropics, the marshes, and the cities from invasion by human beings coming in from healthier conditions outside, especially from temperate climates; that is until Europeans discovered other remedies. They have also continually weakened in health and fertility the people living in the tropics. Notably, until the development and introduction of European medicine, they have prevented or delayed the growth of cities in the lowland tropics.

Indeed they have prevented the development of civilization in the tropics except as an overflow from the northern temperate zone. Recently (8 May 1973), the President of Sierra Leone established an Order of the Mosquito in honour of the insect which kept the white man out of Negro Africa. But this insect had also kept the Negro inside Africa; that is until white men took him out.

The Negroes who were taken to America as slaves carried with them the genes for defective haemoglobin. These they have retained in the United States after the malaria to which they gave resistance had been eliminated. The U.S. Department of Health accordingly proposed, in 1970, to make a survey of the frequency of these genes in the Negro population. It abandoned the project however on realizing its implications. It would unfairly brand a part of the population with a stigma of genetic inferiority; and further the stigma could be removed only by preventing the carriers of the gene from breeding.

Our new knowledge has enabled experts (like Zulueta) to identify what happened in long-disputed historical situations. For example, it seems clear that the Mediterranean region in classical times was free from the dangerous carrier mosquitoes. But Alexander met one of them in India. Its bite gave him a slowly incubating parasite (*P. vivax*) which after twenty months killed him in Babylon. Later, under the Roman Empire, deforestation changed the situation. The work, shared by the iron axe and the goat, led to soil erosion, the spread of marshes, and the introduction of Asian and African mosquitoes carrying several species of *Plasmodium*. These, it seems, served to reduce and debilitate the populations of the low coastal areas of Anatolia, Greece, and Italy, opening the way of invasion for the healthy barbarians who destroyed the Empire.

Another field requiring genetic and historical study concerns the relations of man with his diet. We know how individuals and also races differ in their tastes and preferences for food. We know that one man's meat is another man's poison. These differences, like those of disease resistance, have a genetic and racial basis.

All animals and plants have to produce a variety of ferments or enzymes for purposes of their own nourishment. However wasteful men may be in dealing with the world outside them, their bodies are thrifty and this thrift selection ensures that they do not often produce an enzyme that they do not need, or for longer than they need it. For this reason the infant mammal whose mother gives it milk containing milk-sugar or lactose produces, in its stomach, an enzyme *lactase* which breaks down this sugar. But it stops producing the enzyme when it is weaned. In the evolution of certain peoples, however, a genetic change has occurred. The production of lactase is continued throughout childhood and throughout life.

Why do they do this? Evidently because in no other way could adults live and thrive on fresh milk. With this enzyme they can become pastoral people. The Mongols and the Bedouins in Asia and the Masai and the Fulani in Africa breed cattle, sheep, camels, and horses and feed on their milk. Other peoples like the Chinese, the Bantu, and the Israeli Jews usually have an insufficiency of lactase. They can take milk in quantity only as infants; or when by souring the lactose has been turned to lactic acid as in yoghurt or butter milk or cheese. For this reason the Mongol and the Chinese, the Arab and the Jew, have an irreconcilable racial difference in their diet and in the way of life which supports this diet.

Evidently the full development of pastoralism has depended on polygenic mutations: the two changes to pastoralism and to adult lactase must have spread together through human populations as the populations themselves spread after the development of agriculture. For example, the Negroes from Cameroun to Sierra Leone keep cattle which, as Murdoch has pointed out, they do not milk. The cattle probably came from Nubia in a first wave of pastoralism about 3000 B.C. before the Beja in Egypt had taught the Nubians to milk—and had given them by hybridization the selective advantage of their new genetic capacity which led to the expansion of the Hamitic peoples in Africa.

In Europe the spread of pastoralism seems to have been conditioned by general lactase production and milk-sugar digestion. The advantages have lain partly in the ability to drink milk, and to absorb vitamin D and calcium from it. But in addition it may well be (according to Flatz and Rotthauwe) that the lactase is directly valuable in promoting calcium absorption in the gut. Both these properties would be useful in a climate where sunshine is restricted, where rickets is frequent, and where clothing is indispensable. Thus the genetic basis of milk consumption, apparently newly acquired, shows us how evolutionary changes which are still taking place may have influenced the ordinary healthy occupations, diets, and distributions of human races.

The force of these evolutionary and historic interactions between man, his food, and his diseases is now indisputable. But their variety means that another lifetime's work will be needed to define them. How, for example, are we to look upon the contrasted attitudes of different peoples to salt? We can see that when men began to make pottery and to boil their meat and vegetables they lost salt. Salt, therefore, by natural stages acquired economic, social, and religious importance. We can understand why men sweating in Africa and in Asia demanded blood as a source of salt, drank it with their milk and kept their cattle for these uses alone. But why then did the Jews drain the blood from their kosher meat and so lose the salt? Clearly they came from a salt-rich region as did all the first farmers and herdsmen. But was there also a genetic link in the sequence of events?

Whatever the answer to these questions the principle is clear that human activities have themselves been responsible for the actions of diet and disease in changing the course of human evolution and human history, and *vice versa*. They have done so in ways of which kings, priests, and peasants have been only vaguely aware; and in ways the consequences of which cannot be remedied easily or quickly. Still less can they be ignored or suppressed. They demand for their correction a genetic and evolutionary understanding.

X *How do we recognize Heredity?*

Now we may ask how we came by our ideas of heredity and the words we use to describe it. There have always been, and always will be, two opposite approaches. We may look at individuals and their heredity as a whole, as something undivided although not indivisible. We can compare and contrast these individuals. We do so inevitably, however, by measurement. This method lends itself to the description, a statistical description, of populations. It was the approach of Galton and the biometricians. The opposite approach is that of Mendel. It is to pull the individual and his heredity to pieces and examine each piece separately.

Between these two methods there is an immense gap. Partly it is bridged by looking at the chromosomes. Partly also it is bridged if we look at the whole business in historical sequence. Precise human heredity was first seen, already in antiquity, through the action of dominant genes appearing in family lines. The significance of recessive genes appearing unpredictably could be understood only when Mendelism came to be understood in 1900. The connections between these genes and the chromosomes that carry or include them became clear only with sex-linked inheritance ten years later. At the same time the somewhat different principle of the effects of chromosome mutation and crossing-over became clear in animals and plants. Only fifty years later, with the study of human chromosomes in 1956, did the practical implications of these discoveries for man become fully evident and indisputable.

It is not surprising, therefore, that when we look at the evidence of heredity as a whole we see how many-sided it is and how contradictory and deceptive it can be. The mechanisms of heredity, as I have described them, look like stratagems. They have had, we now recognize, by their capacity for innovation, the effect of forestalling the vicissitudes to which our forebears from the beginning have been perpetually exposed. And they may therefore also have the effect of enabling our descendants to survive the even greater vicissitudes they are likely to meet in the future. But only if they have the advantage of knowing what is happening to them.

So much for the greater and grander field of vision. But for the small and petty problems our evidences of heredity tell us something immediately useful. They tell us, apart from the fact that the chromosomes are the substance of heredity, and that the genetic code within them is its mechanism, that differences are almost our whole equipment in studying heredity. Differences are our evidence of genes. One gene has never been separated from all its neighbours in heredity. Our whole heredity is not therefore the sum either of genes or of differences. They do not tell us how our whole heredity is put together. It is something we know by its differences from other whole heredities, other whole individuals. People, including writers of textbooks who have never pondered these difficult questions themselves, continually speak of the genes doing this, and the genes doing that, when they have no evidence except that some kind of heredity is at work. Nor do they need to know more for practical purposes since no one needs to know how a clock works in order to tell the time. But they should be content to speak of what they know, that is of what is genetic and what is hereditary.

When we do speak of heredity we must weigh evidence of many kinds. We must remember that species, races, classes, and tribes differ by heredity, sexes differ by heredity, and brothers differ by heredity. Chromosomes differ by heredity in different ways: the whole chromosomes in their numbers and proportions, pieces of chromosome in their numbers, positions, and proportions, their activities or their inactivities. The genes vary in their structure from the minutest changes to great blocks displaced. Their effects vary from wholesale disaster to the minute polygenic effect with its statistical indications, or again the specific little change in an enzyme with its specific chemical and medical indication.

It is often said that we cannot experiment with man. But, as we shall see, situations are abundantly available that are as good as experimental. Our immense knowledge of mankind is in process of making the whole species into one vast natural experiment. There is one outstandingly important experimental situation, however, that to my knowledge has not yet been described; that is the strictly Mendelian situation of the human inter-racial F_2. For it seems that, in crosses between races, the backcross always arises to conceal the issue. What we most need to know is thus still concealed from us.

In judging heredity, what it does, how it is carried, and how it varies, we have to bear in mind these types and sources of evidence. We then have to use our experience of how selection and evolution works on differences in heredity. We have also to remember what happens and what has happened in plants and animals, as well as in bacteria and viruses, when we think of man.

Chapter 4

Brain and Intelligence

I *The Study of Differences*

In 1819 William Lawrence, a young medical professor in London, published his lectures at the College of Physicians. Under the title of *The Natural History of Man* he described the differences between human races explaining, for example, that the sexual anatomy of the Bushman and his woman was adapted to protect her from rape. These particulars gave no offence at that time but Lawrence went on to discuss principles. From the point of view of mind and body, race and breeding, heredity and selection, he argued, man could and should be considered as an animal. Such an opinion, in the view of the Lord Chancellor, threatened Religion and the Constitution. He condemned the book and Lawrence, to avoid dismissal, withdrew it. Forty years later, as President of the Royal College of Surgeons, he was able to warn the young T. H. Huxley to take heed of his lesson.

The European taboo on the discussion of man as an animal lasted until it was eventually broken by Darwin and Huxley. But in our dynamic world its place on the forbidden list was already being taken by another taboo, that on the discussion of sexual behaviour and this lasted, as we can still remember, more than another fifty years. In due course in the 1930s there followed a third taboo which now dominates the study of human problems and is likely to continue until another generation rejects and ridicules its parents' prejudices. This third line of defence against the understanding of man is the taboo on the study of hereditary differences. The one belief or emotion that unites the jarring nations today appears to be the need not to notice, and certainly not to discuss, the existence of differences between them in terms of their permanent underlying causes. Innate hereditary or genetic differences must not be admitted between individuals or groups, between classes or races, or even between the sexes. But above all what must not be discussed, what must be rejected, are differences in the foundations of human behaviour, the study of brains, of instincts, and of intelligence.

These foundations are complex and happily concealed from the public view. They must remain concealed. In a world already over-crowded and over-troubled they might cause more trouble.

Concealment, of course, means deception, pretence, and confusion. Successively with evolution, sex, and human differences, it has meant that scientists are pushed into deceiving, first themselves, then their pupils, and then the public. Thus fear of the truth, on the part of the public or of the establishment, which used to protect the central mystery of religion, has now shifted to fields of inquiry which are, next to religion, the most difficult. For in heredity and intelligence we have two subjects which inherently we can never entirely understand. Established opinion is objecting only to our making a start.

The heredity of man is contained in a sperm having atoms in number of the order of 10^{12}. The cells in his brain are of a lower order of multiplication (about 10^{10}). In their totality, in the sense that every cell is qualitatively useful, these numbers are still inconceivable. Yet we can reach illuminating and even revolutionary generalizations about both sperm and brain. They are most illuminating and most revolutionary, as you will see, when we use what we know of heredity to enlarge what we know of intelligence.

II *The Evolution of the Brain*

In attempting to show man's descent from animal ancestors Darwin drew on three great lines of comparisons: anatomy, intelligence, and instinctive behaviour. This was the order of battle with his opponents. Anatomy was settled in his lifetime—or so it seemed—and it is with anatomy we may begin.

The great achievements of the animal world, as we saw, have come from the power of movement. This power is coordinated by connecting the distance receptors, as we call them, of sight, hearing, and smell, with the brain. The brain becomes larger in proportion to the whole animal as it acquires the means of dealing with a greater and greater variety of conditions. This is what has happened in the course of the evolution of the vertebrates. The parts of the brain are themselves differentiated and it is the front part of the brain, the part most closely connected with the distance receptors, which has increased disproportionately in size (Fig. 4.1).

The hind part of the brain, the cerebellum, controls the almost automatic internal activities of the body, like balance, and it does not greatly increase in the mammals. But the cerebrum, the forebrain with its grey matter, where the past is remembered and the future is planned,

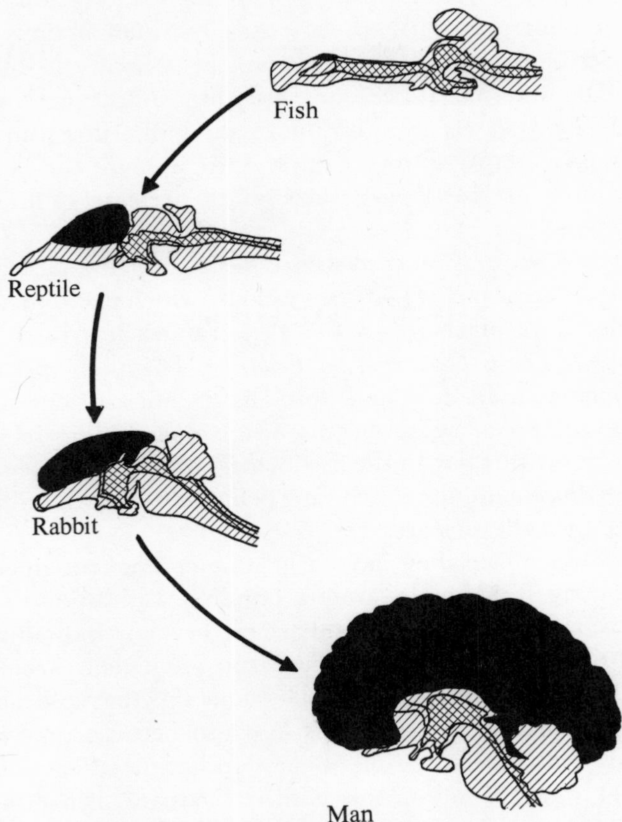

Fig. 4.1 The directed or orthogenetic evolution of the brain in vertebrates due to the enlargement of the new brain (solid) developing in front of the primitive brain (hatched) seen in mid-sagittal section (from Magoun, 1960; after Edinger, 1885)

grows larger. So much is true of the monkeys and the great apes. But in man, as we have seen, two other momentous properties have developed in the cerebral hemispheres: the faculties of speech and of right-handedness.

For understanding how animals behave the experiments of neurologists with reflexes and of ethologists with instincts are both indispensable, but they have to be connected with care since they are using different methods. In consequence they speak different languages, but they agree in showing that a hierarchy of nervous processes is governing behaviour with the effects of heredity and environment variously interacting. The modes of interaction may be illustrated by considering the expression of emotions.

Emotion comes to us through the association of perceptions in the brain and it expresses itself partly by voluntary and rational or intelligent actions. But partly it expresses itself by reflex actions which are involuntary. These are of two kinds which we may call internal and external. The internal expressions are seen in the action of heart, lungs, and blood vessels and also the bristling of a dog's fur. They are often obviously adaptive: for example they prepare the body to take action at moments of danger through the release of the hormone adrenalin.

The external expressions are seen especially in the face but also in the gestures of the arms. These expressions, which are sometimes what is now called a 'displacement activity', were first described by Darwin in his book on *The Expression of the Emotions*. They demonstrate a similarity of behaviour in men and animals, a similarity due to common descent and preserved by its selective value in evolution. Its interest for us, however, goes further. In the first place, all these expressions have an instinctive component since they are behaviour (like blushing) which has not been taught or learned.

In the second place they have a genetic component since they are variable among individuals, among families, and among races. Evidently they are innate in origin and are modified by individual, family, and racial differences in temperament and intelligence which are also innate. In the variation of human behaviour they have become central elements not only for these reasons but also because (as Sherrington carefully argued) the expression of emotion has the effect of enhancing emotion. This amplification, this positive feedback, is overwhelmingly obvious when a skilful speaker (like Antony in *Julius Caesar*) addresses a public gathering, religious, political or military, for his private purposes.

The impulse to look at the action of the brain and hence the character of the mind, and to interpret both in terms of evolution, began in fact before Darwin. It began with Spencer in 1852. And in 1859 the English neurologist Hughlings Jackson argued that primitive reflexes, instincts, and appetites are lower faculties of the mind held in restraint by higher faculties of understanding, of consciousness, and of purpose. Thirty years later the German anatomist Edinger could represent the evolution of the brain in vertebrates as a process of enlargement of the forebrain, the cerebral hemisphere, where in due course experiment was able to locate the capacities of association, sight, speech, spatial sense, and memory. After these developments came two parallel insights. There was the distinction by Pavlov between conditioned and unconditioned reflexes. And there was the conflict recognized by Freud between a lower level of the inaccessible unconnected instincts operating under the pleasure principle and a higher level of rational controls evolving more rapidly subject to heredity and selection; these two levels he supposed to be usually coordinated in relation to the external world but often in conflict.

If we attempt, following Cobb and Magoun, to put these interpretations in diagrammatic connection with one another the result is naive: any diagram connecting the mind with the brain must be. But it is a step in the direction we are likely to follow.

III *The Role of Instinct*

In a striking passage in the *Origin of Species* Darwin says that he will not attempt to define instinct. He then defines it about as well as we can do today:

> Everyone understands what is meant when it is said that instinct impels the cuckoo to migrate and to lay her eggs in other birds' nests. An action which we ourselves should require experience to enable us to perform, when performed by an animal, more especially by a very young one, without any experience, and when performed by many individuals in the same way, without their knowing for what purpose it is performed, is usually said to be instinctive.

To put this another way: the limits of all mental activity are genetically determined. But while rational activity is influenced by the environment and by experience, instinctive elements may be separated in which environment plays little part and experience plays no part at all. The study of instinctive behaviour, however, began seriously only at the end of Darwin's century. Only then did the systematic comparison of man and animals resume from the point where Darwin had left it in 1873. Only then was the scope of the study of behaviour, the science of ethology, clearly marked out.

What interested Darwin in this problem is still what interests the ethologist today. It was that the behaviour of man and animals corresponded in so great a body of observable detail; and it corresponded also in expressing 'the direct action of the excited nervous system on the body, independently of the will and independently, in large part, of habit'. Further, 'the chief expressive actions exhibited by man and by the lower animals; are now innate or inherited.' This 'we may infer from their being performed by very young children, by those born blind, and by the most widely distinct races of man.'

In other words instinctive behaviour must have a structural basis in

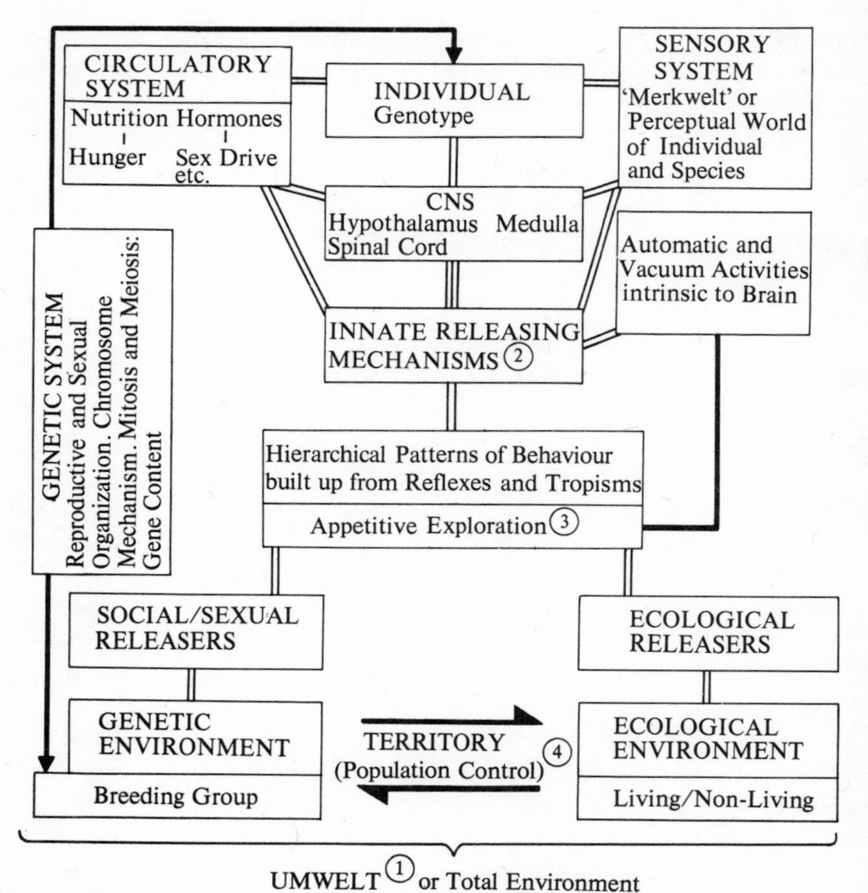

Fig. 4.2 Diagram showing how social life and evolutionary processes are adaptively connected by instinctive and also rational behaviour in Animals and Man

1. J. J. von Uexküll, 1921
2. Konrad Lorenz, 1935
3. W. Craig, 1918
4. R. Ardrey, 1970

Fig. 4.2 *Explanation of Instinctive Systems Diagram* (after Tinbergen and others)

I. The genotype of an individual determines (i) the structure of the Central Nervous System (CNS) at hatching or birth. These are nearly uniform for a species in respect of the lower (non-cerebral) elements of vertebrates below mammals.

II. Non-uniformity or variation gives rise to evolution by natural selection. It arises from recombination controlled by the Genetic System.

III. The genotype also controls (ii) the Circulatory System and hence the production and balance of hormones and their stimulation and (iii) the development of the Sensory System which gives the individual his own perceptual world.

IV. The Innate Releasing Mechanisms coordinate the reactions of the CNS to the

the nervous system which is subject to heredity. Since heredity has its own structural basis in turn in the chromosomes, its study can be used to demonstrate ancestral relationships and evolutionary processes—just as though behaviour were a form of anatomy. This indeed is what the ethologist has done, the outstanding example being in Lorenz's descriptive analysis of the behaviour of different species of ducks and geese.

In making this inquiry it was possible and necessary to examine several opposed explanations of animal behaviour (Fig. 4.2). One was the view that animals were inherently and magically, if not divinely, designed to behave advantageously, having for example, an 'instinct for self-preservation which could not or should not be taken to pieces'. Another was the view that all automatic unlearned behaviour was composed of reflexes, simple connections between sensation and action, connections not passing through the thinking brain.

The comparative study of animals has shown that neither of these explanations works. Automatic, unthinking or instinctive behaviour has an innate foundation and certainly includes reflexes both conditioned and unconditioned. But its most striking quality is in a paradox, namely that, although it is built up of elements that are entirely unlearned, some of these elements simulate the reactions of learning.

How is this? It is that they appear as patterns of response to both external and internal stimuli; and they have variable thresholds related to emotional states. Individuals vary, for example, in their thresholds for violence. They also have connections with one another and various 'releasing' and regulating mechanisms which have a rational basis.

The most elaborate and most far-reaching of these mechanisms is that known, following its discovery by W. Craig in 1918, as *appetitive behaviour*. The principle is that animals and men make exploratory

---

messages from the sensory and circulatory systems. They also embody automatic activities which have been transferred in evolution from the outside to the CNS.

V. The patterns of behaviour released in these ways often require the stimulus of exploratory activities. This Appetitive Behaviour discovers the most effective means of satisfying appetites or desires.

VI. The main responses of insects and fishes are instinctive, unlearned and non-cerebral. In the higher vertebrates these are combined with more and more learned responses seated in the cerebrum.

VII. All responses may be divided into those related and unrelated to the needs of the breeding community. The former are adapted to the needs of the whole community, now and in future generations, and hence to the evolution of the Genetic System, including its chromosome behaviour.

VIII. The possession of Territory is a connecting link between the genetic and the ecological environment and the control of population in man as in animals.

movements which discover for them by trial and error the means of obtaining emotional satisfaction. Of such exploration, such learning by trial and error and by experience, we have evidence in the behaviour of the pigeon. For unlike the cuckoo the pigeon begins to find its way home by experiment and by learning.

An example of the evidence for clear-cut non-learning is the fact that old birds build no better nests than young birds. The first knot the weaver-bird ties is as good as the last. And the cuckoo follows the exact pattern of its parents' immoral behaviour without ever having seen them. The biological problem, however, becomes more complex when we compare the songs of birds. At one extreme the garden warbler (*Sylvia burin*) produces all its parents' calls correctly even if it has been isolated from them by an experimenter. But the starling (*Sturnus vulgaris*) learns, imitates, and uses, not only its parents' calls but those of any other birds it chances to hear. And the cock chaffinch, as we know only after Thorpe's experiments, has to hear his male parent's song before he can perform.

Now the capacity to do these things, sometimes with learning and sometimes without learning, is in all cases the hereditary property of the species concerned. The differences between species as well as between sexes, must therefore depend on the existence of crucial differences in nerve connections, instinctive and associative, between various parts of the brain.

We must recall at this point that the song of a bird is not one of the properties by which it adapts itself to its physical environment. It is a property that adapts it to promote breeding by bringing the sexes together and often to guard the territory on which the family depends. In other words it is part of the breeding system, or in a larger sense the genetic system, of the species. It therefore depends for its value on its extreme uniformity. This is what excludes such properties from Mendelian experiments. The male and the female have to be exactly adapted to one another and not to the females and males of any other species.

From this condition arises the value of a simple instinctive system unencumbered, unconfused with learning. From this condition also arises the fact that each has to respond to the stimuli it receives from the activities of the other. These responses and activities have promoted (and been promoted by, with the customary feedback mechanism of selection) the processes of sexual selection with whose effects on general evolution Darwin was concerned. Hence the relative behaviour of the sexes in animals tells us more about the scope of instinct than any other source.

The most elaborate, indeed extravagant, development of an instinctive element of behaviour is seen when courtship and mating in many animals acquire the character of a ritual. The self-exaggerating feedback mechanism of sexual selection on the plane of visible form gives us (as Julian Huxley pointed out) the spider where the female is 500 times as large as the male. Or the fish where the male is a parasite attached to the belly of his spouse. On the plane of behaviour, human rituals achieve a correspondingly extravagant development for in them we can see instinctive elements variously attached to chains of aesthetic and emotional responses. Simple gestures (of the kinds Darwin discussed) then come to have symbolic meanings and ritual develops as a property of a tribe and as the expression of a religion, at once emotionally satisfying, socially unifying, and hence selectively advantageous.

In animals instinct complexes often break down. We can see this happening in ways which show us how they have been built up. For example an environmental change may give an instinct an unfavourable effect. Thus the flea carrying myxomatosis reversed the advantages of burrow life for the surviving rabbits in Britain. They then lost the part of that instinct which led them to live in burrows. This selective process did not destroy the part of the instinct which led them to dig. They now dug in all kinds of ways and places never knowing what to do with the result. Human beings, individuals, classes, and even nations, often, as we shall see, find themselves in this idiotic kind of situation.

Again, different breeds of dogs have different instincts combined (as Darwin pointed out) by artificial selection. When crossed they produce F_1's like the lurcher used for poaching with useful instincts still further combined. But in the second generation muddled unadaptive genetic recombinations appear. Consequently they are what the dog breeder calls untrainable and the public calls a mongrel. Again this situation arises among human beings.

The one extensive experiment we have as a means of studying instinct is indeed the process of domestication of animals by man, a process we see mid-way in the elephant and the camel. What it shows us is that the integration of behaviour in wild animals is partly lost. Faults occur in instinctive behaviour in nature; in domestication they survive. But also new patterns are built up. In the sheep-dog, whose intelligence and responsibility has been selected in the Balkans for about 7000 years, trials in England since 1873 have encouraged selection for new specialized and, as we may say, professional faculties.

In wild species patterns of instinctive behaviour may well be based on localized gene groups or super-genes in the chromosomes whose stability is preserved by selection. But in domestication their bases seem to be freely recombinable with variation in intelligence. In the absence of selection, however, instinctive specialization and intelligence will always decline. It has been suggested that the chimpanzee, now restricted by the spread of man to a narrower environment, has lost intelligence and the same might be true of the Australian Aborigine and the Bushman. On the other hand there are unskilled types in industrial society (like Ronald Glum in the BBC classic programme) who may well have lost intelligence as well as instinctive adaptation. These possibilities must be borne in mind since the alternative of an inherent progress of human intelligence, taken for granted by many progressive people, is neither inherent nor necessarily progress.

For man important questions arise about instinctive patterns of behaviour, with their pre-emption of the process of learning. How have the learning faculties of the cerebral cortex, for example, been superimposed on instinct in the course of evolution? How has conflict been avoided? The answer is that conflict has not been avoided. Nor has the dissatisfaction, the emotional unrest, of man been resolved. The insatiable curiosity remains with some of us; but not with most of us, and not quite throughout life (as Lorenz suggests) but narrowing more than in our nearest relatives the inquisitive monkeys. Even this result has been reached only by a slowing down of development such that the human infant is born less developed mentally than the ape and takes twice as long as the ape to reach maturity.

IV *Human Instincts*

In the early years of the twentieth century there were people known as behaviourists who were willing to believe that all human beings at birth were mentally indistinguishable. Everything in their behaviour was a matter of learning and the ability to learn was invariable and universal in the human species; and perhaps it always had been. As for instincts, men had none at all, they declared, beyond the infants' impulse to suck. This profession of faith was the behaviourists' way out of a genuine dilemma. Animals seemed to behave in ways which they could not have learned and their behaviour was constant for any species; more precisely for each sex of any species. But human beings learned so much of their behaviour and everyone behaved differently. Surely what they did they must have learned to do, learning differently from people or things outside them.

The mistake of the behaviourists was that they did not pay attention to what ordinary parents or teachers could have told them about the behaviour and intelligence of children; nor to what a number of scientists could have told them about heredity and variation among men. To be fair to the behaviourists, however, it is only in the last generation that we have been able to make a just comparison in the matter of behaviour, especially instinctive behaviour, between men and animals.

One great evolutionary consideration is bound to govern our new approach. It is that man is not a species in the same sense as any other animal. He is as we have seen a super-species, self-domesticated, if you like, with variation in genes and chromosomes, in body and brain, in form, function, and chemistry, corresponding in range with a whole complex of natural species of any other group of animals. Similar super-species in animals, cattle and dogs, pigeons and fowls, have all been made by man's purposive and divergent selection. They vary in behaviour, as he does, and in a very instructive way although on a smaller scale.

Our first task must therefore be to put man's instinctive behaviour in a workable evolutionary sequence:

(i) Man's sexual instincts obviously go back to the origin of the vertebrates and beyond. But they have been greatly elaborated and diversified in the evolution of man himself. This is partly due to their attachment to rational faculties. For example the property of assortative mating has developed rationally at least in the post-agricultural phase. But it is also partly due to the development of the irrational, and indeed anti-assortative, incest taboo. Associated with our sexual instincts, as human infancy lengthened, has also been the growth of adaptive parental instincts, leading eventually to the parental attempt equally among Christian, Muslim, and Hindu, to control mating in the next generation.

(ii) Closely related to the sexual instincts, and indeed stimulated by the sex hormones, are the social instincts, competitive and cooperative, which lie inseparably at the root of the virtues invoked by Kropotkin in his *Mutual Aid* as well as the vices described by Trotter in his *Instincts of the Herd*. Evidently the social instincts which in their cooperative aspects hold each group together, in their competitive aspects hold different groups apart. Their evolution is therefore the key, as we have seen, to the transformation of the multiracial society into the class-stratified society following the spread of agriculture.

In the early stages of this transformation of society the conflicts beween governing classes were always settled by war. Order among the other classes was everywhere preserved by the disciplines of slavery, serfdom, or caste. Under modern conditions, where unskilled manual workers of different origins, racial or religious, are brought together under crowded urban conditions, the herd instinct of Trotter takes control. It produces tension, whether in Ulster between Protestant and Catholic, or in the United States or South Africa between Black and White. Education may of course be used to enhance or diminish these tensions.

(iii) From an early stage of man's evolution there has always been an opposition between two contrasted ways of living. These are the settled and the wandering habits which have an instinctive basis but quickly acquire rational connections. In view of the prevalence of instinctive controls of movement in every group of animals it is difficult to suppose they are not operating in man. They must distinguish attachment to territory and later to the soil, from the opposite urge to move and to explore. These are contrasts of attitude between peasant or townsman and herdsman, between Isaac and Ishmael, as well as formerly between Jew and Arab.

In all such groups we notice that the selective advantage of thrift (as opposed at first to its alternative of theft) made itself felt after the development of agriculture by the development of a new instinct, originally a civilizing instinct, that for property. To the wanderer property took the form of the cattle who wandered with him. His love of this form of property has led him and his cattle to disaster whenever, as has happened recently, the control of population by war has been relaxed. For love of cattle as property has led the herdsman always to breed too many and, abandoning selection, to part with too few. The result has been over-grazing whether with sheep in Central Asia or South West Africa or with cattle in tropical Africa and India. These have created deserts, a process completed by the camel in the Sahara, in Arabia, and in the Gobi desert. Ratcliffe's story of what happened in Australia in this century repeats precisely in an advanced society the sequence of disaster among primitive hersdmen.

For the settled peasant in other parts of the world, the love of property attached itself to the land before it spread to all the things he could keep and collect on the land. Again the instinct for collecting, which began as in other animals as an adaptive property, could always in man spread beyond reason; it could become a hoarding mania, as Karel Czapek showed us in his story of the dung beetle; or as represented by the late Emperor of Ethiopia who stored his gold under the carpet. But in its normal form it provides the means of livelihood at the hunting and collecting stage of human evolution. It is then attached to a variety of rational aptitudes, above all in observing, classifying, and naming plants, animals, and minerals, skills diversely displayed by primitive peoples. These skills with an instinctive beginning were the foundation of most of the civilized arts and sciences. Attached to other skills in advanced societies they promote the formation of museums and libraries; detached, they lead to acquisition and classification by eccentric individuals often without any purpose or value at all.

In advanced societies, with the extreme heterogeneity which follows outbreeding we see instinctive behaviour of ancient origin mobilized and exploited in three different and entirely modern fields: the occupational, recreational, and ideological. The choice of occupation is certainly governed by physical and mental skills which are genetic. They are partly within the range of instinct: for example where plants and animals, soil and sea, in other words our habitat, is concerned. Then a judgement which is instinctive and intuitive often seems to direct our activities. The sense of balance or the absence of vertigo in the Iroquois Indians is an example of a purely sensory faculty governing choice of occupation and no doubt many tribal characters are of this adaptive kind. In the choice of recreation such instinctive preferences operate most directly: the instinct for play precedes the skills which later reinforce it. What of the irreconcilable opposition between those who love killing and those who hate killing? For both emotional attitudes we can scarcely avoid seeing an instinctive basis, surely related to the distinction between the hunter and the collector, between the worshippers of animals and of plants.

(iv) A gambling instinct was and is obvious in the hunting phase and continues today to be the mainspring, not only of the hunting activity as a recreation, but of most of the other recreations of civilized man which have been invented to occupy the leisure or relieve the monotony of whole classes of society who lack the resources for constructive recreation. Exceptionally of course an uncontrollable and instinctive gambling addiction, obsession or mania, as described and suffered by Dostoevsky, can seize and destroy the most intelligent of men.

The thousand disconnected and generally useless or even dangerous philias and phobias from which men suffer may be regarded as the materials from which useful instincts might be constructed. But more probably as a rule they are the débris from the breakdown of instincts in the processes of genetic recombination of an outbred society. Whichever they are they have the incurable independence and resistance to reason of instinctive behaviour. When they are attached to particular personalities they can have shattering historical effects as kings and dictators, ancient and modern, have copiously demonstrated.

The variety of recombination in outbred populations tends to break down their adaptive heredity or fitness. This leads, with men as well as with dogs or rabbits to a breakdown of instincts. The modes of breakdown of the sexual instinct, its failure and distortion, the conflict of sex and gender, are well known and are sometimes due, as we have seen, to identifiable changes in the chromosomes. Every combination and every gradation is found between the presence and the absence of sexual instinct, fertility and parental instinct. Indeed the wrong combinations are continually revealed, mildly by the practices of contraception and adoption, violently by the incidence of baby-snatching and baby-battering. Another instinct which can fail, as I have argued from dynastic examples, is the incest taboo itself. The result may then be, as we have seen, another set of disturbances, the segregation of an encyclopaedic variety of rare deleterious Mendelian recessives.

Thus we find, as we should expect, many and variable attachments of instincts to rational processes and to one another. Such attachments would begin in tribal groups whose consequent success would lead to their expansion in numbers and distribution, and to their spreading or diffusion after agriculture, within technical and governing classes, priestly or military, ultimately over the whole earth. The effects of this expansion are surely what we see in Levy-Brühl's contrast between the advanced mind and the primitive mind which it is now, as we hope, superseding.

Man has developed faculties of learning, memory, and reasoning which have not destroyed the instinctive basis of his behaviour but have masked it, distorted it, and above all have combined with it. When the combinations differ merely among individuals and families they are often eccentric and disadvantageous; we may speak of them as neuroses or addictions, phobias or philias. But when they are characteristic of established races and classes it is because they have an adaptive and also a predictive value. More than this, as Darwin suggested in the *Descent of Man*, they become the basis of social customs. They may have the features and the force of morals and of religion.

V *The Genetics of the Brain*

At this point we must ask how the brain and behaviour are connected. Particularly we must ask how heredity and the chromosomes on the one side, and the structure and the chemistry of the brain on the other side, can help us in making this connection. The main fields of evidence are now appearing. They are of five kinds. First, there are general anatomical differences among men and women. Secondly, there are the effects of sex chromosomes and the chemical sex hormones. Thirdly, there are other biochemical effects of particular genes. Fourthly, there are the effects of abnormal chromosome complements arising by accident or by mutation. And lastly, there is something connected with all these studies, but needing to be handled separately, namely the measurement of behaviour in the form of intelligence.

Anatomists formerly used to say much more about variation in the brain than their modern successors. For example, in 1867, Quain wrote: 'The comparison of human brains with one another establishes the existence of a relation between mental development and the complication, size, and depth of the cerebral convolutions and the extent of the grey matter contained in them'. This is true and it is still worth saying.

Our modern anatomists agree that within the heterogeneous populations they study, the size of the brain and of each of its parts, the shape and structure of the cerebrum, are all extremely variable. The analogy is frequently made between the individuality of brains or even of a part, the thalamus, and of finger-prints. Lashley points out that the fissuring of each cerebral hemisphere has a familial character. And the comparison of Bushman or Aborigine with European gives it a racial character.

There are many other individual undescribed variations in the brain and the nervous system which (as the late W. E. Le Gros Clark told me) practising surgeons have to take into account when they unexpectedly discover them in the course of their operations. Such are the variations in the fibre connections between the thalamus and the spinal cord. Some of these abnormalities of the spine and cerebellum have been noted in connection with specific genetic defects such as failures of muscular control. Again the arterial supply varies as to different parts and as to the whole of the brain and any defects in it will inevitably damage, first the development of the brain, and then its mature activity.

At opposite poles of the study of brain genetics are the problems of size as a whole and difference in detail. The evolutionary increase in size we have considered in relation to the fossil record and the selective process. Recently also Van Valen has looked into the question of the possible speed of selection effects. Localised differences in form, on the other hand, are an almost unexplored field.

To obtain decisive evidence of the inheritance of differences of structure and of mental or sensory properties connected with them might seem to be a hopeless enterprise in man. For we have to observe several *propositi* alive and examine one of them dead. Yet this has been done in Oxford. The late Sir Edward Poulton F.R.S. (1856–1943), a Darwinian notable whom I knew, inherited from his father a lack of any sense of smell. Knowing this, he had his father's brain examined *post mortem* in the Department of Human Anatomy where it was found (as he told my colleague, Prof. E. B. Ford) that the olfactory bulbs were missing. The absences of the structure and function were evidently connected in father and son and connected also by heredity; both individuals were probably heterozygous for this rare mutation. Obviously, for the inquisitive there is a great deal more of this kind of genetic evidence to be found out.

Ever since the discovery by Broca of the speech area in the brain, it has been of interest to know whether this area varied in structure naturally between individuals. Now Geschwind has shown that the speech region in the left hemisphere is usually larger than the corresponding non-speech region in the right hemisphere. Sometimes it is the other way round, perhaps in left-handed people with the speech centre on the opposite side. But the difference is present already at birth and it is not found in the anthropoid apes who have developed no speech and no right-handedness.

No doubt racial differences will be found in the speech centres and their auditory connections and these will eventually be related to racial differences concerned with language, notably grammar and perhaps phonetics. All that we know at present, however, concerns the smaller size of brain of the Australian Aborigines discussed by Woollard and Baker, and the character of the septal nuclei in Papuans noted by Gajdusek.

One end of the range of variation in the brain has long been studied, that represented by the brains of imbeciles, which together with their chromosomes constitute our main debt to this unfortunate section of the population. Thomas Willis, the Professor of Anatomy at Oxford, in his marvellously illustrated account of 1681, described 'the brain of a certain youth that was foolish from his birth . . . the bulk of the whole brain was . . . thinner and lesser than usual . . . the interior parts could be lifted up and turned back'.

Today we can go much further with imbeciles. We can classify them by their particular defects which prove to be of four kinds: those due to chemically specific genes like phenylketonuria; those due to identifiable chromosome abnormalities; those due to environmental defects such as rubella infection or drug damage; and finally those clinically classified but of still unspecifiable origin.

The work of Crome and Stern on these lines already gives a picture of the lower end of the normal curve in the variation of the human brain. Nearly all imbecile brains (95 per cent) are defective in structure. A few seem to be only reduced in size—down to the microcephalic limit of 100 c.c. The greater part, however, have specific defects. Of these the most remarkable are absence of the hindbrain, the cerebellum, absence or reduction of the connection between the two cerebral hemispheres, fusion of the two hemispheres and calcification of the inner surfaces of the ventricles. Many have combinations of these defects with one another and with other bodily abnormalities.

Two specific chromosome abnormalities have effects on the brain which will serve as examples of their range. Turner's syndrome, the XO type of sterile female, is the mildest deficiency; Money explains that it shows no general mental defect but only what must be a localized and parietal error in the cerebrum causing space-form blindness. The opposite extreme, which is only just compatible with life, is the trisomic for No. 13 chromosome. It rarely survives to be born and when born shows polydactyly, microcephaly, and usually undivided cerebrum, with ear, eye, and lip defects. In some individuals there is no olfactory lobe of the cerebrum but in others there are only internal malformations of the brain.

The contrast in effect between these chromosome abnormalities and specific deleterious genes is remarkable. The defect known as *phenylketonuria*, like the alkaptonuria studied by Garrod, is due to an error in the body chemistry, the absence of an enzyme breaking down certain proteins. As a result a particular molecule (phenylalanine) is left in the blood and causes irreparable damage to the developing brain. If the error is detected soon after birth and the diet is corrected by removing the difficult proteins, mental defect can be avoided. Conversely, according to Harlow, introducing excess of phenylalanine into an infant monkey's diet will cause imbecility, something which is otherwise unknown in wild monkeys because they do not accumulate recessives like the more widely outbred human beings. A number of such devastating genetic defects, due to failure to break down fats or proteins, are known to damage the human brain and cause mental defect.

The contrast in effect between specific deleterious genes and abnormal chromosome types indicates how the whole machinery works. The chromosomes control chemically the total development of the body and they do so in a variety of ways throughout its whole course and affecting many structures. The genes whose specific and separate effects we can see are those with chemically limited effects causing damage at a late stage of development and at a molecular and cellular level of size. In either the chemical or the structural situation the damage, once it has occurred, is irreparable. But both chromosome and gene defects can often now be recognized early, even before birth.

The study of abnormal chromosome types has shown that all of them affect the brain and depress intelligence. As in our two examples the lowering due to variation in sex chromosomes, X or Y, is slight; that due to autosomes is severe. Individuals with abnormal numbers of sex chromosomes, X or Y, occur not only in the range shown in Table 3.1 but up to the number of five or six. Always we must remember, however, that in abnormal individuals it is the chromosome outfit as a whole that decides the character of the body, the brain, and the intelligence and this aggregate effect for the normally represented chromosomes is as variable in abnormal people as in the crowd of normal people.

The existence of a wide range of abnormal numbers of sex chromosomes offers us a fertile field of study in what is man's great natural experiment. Here are these chromosomes which govern sex; they also govern the brain and intelligence somewhat differently in the two sexes. They vary in number giving a variety of abnormalities whose genetic cause is precisely known, simply because the chromosomes, as I have said, carry their pedigrees on their backs.

As we have seen, genes on the Y chromosome cause testes to grow instead of ovaries. These testes secrete hormones which, when the blood circulation begins to activate the hypothalamus in the brain, shift the relative development of the two cerebral hemispheres in the male, rather than in the female direction.

The difference between the male and female hormones takes effect, not only in development, but also in the sexual and general behaviour of the mature man and woman. It is for this joint reason that the male and female think differently and behave differently, as the mother can observe in the child soon after its birth. Taking the sex difference as a model of genetic variation in the control of behaviour, we see that it works through variable cellular structures interacting with variable body fluids both during development and during working life. The ways in which the interactions take effect are of course innumerable

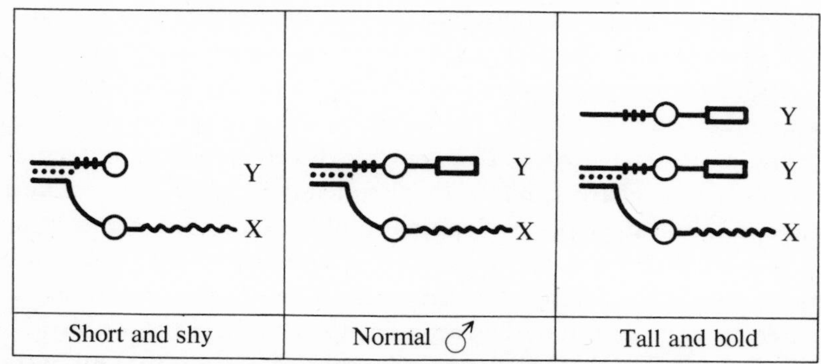

Fig. 4.3 Three types of sex chromosome complement in man compared. Left: X, small Y (Langmaid and Laurence, 1974). Middle: normal, see fig. 3.1. Right: XYY (as in Table 4.1)

owing to the endless abnormalities of both structure and behaviour, of sex and gender.

In understanding what happens, abnormal chromosome situations take us several steps further than the normal sex difference. In both sexes the activity or intelligence of the brain is depressed in proportion to the number of these extra chromosomes. In all the extra X chromosomes there is a mechanism putting out of action the main part of the differential segment (Fig. 3.1). But evidently the rest is active enough to do the damage. Also, the mere presence of extra useless chromosomes, as Barlow suggests, probably slows down the multiplication and migration of nerve cells which are needed before and after birth for the full development of activity in the brain.

These are matters of developmental interest. But there is also a matter of psychological and social interest. All males with an excess of either X or Y chromosomes tend to produce an increased amount of male hormone and this is associated, as it is in the normal population, with a varying but increased aggressiveness, a lower threshold for violence, as compared with the female (Fig. 4.3).

This connection was first picked out in a detention centre for violent criminals in Scotland. Here among 315 inmates 9 were found to have two chromosomes (XYY); that is 3 per cent or a sixty-fold increase on the general population. Now the bulk of XYY men do not get into trouble in this way: it is rather that an augmented supply of hormone, a slightly diminished supply of intelligence, a slightly disturbed personality, and a dominating stature, all due to the extra Y, combine to make harmony more difficult and violence more easy. The result will, of course, always be influenced by the contents and character of the other 22 pairs of chromosomes. Many XYY men, shifted by their extra Y towards an aggressive type, may well have been helped by their autosomes to an anonymous salvation as guardsmen, boxers, warders, and moderate militants of many kinds: outside prisons there is a wide field of activity and of inquiry.

For what those autosomes are doing we have to look to other evidence. Some of this, as we shall see, arises from the measurement of intelligence. But some can be taken from the records of personal and family history. First, it seems, the violence of the XYY men begins early: at 13 years instead of the average 18 years of the ordinary autosomal delinquents. Secondly, the XYY men are mutational: like the Mongolian idiots they come from a fairly normal sample of the population with its normal environment. A random group of XY men, on the other hand, come from a genetically criminal section of society with its criminal heredity and environment (Table 4.1).

Table 4.1 *Comparison of XYY and XY defectives in Carstairs State Hospital (from Price and Whatmore, 1967)*

315 violent ♂ defectives	X-YY_{tall}	X-Y
nos. of men	9/92	18*/210
—offences		
age at 1st offence	13·1 yrs.	18·0 yrs.
against		
—person	9%	22%
—property	88%	63%
siblings	31s.	63s.
offenders	1 off.	12 off.
convictions	1c.	139c.
∴ families	non-criminal	criminal†

* Sample from 306 XY excluding those with accessory defects (epilepsy, psychosis, brain damage)

† Criminal families are estimated by the Portia Trust to number 114,000 in the U.K. (*Times*, 29 Nov. 1976)

Apart from the causes of these two classes of delinquent behaviour, the consequences are also to be noted. The XYY class is sterile but the XY's are fertile: when not detained they breed; they breed a class of people like themselves and like their sibs.

What happens to individuals with 0, 1, and 2Y's is now apparent. But there is a gap. The results are not quite comparable with the 0, 1, and 2 of No. 22 chromosomes, giving the Mongol and the rare anti-Mongol types. Where is the anti-aggressor type? Recently, however, a fourth type has appeared in England which completes the critical range of Y chromosome abnormalities from the point of view of behaviour. An anti-aggressor individual has been found, aged 28, with half a Y chromosome. We may call him Xy. He has the arm of Y which determines sexual development, but he lacks the other arm which gives the two accessory male qualities of aggressiveness and height. He is described as 'timid' and is 150 cm (5 feet) in height, 23 cm shorter than his father and 13 cm shorter than his mother (Fig. 4.3).

The different determinants or segments or genes necessary for male and female development are evidently distributed along the X and Y chromosomes. When accidents occur in heredity which break these chromosomes at different points, individuals are produced with different combinations, deficiencies, and exaggerations of male and female structure in body and brain and of course in behaviour. This kind of variation has been known and understood very generally in plants and animals for over fifty years. What is seen in man confirms the established principles while, owing to our immense understanding of our own species, it allows us to define many new details.

Such evidence is derived from hundreds of different types of chromosome abnormalities found among the vast numbers of individuals examined. It shows that a large part of the detectable excesses or deficencies in the chromosomes lead to bodily and mental defects in combination. This is one way of saying that the brain is a part of the body and like all other parts it is connected with the rest in development. But we have to add that by its structure, activity, and behaviour, which are inevitably linked, the human brain is the most sensitive indicator of varying efficiency in the development of the body as a whole. This is not surprising. The brain is the most complex, the most slowly developing, and being the most variable it is also the most rapidly evolving part of the human body. To survive, moreover, the brain needs a great deal of body; but the body needs very little brain.

We shall later know far more about the differences in development of the brain between the two sexes and its relations with all the other differences between individuals, between races, and between classes of people. But already the sexual difference provides us with a model of the interactions in development between the chemical code in the chromosomes and the chemical processes and structural differences in the brain which arise from it.

VI *Can Intelligence be Measured?*

Observation has led men to suppose that they have a faculty of understanding, of learning from experience, which is seated in the brain and varies among individuals. Our modern sources of knowledge assure us that variation in this faculty in any heterogeneous society must have an hereditary component which has allowed its improvement in evolution by natural selection. They also assure us that this faculty is connected with sensory, motor, instinctive and emotional properties which are also variable in heredity but have changed less quickly in evolution. We believe therefore that within the whole apparatus of what we call intelligence or cognitive ability or native wit or common sense is something which men and women derive not from heaven or earth or the world outside them but from within themselves, something which is inborn or innate or genetic.

Now if intelligence is the ability to learn from experience it is also an ability which grows with experience. It is a property of the individual whose perceptions and actions, and the reasoning which intervenes between them, show that he understands space and time, form and motion, words and numbers. Remembering the past he foresees the future and hence can use his judgement to distinguish between cause and effect and to cope with the situations that arise in a changing environment or an evolving society. But we also recognize that individuals understand these things with different speeds and with different degrees of success. Individuals develop from birth to maturity at different rates, and they develop different kinds of understanding which lead them to choose different environments and to follow and to excel in different pursuits.

These are matters of common observation and inference, common to ordinary parents and teachers who observe the young with a care and success which the most learned men are often unable to achieve. The basis of these individual differences lies in the development, structure, and working of the brain. The brain is less advanced in man at birth than in any monkey. Owing to its great size it has to leave more of its development until after it has emerged from the womb.

In developing after birth nerve cells grow and branch. Small cells even migrate. Many attach themselves to one another. By the connections they form they communicate with one another, chemically and electrically, and by these communications memory is stored, activity controlled, and intelligence developed. Where the connections fail intelligence fails in the ways we have seen and from both environmental and genetic causes.

Such inferences lead us to a further question: how can we say that people are alike or unlike, equal or unequal, in intelligence? This was the problem that was faced by the Minister of Public Instruction in Paris at the turn of the century. Surely it might be possible, on their first coming to school, to recognize children who would not be effectively teachable along with the general body of pupils in the classes of the city schools? In 1904 he put this question to the psychologist, Alfred Binet, who had recently taken up from Galton the idea of measuring intelligence. He had already devised certain 'mental tests'. These he proceeded to develop by trial and error so that the schools using them would be able to separate the backward from the more hopeful children. They would be able to save years of effort for the teachers and of frustration for the pupils, both for those who succeeded and for those, about 2 per cent, who failed.

From this modest beginning there grew a system of tests adjusted or calibrated to suit the capacities of children at a succession of ages. Using these tests, the expert might claim that he could now assess in a few hours the abilities of each child in relation to the whole population of children in the same community and of the same age (Table 4.2).

Table 4.2 *The historical development of intelligence testing* (*cf. Herrnstein 1971, Eysenck 1972*)

Year	Development
1869:	Francis Galton (1822–1911) discusses individual and racial variation in 'grades of ability'. 1882: sets up laboratory for sensory testing of mental defectives in *London*. 1888: uses correlations to show that heredity follows the same principles, whether in mind or in body, in men or in animals.
1890:	J. McKeen Cattell uses 'mental tests' for sensory, motor, and memory faculties in *Philadelphia*.
1895:	Alfred Binet (1857–1911) pupil of Charcot, begins coordinated tests on all mental faculties of children in *Paris*. 1904: Minister asks Binet to pick out sub-normal children in schools. 1908: Binet publishes tests to fit normal children by age whence the principle of Mental Age.
1912:	Wilhelm Stern (*Hamburg*) proposes mental age/physical age × 100 as Intelligence Quotient or I.Q.
1904–27: 1931–48:	Charles Spearman (*London*) L. L. Thurstone (*Chicago*) } show that different mental faculties are independent but correlated.
1913–61:	Cyril Burt (1883–1972) surveys intelligence of *London* schoolchildren and their fathers by occupational class of fathers.
1925–59:	Lewis Terman carries out life-long developmental tests on a selected 'gifted' group at *Stanford*.
1959–66:	Audrey Shuey summarizes racial differences in I.Q. tests in *Virginia*.
1969–72:	Arthur Jensen summarizes correlations of I.Q. between kindred (world tests) at *Berkeley*.

Naturally, as the Swiss investigator Piaget was later to show in detail, ideas, notions, concepts arrive in the child's mind, step by step. They are conditioned by his understanding of his whole environment, by his learning from experience. But Binet had long ago found that they arrived with different children at different rates and hence at different ages. He fixed the value of 100 for the average performance or score at each age. Children having a score of 100 were of their own proper 'mental age'. Later the child's mental age could be expressed as a percentage of its real age to give its Intelligence Quotient or I.Q.

Children falling below 70 were then reckoned to be defective, feeble-minded or educationally subnormal; in other words unpromising pupils.

Two difficulties at once occur to us. We are offered a scale of values for intelligence like the scale of degrees for temperature. How is this possible? There are obviously so many different kinds of intelligence, keenness of senses, skill in manipulation, verbal memory, spatial judgement, logical reasoning, imagination, capacity to concentrate, and so forth. The answer is that between these different faculties there is a partial connection, a statistical correlation, as Galton had expressed it.

Why is this? It is because there is a structural connection between the parts of the brain which are composed of similar tissues, nervous, vascular, and the blood itself. Each part helps and is helped by the other parts. By measuring them all we therefore obtain a measure of the whole. That measure is not all we want to know, but it is a beginning. By using it we can discover more of what it means in practice.

Again, how can we measure something whose processes we do not, except in the most general way, pretend to understand? Here the answer is that we do not need to understand. We understand more and more about temperature or gravitation, heredity or race, about their causes and their effects as our enquiries proceed: we use them with caution before we can fully understand them. So is it also with intelligence.

When a number could be put to a child's intelligence new inferences could be made about the quality as well as the quantity of understanding. First, came the discovery that the I.Q. varied very little after seven or eight years of age. The bright stayed bright and the dull stayed dull. Early and late developers were uncommon extremes. Intelligence was, as experienced teachers had long understood, a property of the individual.

Secondly, came the discovery that one-egg twins were correlated with one another to the extent of nearly 0·9 when reared together and between 0·7 and 0·8 when reared separately. How then about the correlations between kindred which were already taken as the measure of heredity in physical properties such as height? From a variety of studies in Britain and America these connections were established. Both between parents and offspring and between brothers and sisters (sibs) the correlation proved to be close to one half or 0.5. With each degree of kinship the correlations followed the rules laid down by Yule and Fisher. Further, husbands and wives, although unrelated, proved to be positively correlated with a value of 0·4, 0·5, or even 0·6. Why? Through like marrying like. It was a measure, in Galton's phrase, of assortative mating.

A second step was to compare the abilities of pairs of sibs brought up together with those of pairs brought up separately. Or to compare the abilities of adopted children with those of their natural and their adopted parents. These comparisons enable us to see how far differences in the environment modify the effects of differences in heredity, that is in innate intelligence. Studies in Britain and America have agreed in showing that while the influence of the environment can never be eliminated, it is greatly reduced in the intelligence test as compared with ordinary scholastic tests in reading or arithmetic. The intelligence test comes near to measuring an innate capacity (Tables 4.3 and 4.4).

Table 4.3 *Correlations between sibs reared together and apart showing the greater effect of differences in environment on scholastic than on I.Q. tests* (from Burt, 1975)

	No. of pairs	*I.Q.*	*Reading*	*Arithmetic*
One-egg twins				
together	95	0·93	0·95	0·86
apart	53	0·87	0·60	0·73
Two-egg twins				
together	127	0·53	0·92	0·75
Full sibs				
together	264	0·53*	0·84	0·75
apart	151	0·44	0·50	0·56

* Established, for example, excluding totally uncorrelated imbeciles, by J. A. Fraser Roberts, 1940.

The next step was to discover the range of I.Q. values in groups or communities of people. Did they show any characteristic relationship? The answer emerged that all communities or populations or classes had their own characteristics. Like the range of heights or any other measurably varying property, they followed a pattern of variation with a maximum frequency close to the average and lower frequencies for measurements on either side of this maximum or mode. The rule which I.Q. follows in common with all other such biological measurements is the Normal Law of the Frequency of Errors: it has the bell-shaped curve of a 'normal' distribution.

We do not need to follow Fisher's argument, however, in order to see that these 'errors'—whose estimation was first used to correct the betting of gamblers and the observations of astronomers—were, among

Table 4.4 *Correlations of the child's tested ability with its hereditary and environmental circumstances* (from Burks, 1928)

	Natural parents (nature + nurture)	*Adopted parents (nurture alone)*
Father's I.Q.	0·55	0·09
Mother's I.Q.	0·57	0·23
Father's vocabulary	0·52	0·14
Mother's vocabulary	0·48	0·25
Home grading	0·48	0·24
Income	0·26	0·26

1 All Californian families of North European origin, English speaking

2 Average age of adoption: 93 days

3 Age at testing: 5–14 years

4 Controls matched for age, sex, schooling, and profession of father

5 Numbers tested: 99 to 206

6 Scale used: Stanford Binet

7 The author, Barbara Burks, was in fact one of Terman's sample of Gifted Children

human beings, the result of differences in the heredity and in the environment of the individuals concerned. Those in the heredity are due to recombinations and mutations of genes and chromosomes which make heredity what it is. Deviations from the mean and the mode are the accustomed result of the processes of variation by which man like all other sexually outbreeding organisms maintains his adaptability to a changing environment. But how about the differences in that environment? The intelligence test is designed to separate, as far as possible, what is inborn from what is acquired by experience. How far does it succeed?

To answer this question we have to go back to 1913 when Cyril Burt, at the age of 30, had been given the task of advising on the education of children by the London County Council. The authorities gave Burt very little assistance or equipment. But at this time statistical and testing methods resting on psychological and genetic theory, were in rapid development. And the centre of this development was at University College to which Burt became attached. Burt's appointment therefore gave him an unexampled opportunity. The immense range of his studies over the next fifty years shows how well he used it.

Burt's achievement was to replace the old genetical assumptions and statistical methods by the new: to replace Galton and Pearson (where he saw the need) by Mendel and Fisher. The result reached far beyond the conventional problems of intelligence testing. Consequently it has not always been understood by specialists who, absorbed in the conventional detail, have missed the revolutionary meaning. Specialists, as well as the general reader, may therefore learn something from Burt's own words (written in 1961):

> On the Mendelian theory genetic influences are responsible not only for resemblances between members of the same family, but also for differences, i.e. for individual variations. Genetic variability within families receives little or no attention from those psychological critics who still accept the Pearsonian view, and think mainly in terms of correlations; yet . . . variability within families forms one of the chief causes of (social) mobility. Moreover . . . to a large extent . . . correlational analysis was responsible for the abnormally low estimates which Pearson and his followers reached for the influence of environment . . . (Fisher's) variance techniques make it far easier to give due weight to environmental influences, and to the further complications which result from the fact that environment and heredity so often work in the same direction.

In this argument Burt was going beyond Mendel and Fisher. As his pupil Miss Conway had explained in 1958, he was moving towards my view of a created or genetic environment, not opposed to heredity but reinforcing it. This argument I shall explain in several stages.

To understand both the opposition and the incomprehension to which Burt's views gave rise we must recall that nearly all social and economic policy is bound up with the understanding of intelligence. This is most explicit in Soviet Russia because Marxism always attempts to be explicit. For this reason, when genetics was suppressed in Russia, intelligence testing was (in 1936) the first of its applications to be destroyed. And it has never since been allowed. Elsewhere, for the same reason, misunderstandings (for the opposite faces of which we may refer to Jensen and Kamin, both in 1974) have been widely and hastily propagated. We must therefore look closely at the critical points in this study where so many sciences now converge. These are notably in regard to class and sex relations and the nature of twins.

VII *Class and Sex Relations*

The evidence of history tells us that social classes arise from the meeting in one society of different kinds of people, tribes and races, who need, use, and exploit one another but prefer to live, work and breed apart. How do such classes vary in intelligence? It has always been taken for granted (since Plato) that they differ. But if every group shows a normal curve of variation how are these curves related? And how are they maintained from generation to generation?

This was one of the questions that Burt had to ask. As he explained, he divided the population of children into the six classes of occupation by which the census recorded their parents. He then had to correct the proportions to allow for the diversion of some children into private education. His results show the expected gradation from the unskilled to the skilled and professional classes. They show also the expected overlaps between the classes. Now with such overlaps, if all children followed the occupations of their parents, the distinctions of classes in intelligence would vanish in a few generations. But as we know, and we shall hear further of it in regard to education, such distinctions never have vanished except with the disintegration of society. How then could these findings be understood?

The answer that Burt gave to this question was that commonly given by sociologists then and now; none better than Sorokin. It was that children at the lower end of each class fall in the social scale and those at the upper end rise. To estimate what proportions rise and fall Burt examined the intelligence of a sample of the fathers. His results showed the fathers correlated with the children and the children closer to the mean in each group than the fathers. But the fathers' curves of variation were narrower than their children's. To maintain stability in this situation would require some 30 per cent of movement between classes in each generation (Fig. 4.4).

Several questions arise from these graphs. First, do we know that social classes, as opposed to castes, are mobile? No one doubts the upward movement of gifted men, women and families. Dictionaries of biography are compact with examples. The effects of education reinforce the efforts of the individual. The downward movement is less conspicuous but also undeniable. The effects of both movements, however, by no means assure a stability in society as a whole since the several classes always differ in their fertility and their survival. In addition immigration and emigration always have selective effects which we shall have to consider, effects on class and on intelligence. Burt's estimates therefore provide us with a model which we have to test continually by contemporary events.

Turn now from these generalities to particular details. Are there qualifications to be made to these rules? Clearly it is at the extremes of variation that we are likely to find them. The genius at the top and the

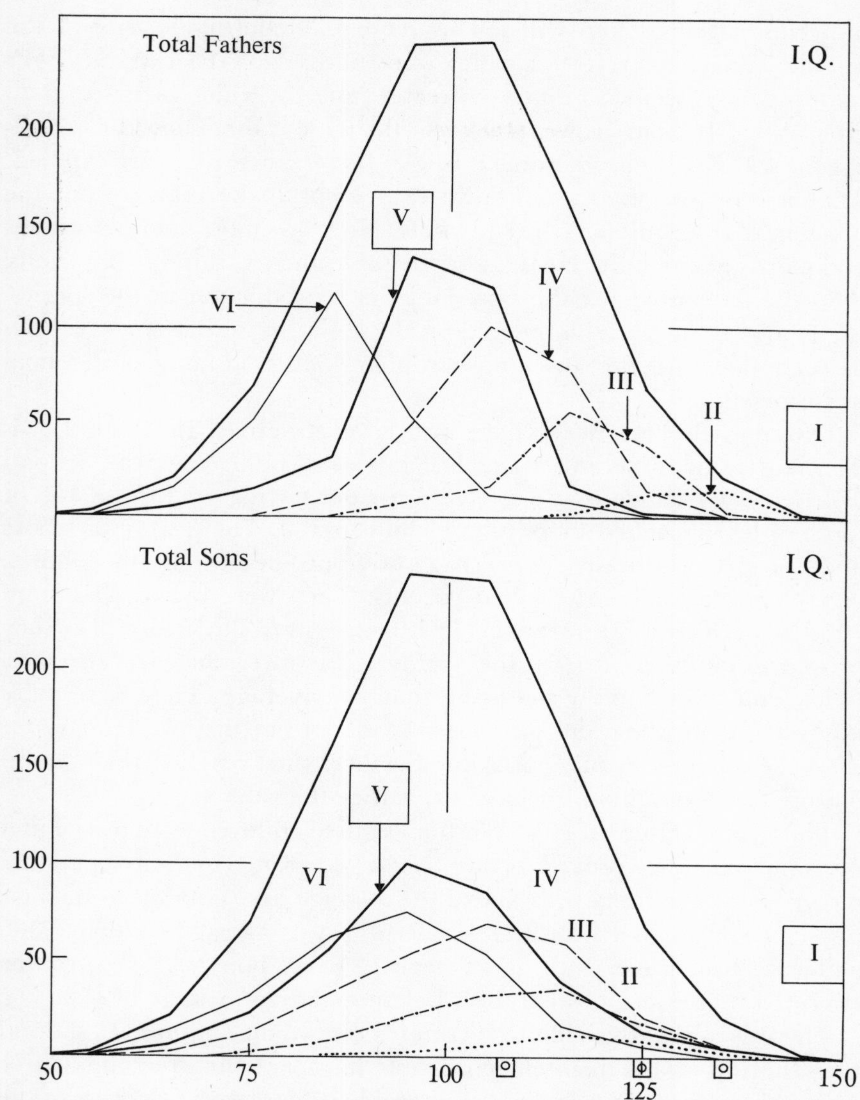

Fig. 4.4 Graphs to show the distributions of I.Q. among London schoolchildren and their parents, separated according to the occupations of the fathers in six classes. The stability over the generations is maintained by (i) regression to the mean combined with (ii) selective movement of the extremes of each class up and down the social scale. Where society has been divided as in America in the past into non-interbreeding castes, Christians and Jews or Whites and Negroes, the distributions of the castes are kept different by non-interbreeding. These differences are expressed in a different apportionment of occupations. By American tests classes I, II, and III are more frequent among European Jews than among Christians; class VI is more frequent among Negroes than among Whites (after Cyril Burt, 1961; *cf.* Eysenck, 1972; Shuey, 1966; Jensen, 1972; see this volume, Chapter 6)

imbecile at the bottom will tell us more than the mediocrity in the middle. Early, some irregularities were noticed at the extremes. For example, boys seemed to have a greater range, a wider variance, than girls. Why? In man, as we have seen, the male is the hybrid or heterozygous sex. His X chromosome is single. Its recessive genes are exposed. That is why the male's mortality rate seems to be higher from the moment of conception to the end of life. He shows more colourblindness and more haemophilia. He is less predictable and less durable physically than the female who is the very hinge of reproduction in the species. He is also more variable mentally. He shows more extremes of both defect and genius. He causes more trouble whether at home or in school or in society.

Extremes in both sexes have proved instructive. In 1926, Lewis Terman, using Binet's tests, picked out over 1500 American schoolchildren between eight and twelve years old having an I.Q. of 150 or more, a level reached by only one child in 300. There were 857 boys and 671 girls. Naturally they were mostly but not entirely the children of professional or highly skilled parents. They were mostly also from families of North European or Jewish ancestry. Physically also they proved to be different from the average. They were heavier, stronger, taller, and more rapidly maturing than the average. They were more interested in reading and did better at school but they were no better than the average in manual skills. Further, they reached their moral maturity, a reliability of behaviour, earlier than the average.

Thirty years later (in 1958) Terman's gifted children were traced and re-examined. They proved to vary over a wide range in their vocational records. But the range was above the average and notably so in their physical and mental health. Their fertility was attested by their 2500 children. And these, with an average I.Q. of about 130, showed the expected regression towards the whole population average of 100.

There is a negative side to Terman's marathon enquiry. It showed that the top scores in intelligence tests have not the great indicative value which Binet had discovered in the bottom scores. Contrary to the suggestion of his title, they provide no means of identifying genius. That desirable aim, nothing but the arduous test of life can properly achieve.

The bottom end of the scale tells a different story. There we can distinguish two important classes. There are the feeble-minded with I.Q. between 50 and 70 who arise from parents of low I.Q. by the usual polygenic recombination. And there are the imbeciles with I.Q. under 50, who mainly arise by chemical and chromosome mutation, and equally in all classes of society. Both these problems I shall return to later.

VIII *The Identity Of Twins*

For a long time it has seemed enough for us to say that twins in men and animals were of two kinds, those arising from one and from two eggs. The idea, the hypothesis, came from Galton in 1875. But eight years later in his *Human Faculty* Galton said much more. He qualified his hypothesis in the light of what he had learnt from it. One-egg twins, he explained, looked the same in infancy but later they developed in three ways the differences between which his successors have disregarded:

(i) Some never diverged, remaining indistinguishable even in their accidents and diseases throughout life.
(ii) Some diverged slightly as a result of differences in damage from accidents or diseases.
(iii) Some diverged in various degrees without any discoverable external cause.

The first two classes contrasted with two-egg twins and were capable of yielding decisive evidence of the relative effects of differences in heredity and in environment. But what was to be said of the third class? Galton, acknowledging the difficulty, attributed their divergence to 'a want of thorough similarity in their nature'. He was right.

As the twentieth century advanced examples of this 'want of similarity' multiplied and its various causes slowly became evident. Galton had been surprised to find a divergence of most one-egg twins in right- and left-handedness, a faculty known to be connected with manual skills, speech and therefore personality. It is a symptom of the unlikeness of the two sides of the human body which particularly affects the brain, the heart and the circulation. Mirror-imaging of these structures occurs in one-egg twins and must be connected with their origin by splitting.

The extreme example of the effects of splitting in causing differences between one-egg twins is the case of the Siamese twins. The classical pair, Chang and Eng (1811–74) had contrasted temperaments. With the same temptations, Eng cared nothing for liquor, Chang loved it. No less striking are the examples of twins so like in appearance that one is regularly mistaken for the other, but so divergent in character that the virtuous one in desperation kills his delinquent partner (*Times*: Brazil, 20 Dec. 72; France, 10 Aug. 76).

Some of the differences between one-egg twins are outside the range possible for ordinary sibs. When a defect of splitting leads to one twin having two feet and the other only one, it is clear that by the *insult* of splitting, the character of one or both products may be violently, variously and most significantly disturbed. It is disturbed (as I pointed out in detail in 1953) in respect of the organization of development, through the misdivision of the great bulk of the materials of the egg. These lie, not in the nucleus or the chromosomes, but in what we call the *cytoplasm*.

These little things seemed of small account in the blazing light of the genetic discoveries of the time. The decisive success of experiments with the fly *Drosophila* brought with it a certain dogmatism. Nothing mattered in heredity except the nucleus. The chromosomes became an article of faith even for those who had never seen them. Plant pigments being controlled by the cytoplasm were brushed aside. The coiling of a snail's shell, and indeed left-handedness in man, with their maternal or cytoplasmic effects, were ignored. Those who attacked the problems of crime, disease and intelligence in man in the 1920's thus naturally all agreed that what they assumed to be one-egg twins must have the same nuclei, the same chromosomes and the same heredity. Any differences they might show were inevitably of external origin.

We now see that small as their differences are, whether they are raised together or separately, they are in large part due, neither to heredity nor to environment, but to the act of splitting. All the estimates of the effect of heredity on intelligence by Newman, Burt, Shields and others are therefore bound to be under-estimates. But they are under-estimates to an extent that we cannot measure unless we take by themselves the class of utterly identical one-egg twins.

To those who reckon that science is measurement such a conclusion must be painful. For the relative influence of heredity and environment which was arbitrarily estimated can no longer be given as a percentage. We must however tell them that in all scientific advance there has to be from time to time an intrusion of qualitative between quantitative judgements. A second of these intrusions now arises from the chromosomes themselves. Let us see what they do in identical twins.

The moment of fertilization is the trickiest event in the life of a chromosome—or of a man. It has also recently been translated from a most private to a most public event. For a variety of accidents at fertilization are now known to give rise to abnormal embryos. Most of them are aborted but some survive to give the kind of abnormal progeny we have seen. But what happens when such embryos split in two? The answer is that one of the halves often suffers the abnormality and the other escapes it.

The sexual examples are the ones we know best. A sperm enters an egg and its 23 chromosomes unwrap and join those of the egg, all ready to divide. But the sperm's Y chromosome is delayed and one of its halves misses the connection. So that the two daughter nuclei are XY and XO. If these give one embryo it will be a kind of hermaphrodite. This has happened. But if they give two embryos they will be one-egg twins of opposite sex, a male and a sterile female (of Turner type). This also has happened.

This is not all. If a single mixed embryo is formed, it may split after many cell divisions. The split, however, need not be in the plane of the first division. It may be crosswise. The two embryos are then both mixtures. If the sex primordia are started in one by an XY cell and in the other by an XO cell, they will again be of opposite sex. But then their cleavage has been asymmetrical. This we know because, as I have said, the chromosomes carry their pedigrees so publicly on their backs.

Summing up: two internal and genetic anomalies of development cause differences between one-egg twins. First, there are some 20 or 30 per cent of errors in the splitting of the cytoplasm. The differences that ensue being internal are strictly genetic. But they are not hereditary. Secondly, in the development of all eggs, there are 1 or 2 per cent of errors in the splitting of the nucleus. Most of them are lost before birth. But when twinning follows and the twins survive yet another class of twins appears which is neither identical nor fraternal.

When we turn back from these new sources of evidence, we see that the old generalisations about these properties have to be adjusted. The study of cells and chromosomes has given us a new exactitude, not of measurement, but of analysis and inference and understanding. In

Table 4.5 *Comparison of similarity of reactions or concordance under various tests of twins in man (after Darlington and Mather 1949)*

	1	2	3	4
Test	Sex	A B O	Crime	Disease
ONE Egg	100%	100%	87%	60%
TWO Egg	50±%	50±%	37%	22%

1 Male or female.

2 Agglutination (blood groups).

3 Institution records (cf. Darlington 1953, 1964; Fuller and Thompson, 1960).

4 Tuberculosis: infection is the most important environmental factor differentiating separated twins.

our old view of the properties of twins (Table 4.5) we claimed to see a gradation of likenesses reflecting a gradation in interference by the environment. It is a gradation in which measured intelligence stands between the total identity of sex and blood groups and the moderate divergence of crime and disease.

There is no reason in theory or practice to question this rule. But when we look at our table in future we must reflect that no one has ever seen one-egg twins arising. We seemed to have inferred certain identical properties from their belonging to one-egg twins. We had in fact inferred the one-egg twins from the identical properties. And with accidents and mutations this is not true.

We have much further to go in this study. Already we may say that some dogmas and many polemics have been misplaced. Yet Galton's, like Mendel's, enquiries have not so far led us astray. They still show us the way ahead.

IX *Mental Defect: a Social Problem*

The relation of intelligence testing to genetic analysis has immediate consequences. The two, of course, agree in showing, apart from exceptional and extreme situations, the primacy and preponderance of heredity in determining mental differences between individuals and communities. But in what they reveal of heredity they profoundly differ.

Intelligence testing naturally admits and records the importance of the individual. But it does so in terms of the family and the population. Its curves of variation show, within the population or breeding group, a continuity which overrides the differences between individuals; as we saw, they even have to be adjusted to equalize the sexes. The correlations of kindred within the breeding group are also a property of the family. All these are genuine notions of practical value in themselves but they are only one part of the story.

The other part of the story is analytical. It is what we get from considering the causes of mental defect in the individual and the consequences which follow for society. These causes and consequences are, as we saw, distinguishable in genetic terms. Above all there is the distinction between two kinds of defect: the mutational, like the XYY male, and the recombinational which, whether grave and biochemical or mild and polygenic, can float in the population for many generations.

One qualification, however, is needed in practice. Mutations due to losses or gains of very small pieces of chromosome are not yet distinguishable under the microscope in man or mammals as they are, for example, in flies and in many plants. The contrast between the two groups as a whole, however, divides our social problem into two parts. The mutational defectives are important only in themselves. The recombinational defectives are important more for the effects of their breeding on future generations of men and women.

Consider first the individual problem. Here it is that legal reforms (notably the reform of abortion law in Britain for which great credit is due to Glanville Williams) and medical techniques (notably in the U.S.A.) have already changed our prospects of reducing human suffering. If the amniotic fluid or placental blood is examined during pregnancy, chromosome abnormalities and many big gene recessives can be identified in an embryo and its abortion can be procured. Where they are expected, as Friedman has explained, this has already proved worth-while; it does for advanced society what infanticide has always done for the primitive society.

There remains the largest class, that of the polygenic defectives. Here we meet another genetic variable, that of sex, which has been almost totally overlooked. The mental causes of low intelligence are comparable in the two sexes. But its social effects are contrasted. Take the case of the XO female. She is somewhat helpless and quite inconspicuous. The XYY male on the other hand can make himself very conspicuous indeed. The contrast in behaviour between the male and the female who are polygenically defective or retarded is no less striking. In 1934 the Brock Committee collected evidence of the breeding of mental defectives in England and Wales. It found that the total retarded population known to have children, amounted to 3247 females (two-thirds of whom were unmarried), and 486 males. This means that females may have been more fertile, but the males were certainly less fertile than the normal population. It further suggests that this difference is due to helplessness in both sexes, a helplessness leading to propagation and prostitution among the women but to the opposite effect of non-propagation among the men.

What happened to these children? The whole group of 3733 parents had 8,841 children. Among these the Brock Committee found that 1,848 were over thirteen years of age and could be given reliable intelligence tests. The results were classified as follows:

I.Q.	*Defective* (<50)	*Retarded* (50–70)	*Sub-normal or Normal* (>70)
	599	240	1009
	(32·4%)	(13·0%)	(54·6%)

Similar results have been obtained from many more recent studies, notably by Reed and Reed in Minnesota.

As a remedy for the undue multiplication of defectives the Brock Committee recommended voluntary sterilization. This recommendation has not been followed in Britain: discretion proved the better part of valour. But since 1934 it has been followed in several other countries.

In Denmark a group of women having an average I.Q. of 75, and under social but not institutional care, were sterilized over a period of ten years. Mohr records that before sterilization they were found to have had 352 children (one or two each) whose intelligence and character were later surveyed with the following results:

I.Q.	*c.* 75	75–90	90–100	*c.* 100
Nos.	112	127	108*	5

* including many with disturbed behaviour

Evidently in populations where they are intelligently applied, sterilization and abortion can have valuable effects in reducing mental deficiency with its attendant ills of pauperism, crime, prostitution, and insanity. The effects are of course complex. For example, sterilization of defective women may make prostitution safer for them; but it is going to reduce the population inclined to prostitution in later generations. Before jumping to conclusions, we need to look at the development of these ideas during the last century.

Francis Galton's studies on the inheritance of ability and intelligence carried out from 1865 to 1905 led him to consider the social and evolutionary implications of his work. He wanted to know how society should make use of the principle of heredity for its advantage, both in the present and in the future. Health of body and mind had obviously been preserved in the past by natural selection, the survival of the fittest. Now that men's affairs were being brought more and more under a conscious and often compassionate control, how could they ensure that this control was used to avoid suffering, not only for the present but also for future generations? This question suggested to him (in 1883) the programme of what he called eugenics.

In classical times the theory and practice of eugenics had been taken for granted by all Western sects except the Jews and the Pythagoreans to both of whom human life was inherently sacred. Their views, prohibiting exposure, abortion, euthanasia and suicide (as well as masturbation and homosexuality) were taken over by the Christians and are only now being challenged.

One Jewish prohibition adopted by the Christians was however given a eugenic interpretation. Pope Gregory the Great explicitly rationalized the veto on incest on the grounds that inbreeding yields sterile progeny. The genetic grounds were misunderstood although, as I have explained in *The Evolution of Man and Society*, the genetic consequences were uniquely beneficial. The European royal caste was sustained in the Middle Ages by the papal prohibition of inbreeding.

In modern times, owing to ignorance of heredity, eugenics has lent itself not only to misunderstanding but also to political abuse. In Germany a bogus eugenics was made the ground for persecution of the Jews. In Russia, the equally bogus theories of Lysenko were made the grounds for the persecution of the science of genetics itself. Now, however, what we know of genetics and of the chromosomes, of the evolution of society and of the character of populations, enables us to look again at the evidence on eugenic problems collected in the last century and take up Galton's problem from where he left it.

Galton's ideas made us healthily aware of the socially discriminating effect of the development of birth control which came after his death. The use of birth control was itself a test of education and intelligence. It therefore inevitably distinguished between individuals, classes, and races by their education and intelligence. The birth rate fell first in the upper classes rather than in the lower (in the U.K.), in the whites rather than in the blacks (in the U.S.A.), in the upper class blacks rather than in the lower class (as Ingle points out), in the Europeans rather than in the Asiatics (in the U.S.S.R.), and so on round the world. It seemed that, for the first time in evolution, for a short time at least, the selective advantage which I have attributed to intelligence was being reversed. But as we shall see, this is only one of the evolutionary dislocations which are now occurring. It is part of the world problem of population which we shall have to examine as a whole.

The smaller problem of the connection between intelligence, delinquency, and fertility is however clear enough for us to consider separately. Here it was the Prison Association of New York which took the initiative. Already in 1874 they asked their investigator Robert Dugdale to study the family and social origins of criminals. In doing so they had no idea that he would uncover a history going back to 1740 and a family, which he named the Jukes, numbering about 1200. Similarly, when in 1912 Dugdale's successor Goddard began to investigate the descendants of another comparable family he did not expect them to number 1533 in two families, the legitimate with 1 per cent, the illegitimate with 25 per cent, of defectives. He had indeed demonstrated rather clearly the connection between assortative mating and hereditary defect.

The lessons learned from these pioneer enquiries could, no doubt, be confirmed by criminologists in any country willing to undertake the great labour of similar studies. They foreshadow important principles of social genetics. 'The tendency of heredity', wrote Dugdale in 1875, 'is to produce an environment which perpetuates that heredity'.

Our later knowledge has confirmed his opinion that mentally and morally defective individuals do produce more mentally and morally defective offspring than other people. They do so because they provide both the heredity and the environment for the 'problem families'. From these observations the conclusion was not unnaturally drawn that society might well be ruined by the propagation of defectives. This fear, as Higgins and Reed have shown, was sometimes exaggerated by a statistical fallacy. Such people, when they have children, occasionally have enormous numbers—with conspicuous and painful results which no student of these matters can fail to notice. But commonly they have no offspring at all; more commonly than ordinary folk. The feckless propagation of a few is therefore less dangerous in an evolutionary sense than it appears. Undoubtedly, however, it is costly and troublesome for society and tragic for the unwanted progeny. It should be avoided and now it can be avoided.

The important social aspect of mental deficiency is evidently its connection with delinquency and crime. Indeed we may say the two important hereditary components of crime are mental inadequacy and a variety of more specific mental disturbances coming within the field of the psychiatrist. While keeping in mind our distinction between the hereditary and the mutational sources of defect, we do well to note the records of intelligence testing of delinquent and criminal populations which have been made on a large scale during the last fifty years in all parts of the U.S.A. The most interesting of these distinguish between offenders by race and sex (Table 4.6).

Table 4.6 *Average results of comparative intelligence testing of probationary and prison populations, chiefly male, in the United States (44 investigations, after Shuey 1966)*

	*Delinquents**	*Criminals*
Negroes	3,480 have I.Q. 74·4	1,670 have I.Q. 81·3
Whites	*c*. 6,000 have I.Q. 80·6	2,407 have I.Q. 91·8

* In a rare separate study of females in N.Y. State in 1920 the I.Q. scores were about 7 points below these averages for both Negro and White. This is in agreement (as the reader will notice) with the Brock Report.

The method of dealing with delinquency and crime by detention and imprisonment is difficult to separate in the public mind from the emotion of revenge and its justification as punishment. But when we see the evidence of the genetic component, whether hereditary or mutational, in all forms of deviation, we see that all imprisonment has three effects: one is in protecting society; a second is in correcting the offender; and the third is in reducing the numbers of his descendants. Now imprisonment does very little good to the prisoner. But, at great expense to the community, it does, or can, or should, stop him breeding. The recent progressive or liberal practice of releasing juvenile gangsters (aged 15) from custody at week-ends is intended to allow them to accustom themselves to freedom and responsibility. But in practice it means that they breed. This is not the best way, as Patrick's study showed, to curb the gang trouble in Glasgow. A French proposal (*Times* 28 July 1975) to allow wives into prisons is designed for another worthy purpose, to reduce the present incidence of homosexuality. But, in contrast to homosexual relations, it will increase the prison population when the children so begotten come of age.

A more fundamental approach to the breeding problem is raised by the practice of what we may call *negotiable punishment*. The principle has been, it seems, to measure the costs and benefits of all punishments multilaterally, that is in relation to the criminal and both present and future society.

In England, after 1660, convicts were often given the choice between imprisonment at home and transportation abroad. The same principle is involved in the choice between detention and vasectomy which has for some time been given in Holland, Scandinavia, and Germany. In California a more drastic choice has been offered to men convicted of sexual assault. They can decide between the alternatives of castration and life imprisonment. At their own request 900 men between the ages of 29 and 59 were castrated and thereafter released. Only nine are known to have repeated their offence. The 1 per cent of failures is the price that is paid for the immense relief from suffering enjoyed by the other 99 per cent allowed to go free. After vasectomy, we know, it would not have been safe to release any of these men. The eugenic effect of life imprisonment, vasectomy, or castration will, of course, be identical (*Times*, 19 April 1975).

These are elementary examples of applied eugenics. But there is another kind of eugenics which requires us to put together all we know of evolution and history for the unaccustomed purpose of looking, not at our little interests, but at the future of mankind, of all mankind. This demands and encourages more serious thought.

Our knowledge of evolution allows us to draw certain universal conclusions. One is that, when any species of organism varies in quality and also varies in numbers or quantity, the two variations are connected. The other is that all actions of governments in every field of administration affect the quantity and quality of future generations of those they govern. This is their gravest responsibility.

Similarly, every important scientific or technical invention always has had, and always will have, effects on the quantity and the quality of human populations. Above all this is true of inventions in medicine. For example, a cure for any hereditary disease (like diabetes) favours its increase in the population. On the other hand, as we saw, its recognition before birth (through the chromosomes or the chemistry of the embryo), combined with abortion, favours its elimination. With the practices of contraception, sterilization, and abortion we can go much further since they favour the restriction of parenthood to those who want to be parents. They therefore have a short-term social effect on the care of children. At the same time, through the field of marriage counselling, which is a science in itself, they have a long-term eugenic effect on the evolution of society.

What we have learned about human heredity now enables us to catch a glimpse of human life from a new point of view. We have asked society to look at the individual. We must now see what happens when we turn the problem upside down, and ask the individual to look more closely at society.

Chapter 5

The Created Environment: Culture

I *The Word and the Idea*

Human communities or social groups from the simplest to the most complex have each of them certain ideas in common, a body of acceptable assumptions. These ideas are mainly expressible in speech and through speech they distinguish, however slightly, each group from all others. Moreover, each group expresses its ideas in a common form of speech which we call a language or dialect. Owing to this distinction we can recognize what is effective in separating social groups: it is that they are always not only speaking groups but also breeding groups united by kinship. Whether they are tribes or races or social classes, their descendants will have common ancestors. The beliefs and the knowledge, the customs and the speech, that they have in common we describe as their culture.

In saying this I am following the usage introduced by Edward Tylor in his *Primitive Culture* in 1871. His work was to be a study of the history, not of the physical properties of primitive peoples, but of the condition of knowledge, belief and behaviour, religion, art, and custom among them. Strange to say, Tylor did not use this new term of his when he wrote his *Anthropology* ten years later. But anthropologists studying primitive peoples soon found the word and the idea indispensable. Cultures for them began to take on a character at once solid and coherent, static and predictable. Like the form of an animal species described by a Linnaean systematist, it appeared self-constituted or God-created. It admitted no external cause, no connection with the past or with the future, no evolutionary attachment to the animals below or to civilization above.

The study of cultures in this way became for the anthropologist a descriptive science without a theory, a body of knowledge with its own frame of reference, detached like theology from experimental verification. Thus the word culture came to represent a key mystery in anthropology, like intelligence in psychology or, for most people, race in relation to man. Restricted, isolated, and abstracted, the term remained indefinable. For this reason, presumably, the lexicographers next door to Tylor in Oxford did not let the word in Tylor's sense into their Dictionary until after a lapse of 101 years. For them culture remained literate: this thing was illiterate. They felt perhaps that such a disembodied existence had given the word a magical and misleading quality. Unlike intelligence or race, its meaning had indeed seemed to evaporate as soon as we asked for its experimental justification or its evolutionary coordinates in time and space. This, however, need no longer be so.

For the ethologist the behaviour of an animal species has the same coherence and predictability as the culture of a tribe has for the anthropologist. But the ethologist, as we saw, is always aware of the property of heredity and the occurrence of evolution. So that his study is not self-constituted, it is related to the whole body of science. The anthropologist, on the other hand, fights shy of examining how far invention and learning, knowledge and belief, intelligence and behaviour, competition and survival are connected; how far they are the properties of individuals; how far they run in families; how far tribes and races historically agree or differ in these respects. For him these questions are separate, difficult, avoidable, and therefore avoided or *taboo*. But for the student of animal behaviour, like Konrad Lorenz, they are practical problems which must be explored if the vast descriptive work of anthropologists, or indeed sociologists, is to be of use to mankind.

We can now recognize three stages in the evolution of culture based on foundations of instinct and intelligence:

1 The body of behaviour of an animal species or its races,
2 The body of belief and behaviour of a tribe or group of primitive people capable of speech,
3 The body of knowledge, belief, and behaviour of a human society capable of speech and writing.

It would seem that these stages represent a continuous historical series guided by the evolution, always selectively advantageous, of the means of communication. Let us examine the evidence.

II *Speech and Writing*

Our first evidence of how human culture came about we have from the apes. They show us something very close to what the earliest men were and did and thought. More evidence of these things we find in the intermediate steps of the fossil record. And, finally, we have the whole range of contemporary human being and doing and thinking. Earlier we saw the results in terms of human inventions, having a genetic basis in the brain, and genetic consequences for the race and the species through natural selection. Now we must separate these inventions into different categories according to their causes and consequences and the stage in which they came into operation, Paleolithic, Neolithic, and civilized.

The greatest of Paleolithic inventions was speech, a property of whose evolution there is no archaeological record. For it is, we may say, the internal aspect of invention. Nevertheless we can now see that the differentiation of the brain and the development of the vocal organs demanded a sequence of genetic steps, a coordinated sequence since each one had to be adapted to many others. Moreover each one had to have a favourable influence on communication. It demanded parallel changes in articulation, in audition, and in understanding; parallel changes also in a whole breeding group which would indeed naturally follow from their common genetic basis.

In all these respects the evolution of speech, and to a less extent of facial expression and gesticulation, obeys the rules for the instinctive basis of behaviour which in man we call morals. The individual is constrained to conform to the practices of the community so far as he is able or willing. And by the process of constraint, speech, like morals, becomes the cultural environment, the genetic environment, of the group. On account of its manifold effects speech thus becomes the chief instrument of positive feedback in the evolution of intelligence.

What were these effects of speech? The first was that it revealed men to one another; the second was that it revealed nature to men; and the third that it revealed man and his mind to himself. This is to repeat what Johann Gottfried von Herder said in his essay of 1772 on the natural (as opposed to divine) origins of speech. Or as Shelley soon put it, referring to Prometheus: 'He gave man speech and speech created thought.'

Here we may add that it was only as speech grew into language that it forced on man the recognition of a real difference between me and thee, here and there, now and then. We know that this is so because these ideas have different importance in different languages. The distinctions between present, future, and conditional, or as Elspeth Huxley puts it in speaking of witchcraft in Africa, between the actual and the probable, are not equally clear to all races or classes nor even to all individuals, even individual scientists. These are distinctions which have arisen in the evolution of the mind and of language. The invention of tenses propelled their inventors into a new world of thought and action. The introduction of a word for time has both a cause and a consequence for a people and their culture as well as for their language.

The multiplicity of languages in the world has greatly diminished since Paleolithic times. But this multiplicity indicated that language, with its analytical and creative uses, was the last invention of Paleolithic man, coming just before and indeed conditioning the invention of agriculture. In arising it became in another sense a powerful evolutionary mechanism; it enhanced the division of men into groups that could not easily communicate and consequently would not usually interbreed. During this last period, therefore, an evolutionary divergence of peoples in the structure of the brain and the vocal apparatus must have underlain the divergence of language at the grammatical as well as the phonetic levels. Every breeding group, tribe, or class, in the world therefore, has its own natural dialect evolving or stabilized with the group. The same principle operates in the evolution of song in the birds, notably the chaffinch. Language is not, as linguists are taught to suppose, outside nature: it is a part of nature. For these reasons language became the basis of the unity within, as well as of the conflict between, tribes, sects, and the cultures belonging to them throughout the world.

When language was committed to writing in the Mesopotamia of the fourth millennium B.C. an invention was made with an effect altogether disproportionate to what was externally manifest. It slowly brought the whole of each written culture into one field of vision and put it onto a scale of time. By creating scripture it established history, religion, and the law. Belief and knowledge had now the possibility of becoming one.

All these things writing could do only because it first created a class of scribes. These people dug themselves in so comfortably in each society that they did not usually need to travel. But when some of them in Ugarit invented a thing so novel as alphabetic writing in the eighth century B.C. their pupils within 500 years had spread their invention over the whole Western world. From this diffusion spread later the great developments in the West of mathematics and music.

As writing became easier, translation became an instrument not merely of communication but also of the most diverse cultural changes. The translation in the sixteenth century of the Greek and Latin classics, and above all of the Hebrew Bible, into the North European languages transformed not only religion but the whole understanding of man and nature. Having done so the Bible then began to relegate the classical languages and to preserve the new languages into which it had been translated. It kept Welsh alive and only missed doing the same service to Irish.

The Hebrew language here is in an ambivalent position. It has been used to restore, not so much Jewish culture, as Jewish awareness of this culture while establishing the state of Israel. The role of the English language in India is again somewhat different. It gave a literate unity to a vast disunited assembly of peoples. In doing so, by means of a small literate caste, it made feasible, first the administrative unity, and then the political independence of India. On the other hand, the English, French, and Portuguese languages gave an appearance of civilization to colonies in Africa where these languages had been used. From this borrowed appearance the possibility and the expectation arose of independent unified government.

The existence of literature as well as language has often held together the educated classes of a country. It has given shape and endurance to their culture. This has in turn maintained political independence in Persia and restored it to Greece, Finland, and Iceland; and will probably restore it to the submerged peoples of Eastern Europe. On the other hand the failure of literature and a literate class is what makes the political survival of peoples such as the Vlaches, the Kurds, and the Nagas, so precarious. That is a good reason why the speakers of languages, like Basque and Welsh, which are culturally too small to be economic, in view of the cost of public communication, should make economic sacrifices to survive. The reason for wanting to survive is another matter: it is because for a small group language is the embodiment of culture; it constitutes the people's environment, not a natural but a created environment, its own genetic environment. Created over long generations by the character of men and women and attached to it more closely than the land itself, it is the very soul of the people.

People have treated the survival of their language in speech and in writing as a matter of life and death. And they have been right in doing so since language guarantees the survival of the breeding community. This is one reason for a deep interest in literacy which is, however, sometimes misguided. If we look back we see the ability to write and to read spreading from the original class of writers to priests, merchants, and rulers. In Northern Europe it reached the kings in the thirteenth century. From it sprang the growth of science which in turn, without destroying the subterfuges of superstition, made them less respectable. Slowly it forced them underground and into the lower layers of society. This effect in turn made illiteracy itself less respectable. Nevertheless after five millennia no community in the world, except probably the Icelanders, is wholly literate.

A large proportion of mankind still finds the operations of writing and reading insuperable obstacles, inborn genetic obstacles, to communication. In spite of the economic advantage and social prestige attaching to these attainments, illiteracy persists and will presumably persist indefinitely. Its incidence, however, is related to intelligence, race, and social class. It may also be assigned a variety of specific causes. Dysgraphia is probably one, dyslexia is certainly another for ten times as many males as females are described as dyslectic. The male is evidently showing his characteristically greater genetic variance in properties of mind as of body.

Evolutionary causes of illiteracy are not difficult to understand, whether in China, in India, or in Europe. For until the twentieth century only a small professional class has anywhere been selected for its ability to read and write. For the rest, literacy has had no survival value. Outside Europe, however, illiteracy is aggravated by the type of script available. Hebrew and Arabic with no vowels are clearly a deterrent to scholarship.

Similarly, the variety and impracticability of scripts used for Indian languages has also been an obstacle to using them as an alternative to English. The Chinese characters, while they unite the regions and dialects of China, help to maintain classes in a society which now, ostensibly, sets out to abolish them.

III *Invention and Diffusion*

If speech is the internal aspect of man's invention, what it has to tell us is about its external aspects, what he has done with the world outside him. The whole of history and pre-history is available to show us how it has all happened. Before we look back to the beginnings, however, we must look at the evidence close at hand. It does not matter whether we are anthropologists (like Spencer and Gillen) studying primitive people who are improving their rituals, or scientists making material discoveries at the present day, we find that individuals, tribes, classes, and races vary in their capacity to invent. And this is fortunately related to their capacity to learn or copy what has been invented. These are properties of intelligence combined with imagination, curiosity and enterprise, perspicacity and pertinacity, and many specialized skills.

Our studies of intelligence and behaviour leave no doubt that these properties are characteristic of individuals and that they have a genetic component. If it were not so there could never have been evolutionary progress, advance, or improvement in human intelligence or in human culture. In this light we can look at the development of agriculture and metal working in the Old World and the New between 8000 and 1000 B.C.

The changes constituting this revolution have been ascribed to various processes: the diffusion of a method or an idea, the migration of a people, or the expansion of a language. All these things must, to be sure, be separated and identified. But once separated they must then be connected in a practical sense. We must recognize that there is no evidence of ideas or languages, or crops or stock, diffusing among primitive peoples except by the movement of these peoples. These things may fly nowadays but they did not fly in ancient times. They were carried by men in ways we can recognize, always on purpose, by effort and for advantage.

When we make these separations and connections we see that agriculture increased and secured food supply which drew into the farming communities the skilled Paleolithic people around them, traders and craftsmen, creating stratified societies complex at the centre, simple on the frontier. These, expanding their numbers over three or four millennia, were able to expand their territory until they filled most of the cultivable world. In doing so they took with them their crops and stock, now transformed by domestication. But at the same time the traders and craftsmen whom they fed and carried with them, often moved independently of the communities to which their advantage attached them (Fig. 5.1).

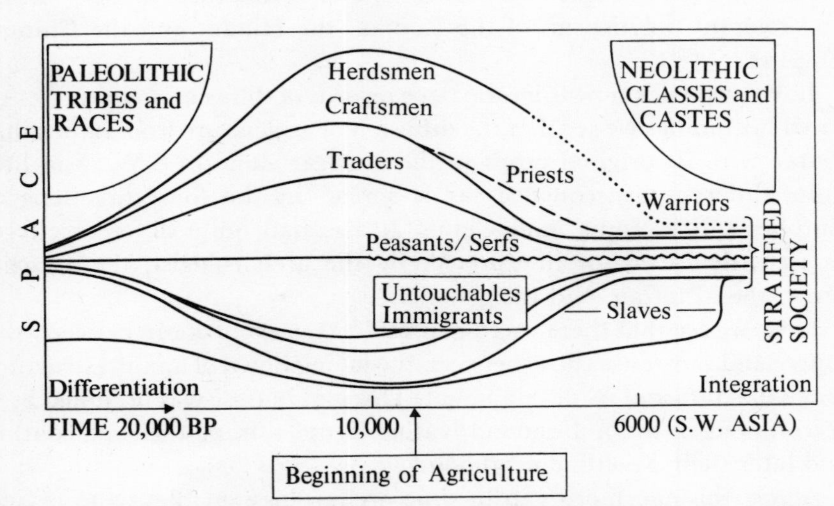

Fig. 5.1 Diagram showing the spatial and temporal relations between the evolutionary differentiation of tribes in the Paleolithic and their combination or coalescence to form the class structure of stratified societies after the invention of agriculture (after Darlington: *Eugenics Review*, **50**, 1958)

Thus the movements of peoples have been of units of different sizes, tribe, class, family, or individual according to the ideas or techniques that they were carrying. The expansions of Semitic and Aryan languages have been the work of conquering and governing classes. But in the modern world single artists or missionaries are effective. Peasants may shift their ground a day's march in a lifetime. Horsemen have taken no longer to cross the whole of Asia. But for peasants without the horse Central Asia blocked the passage of the wheat they grew for 3000 years. Again, between the people of Mexico and Peru the sea was an insuperable barrier for about 3000 years, but between Polynesians, as we have seen, it was over the same period the perfect means of communication.

There is therefore a logistics of human expansion, based on many sciences, which makes racial and cultural sense of the historical record. In the period of the Agricultural Revolution the fundamental imperative was of course that of food production and that is why (as we saw in Table 2.2) crops and stock preceded metal and stone and controlled the migration of people and hence the diffusion of culture.

As the means of production changed, as the hoe replaced the spear and the plough replaced the hoe, as authority shifted from weapons to tools and back again, and from men to women and back again, so priests, religions, and gods accommodated themselves to the changing balance of their perpetually unstable genetic foundations. It was an evolution which reached its diverse climaxes, notably, in the shifting and tolerant polytheisms of the Roman, the Hindu, and the Chinese Empires.

If we turn back now from the later records of diffusion to its authenticated beginnings we see that the diffusion of agriculture from its original source with its original crops in the Nuclear Zone in S.W. Asia had quite different consequences as it spread in the four directions of Europe, Africa, India, and China. It also had quite different effects as seen, described, or interpreted, by the archaeologist, the agriculturist, the historian, and the geneticist.

First, we see that there was a gap of 4000 years or more between the source and the destination, between the laying down of an infrastructure for civilization and its development. This gap in time was occupied by a recruitment of the nuclear cultivating peoples from their Paleolithic and later their Neolithic neighbours.

Across this enormous gap in time archaeology enables us to attach to one another the two great series of human movements in the Old World. The first are the four centrifugal movements from the Nuclear Zone which are botanically authenticated. The second are the five reverse movements of the Aryans breaking into the expanded Nuclear Zone in the second millennium B.C. in Italy, Greece, Anatolia, Persia, and India; these are historically and linguistically authenticated. The whole vast assemblage enables us to see the civilized and barbarian worlds for the first time in their connections and proportions.

What do we find? Just as root cultivation could get no further and failed to give rise to agriculture so the immigrant peoples of Europe who could build barrows in the fourth millennium B.C. and temples in the third millennium B.C. could not build cities until they were recruited by city builders from the Nuclear Zone 2000 years later.

The most valued craftsmen and engineers were drawn into the secure surroundings and favourable climates of Mesopotamia, Egypt, and the Indus and later into the Yellow River Valley in China. They were not disposed to shiver in Europe. Of the originality of Europe there is no doubt but its development was both delayed and starved primarily by the winter climate. Cities were built only much later because building was spread only by city builders. As we know, it was Caesar who took the crucial step into the north.

The comparison of the West with China in this respect teaches us another lesson. In the West inevitably agriculture spread northwards. It spread into regions which, when bronze and iron made them cultivable and therefore intensively habitable, also proved to be healthy and fertile. The Nuclear Zone became an impoverished, deforested, and ultimately disease-stricken centre. But in China, 3000 years later with the help of bronze, imported agriculture developed in the north. The centre of origin, being in the cold north, never became overpopulated, impoverished or diseased. Agriculture had been introduced independently with rice in the south. But from the north, language and writing, cities and civilization, carried by warriors, scholars and craftsmen, spread or diffused southwards. Northern cities, free from malaria, with little interruption have remained the capitals of China for nearly 3000 years.

In the diffusion of culture, therefore, the movements of people are the primary agents. But their genetic character, the structure of classes, the barriers to mating, the types of activity, the means of communication, the incidence of disease, the varieties of religion, the changes of climate, the discovery of new natural resources, all play their part.

IV *Culture Divided*

Two properties separate culture in Tylor's primitive societies from what we call civilization. One is due to writing and the other to the stratification of classes. But two other properties unite the contrasted stages of evolution. These are due to the differences of culture between age groups and between sexes. All species of animals have their own characteristic contrasts between their genetically prescribed stages of development. The recreations of children have seemed to be, as indeed they are, largely the immature stages of the adult occupations. But between the two there are also contrasts, long known among primitive peoples, but now recognized in civilized society in the form of cultures separately transmitted by age groups. The Opies have shown that this culture has been orally transmitted from one generation of children to another over great areas and probably over thousands of years. It has been transmitted largely without the help of parents or teachers and (before the Opies) entirely without the help of writing.

The culture of children consists of song, speech, and play which they have invented and transmitted within one stage of their own development, a stage hereditarily circumscribed. Its purpose is pleasure, its basis is instinct and intelligence, and its value is attested by its origin in play continuing throughout the evolution of mammals. Only in man, however, can we say that the rhymes that children recite are bisexual while the games they play are unisexual. Throughout the world boys prefer one kind of game, girls another. These differences are sexually and therefore genetically conditioned. They are the beginnings of the distinctions of culture between the adult sexes which dominate the evolution of many societies.

How does this happen? The genetic difference between men and women is, of course, primarily prescribed by the needs of reproduction. But in turn it prescribes their differences in occupation and interests or, as we may say, in the ecological setting they have given one another. In spite of overlap in their range of variation the two sexes are genetically adapted to benefit from these differences which in turn create a divergence of culture between what mothers pass on to daughters and fathers to sons.

At the same time their joint sexual and domestic interests converge to unite the sexes. Religion and race combine to balance, adjust, and regulate the two sexual cultures through a gamut of variations. These are expressed in the matri- *versus* patri-linear and matri- *versus* patri-local systems of marriage and inheritance; also more seriously in the division of labour between the sexes among all primitive and civilized peoples. They are also expressed in the contrasted arrangements of the great scriptural religions. For these all attempt, with partial success, to establish a uniformity of sex relations.

One of the religious systems, the European, stands apart from all the others. In introducing Christianity to the Europeans, Paul and his successors made concessions to the view of women and of monogamous marriage which racially and culturally separates Europe from Africa and Asia. In so doing the Church Fathers accepted but also slightly and slowly shifted the foundations of European society, and hence of Western civilization. Their policy, their strategy if you like, had the effect of abolishing polygamy both for Christians and for the Jews living under Christian rule in Europe. Consider the contrasted situation of Islam. Over the last 2000 years, the position of women has slowly improved in Europe under the selective, and practically eugenic, influence of Christianity. But the position of women in Islam has no less obviously declined. Only in the twentieth century has European influence reversed the trend by colonially, industrially, and therefore culturally undermining Islam itself.

The result of this history has been to establish a balance between the culture of the two sexes in Europe which has in turn provided an environment crucially affecting the genetic evolution of both sexes. The special contribution of women to the development of European culture has been one of the consequences of this evolution. But something even more important has been the need for adjustment of the two balanced but perpetually diverging sexes. During the last millennium this adjustment has given an increasing cultural vitality to the idea of a *home* in Europe, something which has conspicuously failed in Asia and Africa.

If you look at Europe more closely you see that the relations of the sexes show a cultural gradient running from north to south. It has the character of a Huxleyan genetic cline between the north where women are treated as social equals and the south where women are the property of men. Is this contrast a legacy of the division between Roman and barbarian Europe? Or between what was invaded and conquered by the Muslims and what was not? Or between Catholic and Protestant? Or between industrial and primitive? It is, we may say, all of these in historical, in evolutionary, sequence. The genetic division has not been shifted, the cultural contrast has not been mitigated, by the technical and social transformations of the north arising from the Industrial Revolution. On the contrary it is the contrast which has imposed these transformations. All that has happened has been a migration of illiterate workers from the south seeking employment in the north. And a less successful attempt to colonize the impoverished south from the industrial north.

A few cultural properties fail to interact with the differentiation of the sexes. One of these, as we might expect, is the instinctive and almost invariable incest taboo. Another is the highly variable attitude to nudity which is surprisingly little related to the need for clothes. In ancient times and similar climates the contrast between the Hebrews and the Greeks in this respect is clear. It is expressed in the wording of Deuteronomy and the stories of Noah and of Susannah on the one hand, and in the Olympic Games and the development of Greek sculpture on the other. Similarly today the highland tribes of New Guinea, which are racially highly diverse, show a complete range between the exhibition and the concealment of the genitalia. In the males we have the penis gourd and the hornbill of the Mitak at one extreme. At the other we have the skirt of the Kukukuku, irremovable, many-layered and louse-ridden. When we recall the role of sexual behaviour in the evolution of man, we see that these contrasts (described by Sorenson and Gajdusek), often emphasized by sexual morality and its mythical background, have a genetic component. Presumably the attitude to nudity is connected with all the other genetic elements in behaviour in each of the differing tribes.

The expansion of Islam into Africa sharply exposed conflicts of attitude towards women, towards their nudity and seclusion, and consequently towards the dancing of men and women together. These racial differences between Arab and Negro were brought into the forefront by the Arab strategy of conquest and conversion which depended above all on the general subjection and seclusion of women for the use of the polygynous conquerors. In two generations subject populations were thus hybridized and Arabized. The wave of Arab conquest broke on the rocks of female independence with Berbers like the Tuareg, and of female nudity with the Negroes. On his travels in the fourteenth century, Mohammed Ibn Battuta was shocked by the one, horrified by the other. In the following five centuries, their Negro slave trade shows us how the Arabs resolved this conflict of race and of culture.

Since men, women, and children each have their own culture in family life they have to switch from one to the other every day. Intelligent children take it as a matter of course to change their language, if need be, between school, street and home. Their parents, also, for much of their lives are working under the auspices of several cultures which, in our heterogeneous societies, may be not a little inconsistent. We need not wonder therefore at the ceremonial versatility of a Roman or Chinese Emperor who would minister to the needs of as many religions as his subjects required.

Nor need we wonder at the Amerindian peasants who accommodate themselves to a multiplicity of ceremonies if not of beliefs. In the Quiche province of Guatemala, Aldous Huxley visited the mountain village of Momostenango where he found that on a day recurring at intervals of 260 days, the Maya year, 30,000 Indians will celebrate the feast of Mindo at a hundred stone altars of the God. Afterwards they repair to the church to confess their sins to the representative of the white man's God. But for their physical salvation they prefer to resort to 300 sorcerers or witch-doctors, medicine men or shamans (depending on whether you wish to follow the European, African, or Asiatic usage). These men, probably dedicated to St Peter, are personal physicians, as well as spiritual advisers. Thus, for people lacking the explicit guidance of a book, professional and religious compartments of culture can be flexibly adjusted.

Belief may sit lightly or heavily on men's heads and hearts. But what they do, the style of their serious work is something always related to their genetic character, individual or corporate. The divisions that result exist on the scale of a village or of a continent. Every village in Europe has, or had until recently, its own character, its own variations of dialect and of culture. These were sometimes minute; but sometimes they were so profound as to cause conflict especially when villages owed their origins to colonization or transplantation a few centuries ago; or to ownership by landlords of opposed religious sects.

Above this minute discontinuity there has been the general movement of the last three centuries which has transformed the character and the culture of the whole of Europe. In England we may see three stages more sharply contrasted than elsewhere. The eighteenth century took its character from the landed aristocracy. It was visibly splendid because those people liked to display their good taste and were used to ignoring the squalor underlying it. In the nineteenth century the managers and exploiters of the industrial revolution, on the contrary, displayed their dark satanic mills with pride, making no attempt to conceal the squalor, but they chose themselves to live elsewhere as they still do. The twentieth century, we were told in 1905, was going to be the century of the common man, and so it has proved to be. It has been devoted to submerging impartially nature and civilization, art and individuality, under the festering sores of economic growth.

How can people who are racially and traditionally almost unchanged produce such radically different results? It is because particular individuals and classes by their inventions have created for the whole of society a succession of new environments. Each of these environments has taken control of society and especially of its means of differentiation. But it is not merely the static environment, it is its direction of change which has taken control. Later we must ask ourselves how far the direction of change has been understood and how far the destination is acknowledged.

V *Genetic Environments*

The contrast and the opposition between heredity and the environment, is primitive and proverbial in human thought. People had to sort out each notion separately before the two could be fitted together. And this has taken many generations.

It was Claude Bernard, with Darwin the most profound biological thinker of the nineteenth century, who made the first necessary step. He recognized that there were two senses, at least two, in which one could speak of an environment. From the external environment he separated the internal environment, the *milieu intérieur*. By saying this, in 1856, he broke into the central problem of the working of the animal body. This environment, he argued, was the product of all the circulating fluids of the body. It was something almost constant, being regulated by what we now know as hormones; regulated also by interactions, which we now know largely as negative feedback processes. This regulation establishes a stable environment, first, for the development and then for the maintenance of the activities of muscles, nerves and glands and, within every cell, the nucleus and the chromosomes. It is an environment which can be specified in terms of acidity and concentrations of solids and solutes, salts, sugars and proteins, and most recently, for warm-blooded animals, in terms of temperature. It is something necessary to reduce the individual's dependence on what happens outside it, that is on its external environment.

For Bernard it was also something characteristic of the species. But when we turn it over in terms of our genetics of a hundred years later we see that it is also something characteristic of individuals and variable between them. Thus, as we saw, when a recessive gene blocks the breakdown of certain substances in the blood it impairs the developing brain of a child. Similar effects may arise from unsuitable feeding, connected either with the mother or with the purely external environment. But the internal environment of the individual is its genetic property and it tends to be genetically adapted by natural selection, by evolution, to be as far as possible independent of what happens outside.

The next step in understanding the environment was taken by Jacob von Uexküll, in 1909. This Danish zoologist translated Bernard's ideas into German and shifted them half way into the world outside. Animals for him had not only an *Innenwelt* but also an *Umwelt*, a social or cultural world. Further they had a *Merkwelt* a world of perception, and a *Wirkungswelt* a world of action. And, of course, a merely physical *Umgebung*. Each of these is a different world, sensory or motor, in which the things are connected in the mind of the observer although they are disconnected in an animal he may be observing. The cat therefore lives in a cat's world and the dog lives in a dog's world, different from one another's and from our world. These are various worlds which a biologist (or an artist) may enter by observation and by inference.

The different worlds in which different peoples live and move are based on the different senses of taste and smell and sight and hearing in which men differ but which kindred people, racially related people, largely have in common. On these sensory worlds rest other worlds of mental association and imagination in which whole peoples profoundly differ. The ancient Egyptian and the Maya, the Indian and the Chinese, the mediaeval and the modern European, have lived in different worlds which are all revealed and reflected, condensed and summarized in their styles of art, styles which can never be translated into one another. Rather they gaze forever at one another across unbridgeable gulfs which challenge our understanding. For this was how they and no one else saw life and nature.

These notions may seem obvious now. But they underlie a revolution in the modern study of the behaviour of animals as well as in my own studies of the evolution of man and of his genetic system. They demand that the activities of animals and plants, and the environments which they make and in which they live, should be pulled to pieces before we can understand them.

This pulling to pieces means that we have to look again at principles which we have taken for granted all our lives. We have to do this in two senses. In the first sense we have to see how environments are given to plants, chosen by animals, or made by men. In the second sense we have to see how plants, animals, and men have made use of these different relations to enlarge their control over their effective environment; how they have indeed, in the course of their evolution, extended Bernard's internal environment beyond the life and compass of the individual.

If we look at the simplest change in heredity—not the accumulated changes that distinguish a cat and a dog or the different races of man—a single mutation affecting the sense of smell in a dog or the sense of sight in a man, we see that such a change, in itself alters the environment in which the new kind of individual lives. It also affects his chances of survival. If it had been a mutation turning a tall into a dwarf pea the plant would have no choice in the matter, no choice of environment. The mutation would change its *Wirkungswelt* but its physical environment, its *Umgebung*, would remain what chance had given it.

Von Uexküll was thinking particularly of animals but these environmental connections show us the cardinal distinction between the modes of evolution of plants, animals, and man. For the evolution of all three, a mixed, a heterogeneous, environment is equally necessary; but the animal, unless it is being controlled by a man, a domesticator or an experimenter, can within limits choose its environment. A variable species of animal, unless it is living in the invariable environment of the deep sea where evolution is commonly brought to a standstill, can and will move to the place that suits each individual best. In this way the cost of selection is economized and the process of evolution is accelerated.

For the plant the problem is quite otherwise. It has no choice at all; when its seeds are scattered the environment of each is thrust upon it as the parable of the sower vividly tells us. It has therefore to provide copious variation as well as numerous progeny if new variants are to meet situations that are ecologically suitable. For this reason it need not surprise us to find that the highest plants have made good their disadvantage by a network of protective environments. These are more elaborate than anything known in the higher animals. They resemble only the situation in man himself. For this reason they throw light on the evolution of human behaviour. Darwin foresaw this and attempted to show it in a series of books on plants and plant breeding which he wrote a hundred years ago when he had finished with man. We may follow in his footsteps at this point and then proceed from where he left off.

The flowering plants or Angiosperms probably had their origin in the Cretaceous period 100 million years ago and they soon swept the world. They owed their overwhelming success to their having invented certain reproductive improvements. Their common ancestors had discovered two new devices for organizing their breeding processes.

The first device consisted in developing a sieve or filter, the style, through which the male pollen had to grow before it could fertilize the female egg. The pollen tubes cannot get through this style if they are too like it; nor if they are too unlike it. A hundred years' work has shown that this reciprocal device keeps the right distance of kinship between the uniting germ cells. It is a device which owes its success to securing a favourable balance between the needs of fitness and flexibility, between the vigour of the offspring and the mixing up of genetic differences in their descendants. It is a device which, as I pointed out thirty years ago, is fully paralleled only in human societies with their cultural and instinctive control of breeding habits, their assortative mating, their restraints equally on incest and on promiscuity.

This first device had its forerunners in evolution. The second device, however, was an entirely new trick. It consisted of a gestation of the embryo combined with an accurate control of gestation itself. The embryo is carried and fed by the mother plant to the point at which it is free to be dispersed as a seed and to fend for itself as a seedling. But in this development the embryo is further protected by an exact genetic control of its food supply. This control depends on a process of 'double fertilization' discovered by a Russian scientist, Sergius Navashin, in 1899. Each embryo in each seed is provided with a half-sister which it cannibalistically feeds upon. This dummy embryo, this artificial but kindred environmental tissue, is known as the *endosperm*. It is half-way in genetic character between the mother and the embryo that it is feeding. It is a triploid formed by the fusion of two nuclei from the mother (M) and one from the father, the pollen (P). In addition to pollen and egg therefore three other organisms indispensably cooperate in the plant's process of generation and gestation. We may represent them as MM:MMP:MP.

At the same time that this unparalleled innovation took place, the ancestors of our flowering plants were developing a style which filtered the pollen so that no embryo could be formed by too remote an outbreeding or too close an inbreeding. Chemically the plant was achieving

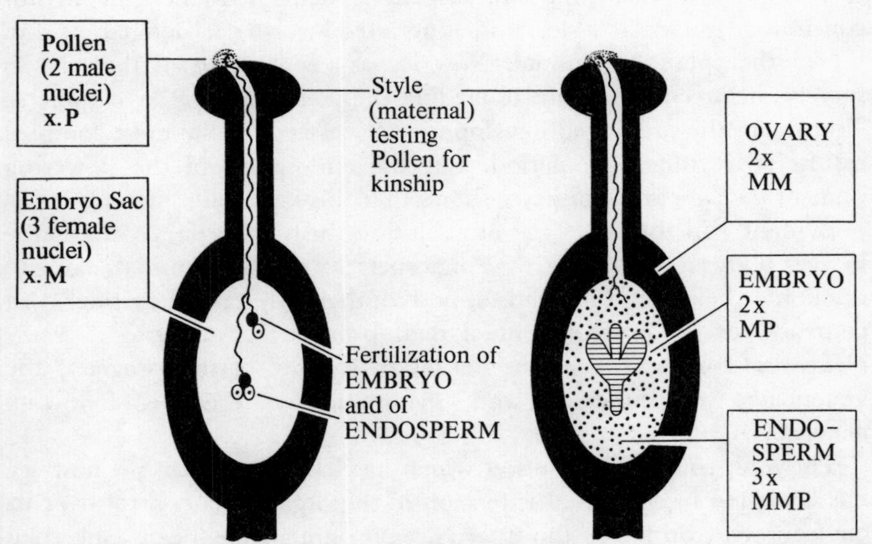

Fig. 5.2 Diagram showing how the development of the style-filter and double-fertilization, combined with gestation, gave the first flowering plants a genetic control of their reproductive systems and initiated a new phase of evolution in the Cretaceous period

a control over breeding which the higher animals achieve by way of instinctive behaviour, processes of courtship with birds, the characteristic organizations of society we have seen in mammals, or instinctive taboos on incest with man (Fig. 5.2).

The combination of these two innovations at the end of the Cretaceous period in one stock of plants led to an explosive change in the character of life on our planet. Within a few million years the flowering plants, equipped with their new breeding system, provided the vegetation which covered three-quarters of the earth. In doing so they provided the sources of food and energy, the grass and the grain, necessary for the expansion of the warm-blooded reptiles, birds, and mammals which quickly followed; and in due course they provided the bread which has fed man himself until today. And, with prudence, will still feed him tomorrow.

The highest animals, the mammals which depend on the flowering plants for their food, do not achieve the same doubly protective environment in gestation but they come as close to it as is conceivable for an animal. They have no genetically intermediate nutritive tissue such as the endosperm. But they have developed a process of gestation followed by lactation. This means that the mother provides not just the food of the embryo but also the environment of the offspring: first the total environment and then later a part of a family environment.

The embryo with gestation, instead of being launched on an uncontrolled, unpredictable, and unrelated world, is lodged within the mother plant or animal. Now it has been supposed that this is merely a convenient means of feeding the young during development. To be sure the prolonged development necessary for the most complex results is a vulnerable period. But the endosperm of the flowering plants by its genetic character shows that this is not all.

Evidently in the last stage of evolution, in the Tertiary period, the highest plants and animals, the Angiosperms and the Mammals came to dominate the earth. They did so, both of them, by extending their own control over the environment of their progeny, by creating a *genetic environment* for the precarious period in the life of the progeny, the genetically experimental and evolutionarily creative following generation.

The long course of evolution which has led up to man, we now see has consisted in a gradual extension of the organism's control over its environment. So far as the internal environment has been concerned this has long been acknowledged. But now we notice that the same principle applies to the external environment. Step by step, gestation and lactation have extended maternal care. The development of the family has introduced paternal responsibility. The growth of society has imposed cultural uniformity. The use of speech has specified the position of the individual who has come to be both protected and subjected by the group, by his or her tribe, class, sect, and nation. And when the individual escapes, as he may, from the genetic bonds of subjection to his kindred, and he chooses by his own judgement what spouse to marry and what other sect or society to join, his choice is still a genetically controlled choice. Unless he chooses solitude and sterility he still has an environment which is genetically implicated and ancestrally bound (Fig. 5.3).

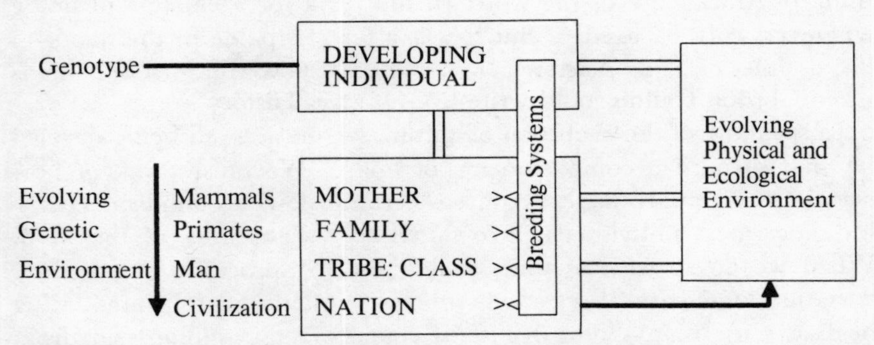

Fig. 5.3 Diagram showing the circular and reciprocal relations of heredity and environment underlying the evolution of human behaviour (after Darlington: *Nature*, **234,** 1971)

The last stage in this evolutionary progression is what follows from man's invention with its effects spreading in time and space: the control of the environment beyond his living kindred, the material exploitation of plants, animals, and the earth itself, leading finally to agriculture and civilization. About this culminating phase of man's evolution there has seemed to be some mystery but it is a mystery we can now see through. It corresponds, as we have seen, to the culminating phase in the evolution of the brain which has developed step by step with the genetic control of the environment all the way up from the lancelet and the lamprey to man himself.

VI *The Psychosocial Fallacy*

In all sciences we find that the ideas which have helped our inquiries in the past become in turn the main obstacle to inquiry in the future. A hundred years ago, Tylor saw how the thing worked: 'To many educated minds', he wrote in 1871, 'there seems something presumptuous and repulsive in the view that the history of mankind is part and parcel of the history of nature'.

What Tylor could not see at that time was that the very words he used would in turn be employed to separate what he wanted to join together and to close what he wanted to open. Man and culture, race and history, heredity and environment, intelligence and selection, all terms used by Tylor, need to be continually re-examined and re-defined. Otherwise they pick up, like magnets, whatever convenient fallacies people like to attach to them. Every term which has brought light soon, in this way, begins to throw its shadow. We have only to think of Marx's use of the word History as a force capable of doing whatever work he needed. But it was a force capable in the hands of his disciples of being mastered by the equally powerful idea of Man as when Gordon Childe could write 'Man makes History'.

In speaking of the evolution of culture we must avoid being dazzled by the splendid accomplishments of 'man'. We must think of how certain individuals have acquired certain new accomplishments—but how most individuals have failed to do anything of the kind. When we do so we can understand how, by processes of heredity, variation, and natural selection, processes usually brutal, humiliating or disastrous, 'man' did evolve in the course of a few million years from a monkey.

We must think therefore, not of man, but of individuals and tribes, sects and classes, races and nations, all of whom are different and behave differently. We must think of culture as being invented, taught and learned, all of which processes are different parts of the behaviour of genetically different people. We must think of heredity not as a block or lump or mass of eggs or flow of blood but as something which is split up in each generation, split up into chromosomes and pieces of chromosomes (not into genes incidentally, as the public imagines, for single genes are never separated in heredity); something split up differently in each individual, and differently according to whether the family is inbred or outbred. We must think of the environment not only as a purely physical environment but also as an ecological environment, a social environment which may be partly selected or chosen by families or individuals; and also as something that is always partly a genetic environment owing its character to kinship and to heredity, something of adaptive value developed in evolution by natural selection on principles which man has derived from his animal ancestors but applied and extended to extraordinary lengths in new dimensions.

When I say we must think of these things I am also asking you, the reader, to do something more. I am asking you to reject what others have thought right and good; to reject the simple terms in which the commonsense of our worthy ancestors was wrapped up. I am asking you to reject the distinction beloved of the most civilized people and enshrined in the great western Judaic religions for the last 2500 years. For these religions tell us in one form or another that man is something apart from the rest of nature, above the rest of nature, divinely appointed and privileged to rule nature, and to exploit it for his own benefit. The principle of divine appointment we may recall, is still widely held among our spiritual and temporal rulers today to apply to themselves. This was the issue (although they did not express it as I am expressing it) on which Darwin and T. H. Huxley disputed the authority of revealed religion a hundred years ago, the issue which scientists, without understanding it, have believed to have been settled.

It has not, however, been settled so as to satisfy the instinctive feelings and hopes of the great mass of mankind, civilized or uncivilized mankind. On the contrary, the idea that man has been appointed by God to rule over nature is and has been the chief reason that Europeans have had for believing in God. It has been God's *raison d'être*. But it is a fallacy and a dangerous one because it offers the pretext of divine support for all the follies that men, and especially the rulers of men, may commit through their own ignorance or stupidity. It is made more dangerous when the flattering argument for man's independence of nature is put in a scientific disguise by men who claim to dispense with God. I will examine one of these disguises.

In an appendix to his study of *Evolution* in 1962, Sir Julian Huxley explained his view that at some point in his development man slipped the traces of natural selection. He began to undergo a novel and peculiarly human form of evolution distinct from anything known in earlier animal history. 'Evolution in the psychosocial phase', he writes, 'is primarily cultural, manifested in cultural change and only secondarily genetic.' Further, 'through the operation of psychosocial selection, the idea-system itself evolves . . . so that each human population possesses a more or less integrated or co-adapted pool of ideas on which it can draw for its maintenance and evolutionary requirements.'

Thus, presumably at the beginning of speech, we are asked to believe that culture began to evolve on its own by a new form of selection. How did it work? 'Psychosocial selection, involving some sort of selection between competing ideas and values, must operate in the human phase and is clearly very different from natural selection.' How did it differ? Natural selection, we all agree, depends on the different prospects of survival of different human beings. Psychosocial selection depends on the different prospects of survival of different ideas. And how do they survive? By being drawn out of the pool by different human beings, or rather by different populations. And how do these populations choose these ideas? To meet their evolutionary requirements. Now where have we heard about 'evolutionary requirements' before? What 'pool of ideas' was that idea drawn out of? It is the pool from which a succession of evolutionary thinkers: Lamarck, Robert Chambers, Herbert Spencer, Michurin, and Lysenko have drawn as they required over the last two centuries. The idea they have drawn is that organisms evolve because they require to do so. We human beings are in the fortunate psychosocial phase when we can always evolve in the right direction because we have all those 'competing ideas and values' to choose from.

Certainly Huxley was right in saying that this is something 'very different from natural selection'. For on this principle 'man' or the 'population' chooses the ideas and, usually (perhaps under the guidance of a Superior Being), chooses the right one. But under natural selection, nature selects the man together with his idea—if he has one. Every teacher who presents his pupils with ideas, as teachers sometimes do, knows that some pick them up. Others fail to do so. Some pupils pick up the right ideas. Others pick up the wrong ideas. They plunge into the pool of ideas and sink forever. Others, again (even acknowledged pundits and professors), we see swimming about in Huxley's pool hoping to pick up an idea and never finding it. Sometimes they find one but then discover with disappointment that it is not 'acceptable'. By this they mean that it is not politically or socially acceptable; and if you are speaking of race or class, or culture or intelligence, there are many ideas which are not acceptable. They do not fit the views of the majority or the interests of an establishment. And there are other ideas, like that of psychosocial selection, which are acceptable. They commend themselves to the majority; indeed the majority of the United Nations Assembly might accept them with applause.

One has to use one's judgement in choosing the ideas one picks up. Even in thinking out one's own ideas, judgement is not to be disregarded. And what is judgement? It comes from the intelligence. And the intelligence comes by heredity. It is an inborn faculty in respect of whose quality or quantity individuals, families, classes, sects, tribes, races, and even Huxley's populations, differ.

It is a faculty which, as history seems to show, is always in short supply. So that even in the most pampered, most affluent, and most compassionate human society, it favourably influences survival. Those with sounder judgement in certain critical connections and junctures (like crossing a road or expressing an opinion on a controversial question) will be favoured at the expense of those with less sound judgement. Indeed, just as with monkeys, we are subject to natural selection in regard to all our physical and mental faculties and therefore all our genetic and cultural prospects.

But I have left something out which must not be left out. For the development of all our faculties we need an environment, an appropriate environment. And our human societies are deeply concerned to provide this appropriate environment for the rising generation of children on whom our hopes are fixed. This we do in the form we describe as education. How do we do it? How ought we to do it? This is a question we can now try to answer.

Chapter 6

The Created Environment: Education

I *Origins*

The extension of a genetic control of the environment, we now see, has played a crucial part in evolution. The mammals began as very small animals, developing individually on a scale of time and size probably like that of mice. In evolution they extended their period of gestation as they and their brains grew larger. In parallel they extended their period of parental care. These changes continued in the evolution of man. Our infants have less mature brains than our ancestors had at birth; and, of course, their development of body, of brain, and of intelligence is slower. The control of the parent is extended.

Parental care and control have obviously developed into what we call education. But in this development the community, the breeding group to which the parents belong, has always played a part. Later on, when the child fends for itself, if it wants to choose another group, it has a choice which is governed by its own genetic disposition. So it is in man, and in each society of men, that the child graduates from one genetic environment to another until it chooses a mate. This choice is subject to greater or less parental control, and this control is in turn subject to the breeding system which is a part of the culture of each community.

How far do these terms correspond with what we know of evolution in general and its selective processes in particular? Most species of animals and plants consist of individuals which differ in their preferences for mode of life and place of living. Outside the uniform environment of the deep sea they also live in situations where these preferences can be exercised. That is to say their surroundings are physically diverse, varying in time and in space.

Man in these respects covers the whole range of possibilities. Stable tribes and caste societies are highly uniform and live in highly uniform surroundings. Unstable societies, tribal or stratified, are diverse in themselves and in their surroundings. These are the kinds of people and of situation which, being most flexible have the most promising future. But their flexibility also makes them hazardous for each new generation. That is why the trend of evolution has been to extend the control of the animal and plant over the environment of its progeny. In man this control has obviously surpassed anything known in any other animal. And it has done so above all by the conscious and more or less intelligent processes of education.

The earliest source of education lies in the guidance, the warnings, and the correction, which the mammalian mother with paw or teeth gives to her young. It also lies in the play which her young instinctively have with her and with one another.

A second source we may trace in the systems of initiation which introduce the child to his or her duties as a mature member of the tribe, whether hunting or collecting, tilling or herding. This ritual indoctrination is a basis of belief and behaviour which is often irrational and overrides rational inquiry. We see it surviving in the Hindu reverence for the Earth, the Mother, and the Cow; and for the social division by caste; all of which together have helped to make but could help to destroy the Hindus.

A third source of education lies in the parental training in the skills which will provide the livelihood of the child. This training becomes differentiated in the stratified society where the vocation itself is hereditary. It exists in two stages. The first depends on the invention of speech. The mother teaches speech. Then the father teaches his son with the help of speech. The two together provide the genetic environment. For the parents provide both the heredity and the environment, either harmoniously in an inbred society, or less so in our own outbred societies. The second stage comes with the invention of writing in Sumer and Egypt. Here with the teaching of this profitable new invention, for which parents were often unqualified, the theory and practice come into historical view.

In Ur and later in Akkad and Assyria the pupils at school are mostly the sons of scribes, priests, officials, and military officers but some are of lower origin presumably chosen for their merits. Later the writers were to become a caste, notably so in Egypt, but in Akkad they are still a mixed class, an ambitious, rising, and privileged class, admitted as pupils after examination of their physique, eyes, teeth, and hands. They are taught both literacy and numeracy. Their languages are Sumerian and Akkadian (in cuneiform) and later for governing subject peoples, Aramaic (in alphabetic script). There are 'scribes of counting' for calculation, surveying, and engineering and there are royal, military, civil, and administrative classes. The teacher is paid by the parents and the pupils are taught to respect him, and the value of what he teaches for their future careers. And in case the pupil forgets there is the sanction of flogging sometimes no doubt applied with anger.

This earliest education, we notice, derives from the structure of the stratified societies in which it arose and it contributes to this structure. How is this? The teacher selects his pupils and is selected by their parents. The parents' interest and the child's ability are the keys to the contract. It is a social arrangement between the three parties. It is also an economic contract establishing two new and skilled professions, those of the teachers and of the practitioners of writing, the scribes and officials. These professions prospered by virtue of the talents of their members, all of whom later became castes; and also by virtue of their inherent value to society which became evident as they transformed the processes of government and their basis in written law.

European education is important since it led to the scientific and industrial revolutions which made the modern world. On the manual side it came from the growth of guilds and the training of apprentices. On the literate side it came from the Church, from its needs to administer its work and its possessions. Cathedrals and abbeys began to teach boys reading, writing, and singing. Their schools began to study scripture, law, and commerce—not without help from Jews and Muslims. In a world where kings could not write this training opened the door to civil administration. Slowly all the uses of education came to be bound together and when great endowments began to be bequeathed to advance them the teachers sought to protect their independence by the incorporation of universities, intermediaries between Church and State.

Outside this system the sons of the rich had always been trained in the houses of the nobility and the royal courts. It was the children of the poor who were intended to benefit. For them schools and universities became the great ladder of selection and promotion in society. This was even true of schools and colleges founded to support the relatives of the benefactors, 'Founder's Kin' as they were known in England. What we may call an academic profession, an education industry, with its own social, political, and religious opinions and its own economic interests, came into being.

Ever since the University of Salerno was founded in the ninth century on what was to be a characteristically international basis, European universities have been enlarging the work of schools. They have been selecting, maintaining, and distributing a professional class. They have been concerned with separating the Neolithic classes of priest and craftsman from their pre-Christian superstitions and putting them on foundations of literature and science which came to be regarded as civilized. In doing so they have nearly always collaborated with and mediated between the contrasted authority of the rulers and the Church in each European country. But sometimes in making a third estate they have contributed to reforming or overturning one of the other two.

II *The Pursuit of Equality*

The consequences of universities were seen in their full gravity through the works of Wycliffe and Huss for they revealed that the Bible could be a revolutionary document. When the revolution burst upon them, the Protestant rulers in Europe sought to repair the damage with the help of education or, more precisely, with the help of paid teachers. They hoped to restore the respect for authority which the Roman Church had for a thousand years sustained so well. In England, Edward VI re-founded almost as many schools as he had dissolved. But it was in England that this defence first broke down.

The revolt of the newly educated literate, professional classes against traditional, aristocratic rule began in England (1642). It followed in the English colonies (1776) and in France (1789). But to succeed, in each of these countries, the revolutionaries had to involve the illiterate urban workers on the side of their literate masters. They had to suggest, or later to proclaim, a principle of equality and to represent the manual workers as having the same interests as their masters. Hence, when the battle was won, it was also necessary to turn about. Cromwell, Washington, and Napoleon each accomplished this difficult manœuvre in his own way. Gibbon's comment on Justinian: 'The perfect equality of men is the point in which the extremes of democracy and despotism are confounded' was written between Washington and Napoleon. It was both a reflection of the past and a prediction of the future. It was a prediction to be further confirmed by the success of Lenin. The pretence of equality was the key to power, or, we may add, exploitation.

This was the situation which, when they were all dead, the heirs of the revolutionaries inherited only to be overtaken by, what none of them had foreseen, the Industrial Revolution.

Each of the industrialized countries was of course hit by this second storm in a different way but Britain, which again led the way, having made the Revolution, was hit first and hit hardest. The impact was buffered by extraordinary circumstances: a religious revival, a successful patriotic war, a system of transportation of dissidents to overseas colonies assisted by the explorations of Captain Cook, and a continual public argument which rarely became violent and in which each social class was articulately divided. These circumstances had their counterparts in France and the United States although they were not enough to avert great political disturbances and one Civil War. In all three countries the upshot was that some kind of principle of equality came to be accepted as the basis of legislation and administration; and representative government came to be attached to universal suffrage.

The notion of equality was admitted by the ruling classes in each country the more readily because some rightly believed it would curtail social injustice, and because others believed it could do no harm, its meaning not being quite clear: the resulting system of government could be manipulated by those who owned the land and possessed the wealth and were, in any case, experienced in the business. For these reasons, the slave owners of Virginia and the landlords in England, almost at the same time, were persuaded to relinquish their authority to the new industrialists who in turn were persuaded to hand it over to the masses, to the proletariat.

What was necessary in Britain, France, and the United States was that the principle of equality and hence democracy (or later in Soviet Russia the dictatorship of the proletariat) must from time to time be asserted, while the powers of government should remain where they had been. During the nineteenth century one way of postponing any loss of power was to accept or seem to accept the unlimited capacity of education to improve the lot of the whole people. Not that the present generation would benefit but their children, if they worked hard, would enjoy the prospect of a future with continual improvement.

A proportion of the children did benefit. A large proportion benefited a little. A small proportion benefited a great deal, as well as benefiting the whole of society. The effects were obvious enough to suggest the noble prospect that if all had equal education all in the end would benefit equally. What was needed therefore was more education. Moreover it must be the kind of education that had made the educated professional classes successful in the past: all social classes, and in the United States all races, must be taught the same things by the same teachers in the same schools. The teaching must be free and compulsory, universal and prolonged, and above all literate. These principles were carried furthest and earliest in the United States. For this there were two main reasons.

Coming into the United States were great numbers of intelligent immigrants some of whom had had little opportunity of education in their home countries. In the United States school education in English was seen as the obvious means for the nation (especially after the Civil War) to instil unity and loyalty in its new citizens. The Constitution, owing to the diversity of the colonies, had abandoned the European method of using religion as a means of unity. It therefore put the English language and American history in its place. In the United States saluting the flag at school each morning took the place of singing a hymn in the United Kingdom.

The second reason appeared much later, in the 1960s. It was that the Negro population, separated from the white population as a visible caste, continued to be at a visible social and economic disadvantage. It was felt that this was not due to a racial difference because such a difference would be irremediable and its acceptance would be a defeat. Rather it must be the continuing result, an abiding and evolutionary consequence, of the former injustice of slavery. Education, therefore, equalized and integrated, would remove the disparity and distribute the Negro population equally and harmoniously through the whole of American society. On this assumption it was decided to remove the bars to Negro admission to Southern schools and universities, to transport Negroes from their own districts so as to mix them in similar proportions in all public schools; and for universities even to remove mental tests which might discriminate between races in admission.

Comparable changes took place in parallel in the 1960s in the United Kingdom. Here immigration had produced some analogous situations. But there was, in addition, a double system of endowed schools established before and after the Reformation, which admitted pupils by competitive examination on two scales; side by side were some children whose parents were willing to pay for their schooling and others who were given scholarships on their own merits providing for free education. These 'grammar' schools, with pupils selected either for their ability or for their parents' abilities, attracted the best teachers. They were diverse in character. Although often small in size and poor in equipment they were successful in fulfilling the purposes of their founders. The first of these purposes might be to suppress the differences of behaviour among their pupils. But their second purpose was to discover and develop the differences in their understanding. History records that they often did so. They provided the genetic environment in which great abilities appeared. They were the geese that laid the golden eggs of the Industrial Revolution.

The principle of equalization demanded that these geese should be killed. Their advantages should be removed and schools should be merged in a national system of large well-equipped expensive 'comprehensive' schools. Further, as in the United States, social differences should be broken down by forced transport between districts, the choice of schools by parents or pupils being suppressed. To complete this democratic programme it was necessary only for parents who were opposed to education to interfere in deciding what was taught and whether or not discipline should be used in teaching it (*Times*, 4 September 1976).

The experience of this policy for ten years has shown that the attempt to combine the education of children at the opposite ends of Burt's range of variation in intelligence is harmful to, and resented by, both extremes. Each discourages the other. Each recognizes its own genetic environment. At the upper end there is a failure to train sufficient numbers for the universities without lowering the standards. At the lower end there is the breakdown of the attempt introduced in the United Kingdom in 1970, to keep all children at school to the age of sixteen, whether they or their parents wanted it or not. Many children, 10–20 per cent of most populations, show at an early age that they don't want to read or write. What they learn this way has no use or meaning for them. They are known as 'slow-learners' or 'lesson-resisters'. As we used to say, you can lead a horse to the water but you can't make him drink. Kept at school such children cause trouble and in the absence of strict discipline, sheer catastrophe.

We learn that in 1974 school fires in the United Kingdom cost £9 million, that a large proportion were due to arson, and that the disgruntled pupils preferred to set fire to their own classrooms (*Times*, 11 January 1975). The vandals are not such fools as they are thought to be: they know when they are wasting their time.

Confusion has evidently been produced by mixing the more educable with the less educable children down to the admitted but arbitrary level of 'subnormality' at I.Q. 70. It has led to a desperate remedy which has its origin in the primary schools of the United States. The idea is that the child directs so far as possible its own education within the limits of its own aptitudes, free from the competition with its fellows which may strain the emotions of those who fail to learn what they are taught. And free, above all, from the fear of punishment which might leave a permanent scar on the developing young mind.

These are known as progressive methods of education. They derive originally from Rousseau's novel *Emile* of 1762 and they are not ill-adapted for intelligent children with intelligent teachers. But Rousseau did not believe that the children of the poor were worth educating. He would not have been surprised therefore that with the general practice of his methods most children suffer. Guidance, competition, and correction are needed by all children. But they are least needed by those who are naturally apt and enterprising. Children whose inclinations are to manual work suffer mentally after the age of twelve in schools where manual work is at a discount. Hence the resentment they feel and show in the following years.

The position of the Gypsies or Romany is well worth noting in this respect. Here is a minority which is now and always has been subjected to racial discrimination in Europe. The Gypsies are nomadic people who for 500 years have been persecuted, distrusted, and usually despised by the settled majority. These are attitudes the Gypsies thoroughly reciprocate for they have little respect for property or learning and are entirely absorbed in their love of nature and their own people. To capitalism and socialism they are equally indifferent. They have, in a word, no covenant with the European God.

The 20,000 children of this strange breed in England would be destroyed by the settled Gorgio's odious discipline of regular indoor schooling: fortunately they have so far escaped it. But their character and vulnerability they share with much greater numbers in the settled population who are faced with the problems of universal education.

The Industrial Revolution which forced these problems on us at the same time provided us with a hasty technical solution. It did so in the shape of two inventions: the rotary steam press in the United States and rotary paper-making in England. From these sprang two great enterprises centred in London which were the divergent forerunners of modern reading throughout the world. There was the 'Penny Dreadful' with violence, horror, and sex, often plagiarizing Dickens. This was the incentive for general literacy. And there was the 'Penny Reader'. This was the incentive for serious instruction. Here the demand came first from Scotland, then from England and last from Wales.

This order of events was reflected in the extraction of ability from the working classes of the three countries. Prodigious enthusiasm for learning struck the three countries in turn and produced from each a rich harvest. This wonderful experience, however, has had an inevitable and painful sequel. The libraries assembled in the mining villages of South Wales were the places where men of genius (like Aneurin Bevan) educated themselves. They are now swept away because the men of genius have themselves been swept away. The libraries have been sold and the buildings devoted to the more lucrative activities of billiards and bingo. The brains whose supply was limited have been drained out. Meanwhile, as a study from the University of Aberdeen discloses, the supply of entrants to the Scottish universities from the manual working classes which stood at 33 per cent in the 1920s had, in spite of all improvements fallen to below 25 per cent by the 1950s. And today 80 per cent are leaving Scottish schools at the minimum leaving age of 16 (*Observer*, 19 September 1976). Burt's analysis was correct.

The urban working classes of Europe are, of course, far from being uniform castes. They have been continually, albeit illegitimately, outcrossed with the educated classes, in the Middle Ages with the clergy and later with the gentry. The outbred products, having the abilities of their fathers or grandfathers, and sometimes more, resented being given the social status of their mothers—for the class relations were the opposite of those D. H. Lawrence represented in his famous novel. They were therefore born to be rebels. It was no accident that Keir Hardie, Ramsay Macdonald, and Ernest Bevin in Britain, all gifted rebels, were also illegitimate. The same principle applies to Abraham Lincoln in the U.S.A., Alexander Herzen in Russia, and in our time, Willie Brandt in Germany and Juan and Eva Peron in Argentina. No doubt many others like George Bernard Shaw might be added to this list. It is also no accident that the working class movements of various kinds which these leaders helped to advance were later, as we shall see, stultified by the inadequacy of their successors; and that we now find the sons of peers concealing their origins in order to fill the gap in the leadership of the workers; while the trades unions themselves take revenge for past ill-treatment by misconceived policies. An inevitably selective educational system had raised politically one part, but impoverished intellectually the bulk, of the class it was intended to redeem.

It is on account of their own policy of universal education, therefore, that a profound cleavage, of whose nature they are unaware, has split progressive political movements. The leaders, many of whom have risen by education, believe in more schools, more universities, more education. Their electors, who no longer hope to rise by education, see less virtue in it. And many of their children see none at all. Refused useful work, which they would enjoy while of school age, the children are provided with a false environment; they take revenge on their teachers, on their more intelligent schoolmates, on the school, on the university, and on society at large. Education has come full circle. Instead of heaven it has given the children and the teachers an introduction to hell.

Look back now at the effects of these developments on the working classes themselves. What the future holds for them is the same baneful aim that inspires their employers, the aim of a higher standard of living by which they mean more goods for everybody. An aim which all candidates for election without hesitation promise to fulfil. ('You have never had it so good.') This constant expectation of improvement, this approach to the millennium, has been maintained, as we shall see later, by interests remote from education.

III *Race, Class, and Privilege*

The industrial countries appear to make divergent social and political assumptions according as they are capitalist or communist. But when we look at their practices a kind of convergence appears. For the political reasons we have seen, all compete in asserting that no differences in educability can exist between social classes. They maintain, further, that their school systems have been designed with skill, and are administered without regard to expense, to exclude any possibility of social or racial discrimination. And no doubt they are intended to extract the greatest numbers of citizens usefully trained for the service of society or of the State. But what are their results?

We have several methods of testing how the system works in countries with contrasted methods and materials. All of them show an inability to extract university students in comparable proportions from the

Table 6.1 *University education*

U.S.S.R. in 1972 (H. Shapiro, Times, 23 November)

Class		Total population 220 million	In Universities[1] 4·6 million
Clerical and professional		5%	53%
Lower classes	town	45%	36%
	farm	50%	11%[2]
Jews[3]		0·9%	2·3%

U.K. in 1971 (S. Jessel, Times, 4 October)

	Class	Total population 55 million	In universities 0·6 million
UCCA classes	Professional and managerial	14%	44%
	Lower class (s.l.)	86%	56%
OECD[4] classes	Professional	29%	73%
	Lower class (s.l.)	71%	27%

1 95% members of Young Communist League (Komsomol).

2 Low figure due to the loss of the well-to-do Kulaks destroyed in 1934.

3 Similarly Armenians.

4 Similar results for France, Germany, Norway, etc.

Table 6.2 *Scholastic abilities of London school-children in relation to occupational distribution of parents shown as percentages of population at each level* (from Burt, 1975)

	Total primary school population	*Population estimated with scholarship abilities (1926)*	*Population estimated with University abilities (1939)*
I. Higher professional[1]	0·3	0·2	4·6
II. Lower professional	3·0	16·6	19·2
III. Clerical or highly skilled	12·0	24·4	23·7
IV. Skilled	26·0	39·7	26·5
V. Semi-skilled	32·5	13·6	18·7
VI. Unskilled	19·0	5·2	6·4
VII. Casual labour[2]	7·0	0·3	0·9
VIII. Defectives[1]	0·2	—	—

1 I and VIII are both under-represented in the primary school population.
2 Class temporarily enlarged by high unemployment.

manual workers and the professional classes. Naturally, because the professional classes have been produced by university selection, the results agree with what we should expect from Burt's estimates of the intelligence of these social classes in London fifty years ago (Tables 6.1 and 6.2). To be sure neither set of data reveals all we should like to know. The British results would show a stronger class discrimination if the skilled and unskilled manual workers were separated. The Russian results would show far more race discrimination if the Armenians, the Uzbeks, and the Mongols were separated.

Another part of this problem arises from the age-long process of building up privileged education. In mediaeval England schools were founded, as we saw (like Eton, Harrow, Winchester, and St Paul's), to provide for needy scholars (*pueris pauperibus omnium gentium*). When the rich discovered how well provided these schools were they found easy means to exclude the needy. These schools became the nurseries of a governing class.

It is much the same in communist Russia. Doctrine declares that there are no class differences that cannot be overcome by using Pavlov's method of the conditioned reflex (assisted perhaps by the earthier idioms of Lysenko). It is admitted, however, that the home environment has its influence on success in examinations. For schooling, therefore, it is necessary to split pupils into three streams: (i) the general, (ii) the technical, and (iii) the backward, these last having exclusively women teachers owing to the principle that, with equal pay, women usually get the worst jobs.

The first are not at all general: they are evidently privileged for their pupils are relieved from military and labour service and happen nearly all to belong to the Young Communist League. These are the ones who go to the universities. Just as formerly in England or Ireland or any other European country you attached yourself to the established Church if you wanted to go to a well-endowed school or university, so in Russia you attach yourself and your children, if possible, to the Communist Party. In either case intelligence is secondary to loyalty. And competition, as in the capitalist and bourgeois worlds, is between parents rather than between pupils. It shows itself in the four kinds of schools which are both 'general' and 'special':

(i) Schools of Closed Access: reserved by birth for sons of officers in the armed forces.
(ii) Higher Party Schools: reserved by birth for sons (and perhaps daughters) of Communist Party officials.
(iii) Fine Arts Schools: for children of promise in some fields who are probably chosen by merit.
(iv) Boarding Schools: fee-paying for 'difficult' children. This is a flourishing group; it numbered 2700 institutions in 1961 all evidently reserved for children of well-to-do parents who have not come up to expectation.

Thus Soviet education suffers from the familiar and perhaps inevitable handicaps of the intervention of privilege. But it also suffers from another familiar but not inevitable handicap: the attachment of its privilege to a political party with an openly conformist and therefore anti-intellectual purpose, This is the system which led to the downfall of the Chinese mandarinate and to the decay of traditional Islam. But in Russia it has given us the tragic picture (described by Hedrick Smith as well as by the great body of Russian dissidents) of a society in which the governing class, thinking badly and speaking badly, has severed its connections with the intelligentsia.

Quite different problems are those arising in the United States from the pursuit and testing of intelligence. Here the great racial components of society, all with their known historical origins and still only partly interbreeding, can be elaborately compared. A gradation appears between the Jews at the top, with the Europeans, and Chinese and the Blacks next in order, and the Amerindians (varying according to tribe) at the bottom. This gradation corresponds with differences between the groups in academic performance, professional contribution, and social behaviour.

Within each group there is, of course, an immense range of variation such as Burt saw in the English social classes. It is connected with differences within the class or community. If the classification were made by religion instead of race the same gradations would no doubt be found. Quakers, Unitarians, Adventists, Revivalists and Pentecostalists would each have their own character. But within each there would be less variation, for individuals cannot choose their race but they sometimes do choose their religion.

A number of attempts have been made to compensate for these differences by what is called remedial training. The most ambitious of these was the 'Head Start' programme whose results were summarized in the Coleman Report (published to coincide with the fireworks on 4 July 1966). This programme, it was found, had a slight but rapid effect in improving the responses of backward children to intelligence tests. But such improvements were temporary. The innate character which the tests are intended to measure reappeared after a short lapse of time. It had not been changed by cramming.

In spite of these discouraging experiences the United States and United Kingdom national school systems are still struggling to equalize and to integrate the elementary education of the whole of their populations. But there are a few special exceptions which we may now specially consider.

IV *The Cost–Benefit Relation*

In most countries of our twentieth-century world the largest industry after agriculture and the war business is education. Its benefits, like those of military activity, are not to be measured in conventional economic terms, but they have an economic component. There is a relation between cost and benefit which is connected with the intelligence of the individual who is taught.

This relation must vary with the political system, class structure, social morality, and of course the range of educability of the population. In any particular country some parts of the relations are clear and exact; others are vague and speculative. American investigations have attempted to estimate their connections with individual character,

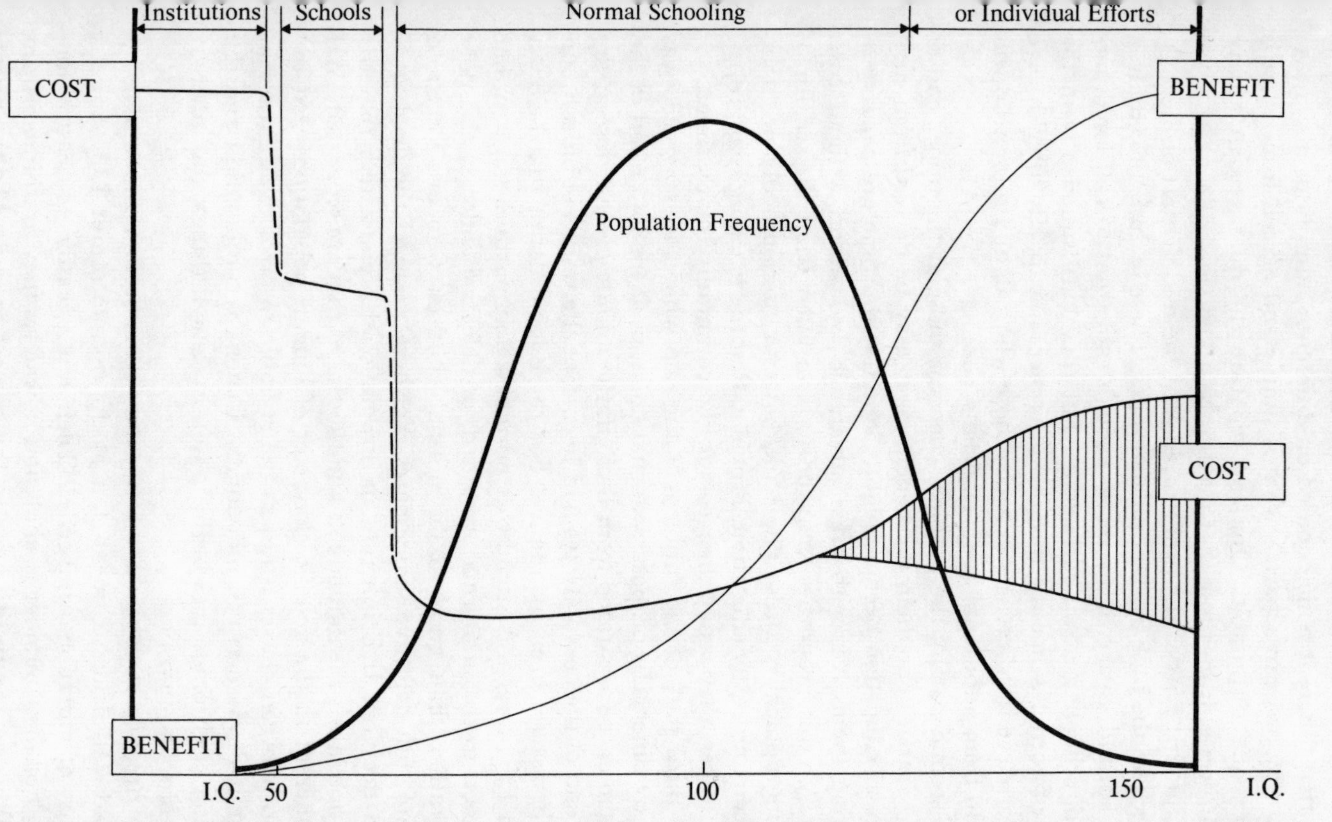

Fig. 6.1 The costs and benefits arising from the formal arrangements usually accompanying universal education for a population estimated in relation to its normal Galton–Burt curve of variation in I.Q. and the separate treatment of individuals in institutions, special schools, normal schools, and universities. The frequencies at the lower end of the curve will vary subject to the techniques of breeding control discussed in Chapter 4; the range of the curve will vary subject to the control of immigration and emigration discussed in Chapter 8. *Note*: I.Q. 50 is the usual threshold in Britain for parliamentary voting and jury service

particularly with the records of intelligence testing, and to compare the effects that different policies based on different assumptions may have. In this way one can separate what is simple and agreed from what is complex and disputable. One can separate the questions that have been answered from those that need to be asked (Fig. 6.1).

For the first part of the problem, look at the middle part of the I.Q. curve where the bulk of all populations lies. These include the children whose aptitudes vary in a narrow enough range not to call for differences in schooling at an early stage. But they vary sufficiently in the course of normal schooling to show differences in capacity after the age of ten or eleven; differences between those who will and those who will not gain from additional or specialized schooling.

The second part of the problem concerns those at the upper end of the I.Q. range. For them the benefits that may be derived from such additional education become highly conditional. Some are capable of educating themselves with great advantage and almost without cost. How large this proportion may be we can guess from the wealth of past biographical records. The bulk, however, undoubtedly profit by advanced and costly education. Provided that the teaching is appropriate, however, they repay their cost to the community many times.

The third part of the problem is the one which, it is agreed, was solved by Binet. His proposal was that children at the lower end of the curve should be separated from those in the middle just as those at the upper end of the curve always had been. But the results of his solution have themselves been instructive. For there is no doubt that below a certain I.Q. level the attempt at normal schooling does harm rather than good to the subnormal, retarded, or defective child. It also does harm rather than good to the normal children who are forced to associate with defective schoolmates. Yet here we meet the need for a painful decision. It is inherent in any national organization that the separation labels the individuals and the classes that are separated. And it is inherent in the genetic character of human populations that the division between classes is not so much liable to error as arbitrary in the line it draws between individuals. Genetic recombination and the mutation of chromosomes begin to appear as evil things, the inherent causes of social injustice.

How dreadful such social injustice may be, is brought home to us by this cold statistical treatment. For at the bottom of our I.Q. curve is our class of mutational imbeciles. Their fate is easily, too easily, forgotten. For their number is small and nowadays they are hidden from the public view in institutions. In this respect they are like the prison population, who, as we saw, are also mostly low on the I.Q. scale. But they differ in that being imbeciles only their kindred suffer from their condition.

The causes and the remedies for the lower I.Q. range concern the whole of education in one important respect: the higher the level at which the 'subnormal' are cut off, the easier becomes a comprehensive treatment of the 'normal' or superior part of the population which remains within the system.

V *The Integration of Pupils*

Those who think about education most seriously, whether they are the ones who work for it or who pay for it or who receive it, are bound to ask themselves whether its effect is to equalize or to differentiate. By limiting our observations to the lowest level of what is called literacy we can make the effect appear to be equalizing (Table 6.3). But when we take the effect at all levels we find that it differentiates. Throughout development it exposes the differences of potentiality that were there, as Binet found, at the beginning. Rightly, people have measured the success of education by the extent to which it uncovers or discovers these differences of ability. Of course this discovery leads on to the business of finding out what the child wants to do, and will be able to do, with these abilities. To that question I shall return in considering the economy of employment.

For the purpose of discovering abilities the good teacher always wants to group his pupils according to their abilities as he discovers them. Here he is confronted with several established outside interests. The greatest of these is religion.

Religion as a rule cannot be separated from the race or more immediately from the parent. But it so happens that in the northern province of Ireland, which we call Ulster, the separation between Catholic and Protestant is not a class difference as it is in Southern Ireland and elsewhere. In the bulk it is a tribal difference within the working class. But it began as racial strife with the first English colonization of the province, when Henry VIII did in Ireland what Henry I and Edward I had done in Wales. It was, however, the separate schooling during the last hundred years of what were now two sects that gave it its present shape. The separation developed from two political steps.

In 1845 the College of Cardinals in Rome had considered the manifold dangers with which the spread of education to the poor would threaten society and the Roman Church. The joint schooling of Catholics and Protestants, they concluded, would constitute a danger to

Table 6.3 *The Equalizing and differentiating effects of education* (from the Coleman Report, 4 July 1966)

Adult literacy in the U.S.A. (percentages, p. 447)

Census	*White*	*Non-white*
1870	88	19
1900	94	55
1930	97	86

Scholastically retarded children (percentages, by age, 1960, p. 452)

Racial origin	*10–13*	*16–17*
White		
Native parents	8·1	12·7
Foreign or mixed parents	8·3	10·8
Foreign born	15·6	28·0*
Non-white		
Chinese and Japanese	4·9	6·9
Asian, Eskimo, etc.	11·2	17·5
Negro	21·6	34·4
American Indian	29·2	43·3

* includes recent immigrants

faith and morals. But separate schooling with a disproportionate multiplication of Catholics, the Protestants saw would constitute a danger to their survival. So it was that when Gladstone (after one short visit to Ireland) proposed Irish Home Rule, the Protestants in 1886 welcomed the retort of a conservative leader, Lord Randolph Churchill, who said with political acumen 'we will play the Orange card'.

From these origins the conflict in Ulster began to take on its terrible character. The teaching of two opposed histories of bloody warfare has proved to be the recipe for ruin. But with integration of schooling between Catholic and Protestant, this conflict would slowly dissolve. Integration (with all being taught the same history) would lead to intermarriage and the disappearance of both religions in the horrible form in which their conflict has shown them.

Neither the Catholic nor the Protestant working class in Ulster would have much to lose in the way of culture from mixing with the other. But the position of the Chinese in San Francisco or the Muslim Pakistanis in Bradford is quite a different one. Among them, again, integration would lead to intermarriage and even the slow disappearance of the separate group. But here the group is one which carries a culture it values and which we may value. And it is of supreme importance for education that all of us who can are allowed to make our own value judgements.

Another situation arises with education in New York. Here there is a Jewish population having an average I.Q. about ten points above that of the general white population of the United States. It naturally provides most of the teachers in the city. There is also a black population having an average I.Q. ten or fifteen points below the whites. The problem is how to give the blacks a chance of university education which a certain proportion will value and enjoy. In the past the City University of New York has been managed largely and inevitably by and for and at the expense of the Jews. Its business for a long time has been to turn the Jewish immigrants, arriving in New York from Europe, persecuted, impoverished and often without any knowledge of English, into the stream of highly trained men and women who now play a conspicuous part in the American professions and universities. In response chiefly to black protest this university decided in 1971 to change its policy. It decided to follow the practice of American State Universities and to admit students on demand without any entrance examination (*Times*, 17 July 1973).

In this way over a period of three years 27,000 students were enrolled including now Irish, Italian, and Puerto Rican (all Roman Catholic) and Negro (mainly Baptist). Of these 20,000 required 'remedial classes' in reading, English, and mathematics; or, as we might say, the three R's. Half dropped out at the end of the first year. It was hoped that one-third would be able to graduate as in any ordinary American State University. But this would be possible only if the standards were lowered or the curriculum simplified. Both these practices have proved possible very widely both in the United States and in Europe. As in the Soviet Union, the faking of examination results proves to be the final assertion of democracy.

Another way out of this difficulty has led to controversy among Negro educationists. Most Negroes at home speak a black English just as the urban working classes in Europe speak their own class dialect. Education and radio do not affect it. These forms of speech, like the pidgin English established officially in New Guinea by the Australian government, are phonetically and grammatically simpler than standard or educated English.

At this point we may ask: Would underprivileged or disadvantaged races and classes benefit by being given segregated education in their own underprivileged or disadvantaged speech? Or would they do better with an integrated education as has hitherto been attempted, Gypsies apart, in all state systems of schooling (*Times*, 26 May 1971)? Surely the answer is that a small proportion benefit by educated speech. But for most, where teaching an educated language proves fruitless, manual training should take its place.

If we turn back to the normal curve of variation in the intelligence of populations, as predicted by Galton and demonstrated by Burt, we see that it makes sense of these situations. Literate education beyond the age of twelve is wasted on the bottom fraction of most stratified societies. Public surveys confirm that after a hundred years of education in reading this section of the population never reads connectedly after leaving school and never reads for pleasure.

The texts of our daily newspapers are adapted to the needs of different social classes. They show that these needs correspond unfailingly with an underlying differentiation which is well understood by those who publish them (capitalists and communists) and hope to sell them for profit, or without loss, to the class of public they serve. Equally striking is the corresponding separation by class made by the national broadcasting system in Britain where, not reading, but the easier tasks of listening and viewing are in question. The BBC, while always attempting to raise the moral and intellectual tone of the listening or viewing population, prudently recognizes that it must offer programmes for the several social classes adapted to their different intellectual interests and capacities. Even more prudently it is careful to avert the evil eye by numbering these programmes out of their intellectual order: 1, 2, 4, 3. Segregated communication is the only practice which adults will tolerate.

The existence, indeed the dominance, of broadcasting in the lives of children brings home to us the changing role of their parents which no society chooses to escape. The parents as a rule provide the best environment for the children since it is a kindred or genetic environment. Many parents, to be sure, have children they do not want as they show by their treatment, sometimes violently, and it is for society, by the means we have seen, to curtail their number. But most parents have children because they instinctively want them, need them, and love them. Are they, however, always adapted to bring up these children, in the unnatural conditions of urban industrial life which society has thrust upon them?

How ill-adapted parents often are appears only too clearly under the conditions of deceptive prosperity recently enjoyed in industrial countries. Under these conditions it has become evident that many parents are not interested in education. Politicians claim to be. Teachers often undoubtedly are. But parents often not at all. If they paid for their children's education, which they could well afford to do, they might be concerned with it. But this possibility has long been discarded.

The inadequacy of parents is now seen, under these conditions, to arise not always from lack of means provided by society but from lack of something provided by themselves, something very like intelligence. Parents at the lower economic levels of society now give their children more pocket money than those who are better off. They do so because giving money enhances pride, removes responsibility, and avoids mental effort. How do the children spend the money? In the U.K. they eat 587,000 tons of sweets at their own expense per annum. And consequently four tons of teeth are drawn from them at the public expense per annum (*Times*, 18 April 1973). Some time ago (in 1962) the Chancellor of the Exchequer, the son of a dentist, had proposed a tax of 15 per cent on sweets. But the population of parents protested and the Prime Minister removed both the tax and the Chancellor. Perhaps it is for parents and for prime ministers that elementary education, free, compulsory, and disagreeable, is now needed.

VI *The Integration of Knowledge*

Are we then to accept a society not unified but disintegrated by education? The answer is that methods of teaching in themselves may either integrate or disintegrate society. Our present methods of teaching serve to disintegrate because they are based on an old belief in the superiority of the written word, a superiority which grew out of the training of the professional classes. From this superiority is derived the separation and also the antagonism between the 'humanities' depending on tradition and the 'sciences' depending on innovation. It is an antagonism which I have described as *The Conflict of Science and Society* and a separation which C. P. Snow has described as *The Two Cultures*. These divisions cut deeper into the educational problem than any of us has probably recognized.

When Goethe wrote that when we want to ask the deepest questions we must first separate and then unite, he was describing the process by which each of us at any point in our lives may attempt to connect events and to understand the causes of things. But it is, I suggest, true in principle of the development of the individual that he begins by seeing things whole. Only when he learns to use words does he start separating and dividing. Almost invariably the teacher gets no further than this. If he is a teacher of languages he may be able to distinguish between hay and straw in many dialects and know where and how each previous word has come and gone. But he still need not know, and often does not care to know, what hay and straw themselves are and do. Those are questions separately classified and often outside the school curriculum. It is not the business of the teacher to unite or to connect them with things that can be seen, handled, and used.

The teacher's habit of fragmenting what the child naturally wants to know as a whole is neatly shown in regard to the baffling problem of sex. In the course of the last century sex has been buried deeper and deeper. The purpose was to get it out of reach and out of sight of the child. So that eventually in the 1960s special teachers had to be brought into schools to explain what the parents and ordinary teachers no longer dared to tell. Meanwhile Shakespeare, the Bible, and Fanny Hill, accompanied by a glimpse of the farmyard, would have told all that was needed. But, unhappily, these four approaches to knowledge fall in four different departments of teaching: literature, religion, pornography, and agriculture.

A proper integration of teaching would partly forestall the need for correction. We have too long derided the practices of the disreputable Mr. Squeers. They are not indeed so far from the principles of the admirable Prince Kropotkin. Those who had been taught how to plant trees would not want to tear them up. Those who had sweated in the churchyard would be less inclined to ravage the church. The habit of doing something useful need not be reserved for the delinquent or inculcated in an expensive remedial establishment. What is needed is to provide an occupational incentive for every child. If it cannot be intellectual it must be manual. And if it is manual it is all the more likely to be cooperative and educationally valuable. The possibilities of apprenticed employment by small employers having now been extinguished, it is all the more necessary that a national and genuine organization should be designed to meet the deficiency we have created. Then socialism could be useful and even profitable.

The climax of disintegration we meet now among the teachers in our universities. The different faculties and departments speak different languages and dread to hear any but their own. Nothing so high as these barriers has been seen since the Reformation and we know what happened then to those who too earnestly debated their academic differences. The leaders of the losing party, if obstinate, were generally burnt alive. Comparable practices still obtain in Communist and Third World countries. Must we then admit, in our supposedly free world today, that such drastic solutions can be avoided only if serious discussion is itself by common consent suppressed?

I recall asking a professor of botany why she needed to teach so many things that could no longer be of any interest or value to her pupils; for medical students since the seventeenth century had to learn botany to prepare their potions. She replied that she taught them in order that they should be able to teach others: other helpless victims in their turn. She was a necessary unit in the respected education industry. So also are those who today write books entitled 'Essentials of Human Anatomy'. They describe the human skull and beautifully illustrate its design with the names of its bones. But they omit to mention that (outside departments of human anatomy) the human skull contains a brain. Why is it left out? Because it is not in the syllabus. It is not essential for medical practitioners. It also suffers from an unteachable unacademic property: it varies; indeed, as we have learned, in its form and in its function, it is the most variable of all structures in the human body.

The late C. T. Onions, who was for many years chiefly responsible for the *Oxford English Dictionary*, I also recall, told me that he owed a great deal to having begun his academic life, not as a lexicographer but as an engineer (at Mason College, Birmingham). This rare good fortune had enabled him to break through from one compartment of knowledge to another. Breaking was the means, but joining was the end. For, although most of those who use a dictionary, or indeed use a language, are first concerned to separate, the grand effect of speech is to unite civilization. This grand effect may be recognized by only a few adults but it is possible for education to show it to children before it and they are swallowed up by the professional machinery.

It is this misused machinery which weakens, in those that have it, the impulse to connect and the curiosity to understand. That is why so many discoveries have been made by those who were trained in the wrong field or never trained at all except by their own curiosity. For this reason education should try to discover and to advance those processes in the development of the mind which are individual and innate and therefore natural.

It is also natural to separate before we attempt to unite. This was easy to do when one teacher, a pastor or a parent, told the whole story. It was also easy when, the teacher having provided the words for pulling things apart, the priest could provide the myths which put them together again; when religion offered an answer, a connected and convincing answer, to all difficult questions. Today, when the convincing and connected answer is no longer there, we have the task of putting the pieces together in the education of each child. It is an impossible task unless the dull and the bright are separated and assembled in their natural groups; groups which see the world (the *Merkwelt* of von Uexküll) through the medium of words and phrases whose meaning is different for every kind of people, every tribe, and every class; and indeed just a little different for every individual.

VII *The Evolution of Society*

From the first stratification of society, between rulers and workers there has always been a middle class. The traders and the craftsmen were indispensable to those above and those below them. But the middle class depends on an elaborate education transmitted without interruption. In times of crisis, therefore, it has always lived on a razor's edge (the phrase is Freya Stark's) and it has had difficulty in surviving. It has done so only by having, apart from particular skills, some judgement and thrift lacking in those more numerous below, together with some prudence and invention lacking in those more powerful above.

Another way of looking at this stratification is to say that the middle class is a professional class. It is composed of those people who, long selected by workshops, schools, and universities, are willing by long apprenticeship to command a choice of the kind of service they and their children may render to society. Above them are those seeking wealth and power. Below them are those who cannot wait but demand their rewards by the day or the week.

There is, however, a third way of looking at society in terms more related to the processes of heredity and the properties of intelligence. It is to consider the prime movers in its evolution as being the creators of culture. In evolving societies there are people, usually one in ten thousand or a hundred thousand, who are inventing new methods of understanding, controlling, and creating new environments, methods which sometimes improve (but admittedly may ruin) the chances of survival of the rest of society.

Much greater numbers are capable of learning and using what these creators have done. They choose their new environments. They are the carriers of this new culture. They can pass on what they have learned for the use of the mass of the community who cannot learn so much and cannot therefore choose so freely but benefit by accepting what they are given. Again, there are a few, outlaws, exiles, and dissidents, who cannot benefit and who refuse to accept what they are given. They reject the culture that has been created. A few of these (like Michelangelo) may be found among the creators who also reject what they were given but know how to do even better.

This division of society with its downward transmission of culture and its upward movement of those who create the culture is no doubt related to Galton's normal curve of variation of intelligence and the genetic recombination on which it depends. The middling people in the centre of this curve are the carriers and receptors. The creators are at the top and the rejectors at the bottom. But the processes of recombination are producing creators and rejectors in every generation: just as the fertile give rise to the sterile and heterosexuals give rise to homosexuals in every generation. Such a view has been foreshadowed if not expressed before by sociologists like Sorokin and psychologists like Burt. Its implication, however, is that the masses of receptors are not (as Davenport puts it) merely space-fillers. A large part of them are potential ancestors of the sporadic scattering of creators who will be needed, in ever-changing circumstances, by future generations.

The creators, however, are produced only by a society which can preserve its culture by means of a professional class which, if it is to recruit, preserve, and expand its numbers, demands education. There are, to be sure, other means of expanding the professional class. One is to encourage its reproduction. Another is to encourage the immigration of trained professional men and women from other countries.

No state or nation or society, it might be thought, would ever have taken the converse course of attempting to extinguish its professional class. But the attempt has often been made, because governing classes or powerful interests wanted to have the present cash rather than the future revenue. Destroying the machinery of selective education, lowering of the standards of education and examination, differential taxation and destruction of savings by the inflation of the currency, these are the obvious ways of abolishing a middle class.

Expulsion of a professional class is another method. It has been tried again and again in European history, always disguised as religious persecution. Such was the expulsion of the Huguenots from France in 1685 which removed the impulse for the Industrial Revolution from France to Britain. The expulsion of the Jews from Spain and Portugal (in 1492 and 1497), followed as it was by the persecution of heretics by the Inquisition, led to the decline in wealth, power, and initiative in those two countries. It was neatly reflected in the rise of the Dutch republic following the arrival in Holland of those same refugees. Israel itself is the most recent example of the recruitment of a highly selected professional class through the immigration of Jewish refugees from persecution in Europe, first by the German and then by the Russian

Governments, both of which gravely damaged their societies in the process.

Indeed so highly professional were the persecuted European Jews that it was only by the invited immigration of the unpersecuted but also unprofessional Jews of the Islamic world that a manual working class for the new state of Israel could be recruited. The Jews entering Israel from the Arab world exactly equalled in numbers the Arabs (700,000) leaving Palestine after 1948. The two races reunited within the Jewish community had diverged in intellectual character. This was due to the millennia of limited hybridization with Christian and Muslim populations since the dispersal and expulsion of the Jews from Palestine in Hellenistic and Roman times.

An example of governments not being absent-minded but actually learning from experience is provided by the comparison of the two European wars of 1914 and 1939. In the first war the Western powers, especially France and Britain, disregarded the special uses to which the professional classes might be put and in consequence they were massacred with an effect from which those countries cannot be said to have recovered. In 1939 Britain at least did not repeat this tragic mistake.

These things are important today because the professional classes of Europe both created and were created by our system of education. Together also they created and were created by the Industrial Revolution whose achievements, glorious or disastrous as we may think them, are now all around us. One of these achievements was the transformation by Europe of the world outside Europe during the last two centuries. This transformation I now want to examine, and put in its historical and indeed evolutionary perspective, before I venture to look at a picture of the world as a whole.

Chapter 7

The Colonization of Asia

I *Range and Sequence*

The occupation of the earth by the migration of men from particular centres, hunters from Africa, farmers and herdsmen from South-West Asia, was a process of colonization. The first stage of mere expansion of territory, and the second of mixing of peoples, were transformed at a third stage into conquest and plunder, government and exploitation. Then it was that the peoples of Europe, themselves born of invasion, subjection, and colonization, invaded, subjected, and colonized the other five continents. I want now to look at these processes the other way round, from outside Europe. Taking the whole continent of Asia I want to look at the impact of nation on nation, of race on race, and of culture on culture during the last five centuries of upheaval.

II *The East India Company*

The intrusion of the British into India was the largest, and most complex of all colonial enterprises; evidently so since the population of India has for the last four or even five millennia represented nearly a quarter of the human race in its numbers and also in its diversity. The British, like the Dutch, entered Asia disguised as their East India Company. This was a body designed to profit by trade and at first little restrained by Crown or Parliament. Its agents enjoyed one significant advantage over their rivals, Catholic and Protestant, in that they cared very little for religion. They sought a market and did not hold Christianity to be marketable. Parliament required them to carry a chaplain on all their ships over 500 tons so they built their ships smaller.

European rivalry soon forced them to raise their own native troops and it was the struggle between France and England in the Seven Years War that led to their encounter in Bengal and its seizure by Clive in 1757. This initial success was followed by a dozen wars leading to one annexation after another. Their advance was based on the new ports they developed at Calcutta, Bombay, and Madras, until the whole of India was brought directly or indirectly under British rule. British India grew as the Roman and Chinese Empires did, and as, according to Fitzgerald, empires must grow if they are to endure 'not by calculated aggression . . . but by occupying places that could not well be left alone'.

The internal effect of the conquest of Bengal was, however, calculated. It was the setting up on European lines of a government which was without precedent either in Asia or in Europe. For here was a European dictatorship in Asia established by Acts of Parliament in London. And it arose at the very moment when European ideas and practices were being transformed by the Age of Enlightenment and the Industrial Revolution.

The speed with which these ideas and practices were carried to India, into a world shut off from Europe for 2000 years, was almost unbelievable. Already in 1767 Harry Verelst, a Dutchman, the first Governor of Bengal was founding a new administration, an Indian Civil Service. Warren Hastings, the second Governor, while establishing British power over the adjoining states had time to think in terms of law, language, and education. In 1770 he had begun by founding an Islamic College in Calcutta which in 1791 was balanced by a Sanskrit College in Benares.

These were the expressions of a first, an orientalizing, phase of British sentiment and policy which strove to revive the ancient cultures of India. But what it revived proved to be the roots of the political division of India which in the twentieth century undid everything else. Benares became the source of Hindu nationalism and the Islamic College was the root of Pakistan. It launched on his fatal career Shaikh Mujib, the founder in 1972 of Bangladesh.

The next step Hastings took was in a different direction. In 1783 he was able to attract from London, for his Judicial Council, one of the most enterprising scholars of the age, the lawyer and linguist, Sir William Jones. Although Jones was to live only ten years, his appointment established the most momentous of all British initiatives in India. Within a few weeks he had gone far beyond his judicial commission: he had set up an 'Asiatick Society of Bengal'. This enterprise he undertook in collaboration with his friend Sir Joseph Banks, the President of the Royal Society in London.

Jones did not understate his expectations. 'If it now be asked' he declared in his opening address on 15 January 1784, 'what are the intended objects of our enquiries . . . we answer MAN and NATURE; whatever is performed by the one or produced by the other'. How far were these expectations fulfilled?

For his part Jones himself discovered the relations of the Indian and European languages, relations whose meaning for human history has been unfolding gradually ever since. He then proceeded as part of his official duties to examine the Hindu and Muslim laws and customs which were later to be codified by Macaulay and have guided Indian administration to this day (except during the recent 'emergency').

Parallel with these works was the development of the Company's administration. Jones's successors were able to create an edifice of surveys and services of a scale and connectedness which has never been attempted in any other region of the world or at any other period of history. This work, continuing long after the disappearance of the Company and embracing most of the South of Asia, was its most memorable achievement.

First there was the Trigonometrical Survey of India begun in 1800, quickly following the first such enterprises for France in 1780, and for England in 1785. On this basis proceeded the exploration which culminated in the man and the mountain named Everest. The Calcutta Botanic Garden, founded by Roxburgh in 1776, became the clearing-house for the economic plants of India. The search for a substitute for China tea led to the discovery of wild Indian tea in Assam in 1834 and the foundation of a national industry with a world-wide use, one which finally established the solvency of India's trade.

Following this enterprise came the *Flora Indica* of Joseph Hooker, the Indian Botanical Survey and, in 1859, the Geological Survey which had the practical aim of discovering mineral wealth. In due course, with all the other surveys and with the experience the British had gained in Egypt, it turned out to be the basis of the construction of 40,000 miles of canals, the largest irrigation system in the world at that time.

Out of Geology also came the Indian Archaeological Survey initiated by Cunningham in 1861, which rediscovered or preserved Ajanta, Konarak, Harappa, and in Curzon's day the Taj Mahal. In this way, not only were the treasures of India's past, neglected and forgotten by its rulers and peoples, brought to light but finally also, through the explorations of Sir Aurel Stein, the deepest secrets of India's connections with Central Asia. How much better in these respects is Britain's record in India than in Britain!

The next of these great enterprises, the Indian Census, began in 1867. Over the following seventy years the Census explored, classified, and recorded the unparalleled complexity of the human populations of India, their languages, their customs, their religions, and their physical character. The fruits of this great enquiry enrich our knowledge of all mankind as I have earlier attempted to show.

By the end of the nineteenth century a million and a half of British had died in India, mostly from Indian diseases which took their toll of Indians and Europeans alike. But by this time from the first efforts of the Company there had grown the Indian Medical Service whose work in the end laid the foundations of a new tropical medicine. In 1897 in Calcutta, Ronald Ross, the son of a general in the Indian Army, was first able to trace the transmission of malaria to the mosquito. It was a step in discovery by which, through the activity of hospitals, in Liverpool, Hamburg, and Paris, human life not only in the tropics but throughout the world came to be transformed.

This series of intellectual impulses coming from Britain were translated at first into the Indian vernacular languages which in their orientalizing phase were used by the Company's administration. It met the desire of the Europeans to be enlightened directly and without delay about India. But it was an uphill task and it is easy to see what disunity and disorder its continuance would have created in India. In 1834 therefore the government, persuaded by Macaulay, took the historic step, which in some sense was to be repeated over most of Asia and Africa, of reversing the translation process. English was to be the language of government and of education. India was now to learn its own origins and history, religion and literature, not only from the English but through the English language. And in English it was to learn about Europe—a region of the world which no orthodox Hindu had ever seen.

In the twenty-five years following this decision the seemingly everlasting structure of superstition in Asia was disturbed and threatened at every level of society. The strain and the struggle were as fierce among the British governors as among the peoples they governed. In the first place the East India Company was in repeated conflict with Parliament representing various interests at home. There were the opposers of colonization in any form. There were also the reformers of colonization high-minded but often ill-advised. The early officers of the Company had adopted an easy attitude in both their sexual and their financial transactions. They were in trade and they took bribes; they were far from home and they took mistresses; in both respects they fitted comfortably into the Indian scene, each side learning from the other. It might have been thought that they were on their way to assimilation. But, in 1813, the evangelical Wilberforce, fresh from his successes with the slave trade in Africa, persuaded Parliament in London to force the Company to admit missionaries in India. Slowly then the scene began to shift. The missionaries had no success in making converts except among the Eurasians and the aboriginal hill peoples such as the Nagas and the Mizos. But they divided the Christians from the Natives, Muslim and Hindu alike.

The consequences of this division were at once admirable and deplorable. Christian influences supported a tradition of incorruptibility in the now purely European administration. They also helped to suppress two of the most damaging practices of Hindu society, suttee and thuggee. Every success in preaching against evil practices at this time gave the Christian churches in Britain as well as in India a feeling of power laced with virtue. The Church of England (like George III a little earlier and just as ill-equipped) began to see itself taking over the British Empire. But the hope that religious teaching might change or harmonize racial characters in the absence of genetic fusion was disappointed.

The changing class structure and moral climate in Britain itself stimulated a confidence in the superiority of Christian belief which could not be separated from a belief in the superiority of Christians and a contempt for the malpractices of the heathen. In the army between Indian troops and British officers the devotion to the service and to one another has been faithfully portrayed in the memoirs of Sita Ram. In one section, however, the Bengal Army, this bond suddenly snapped and one disaster led to another. The native troops were forced to use cartridges dressed with animal fat. That was foolish. Those who rejected the cartridges were punished. That was arrogant and brutal. The result was the Mutiny with its panic killing, its mutual atrocities. The trust, understanding, and communication between the Indian and the European were partly lost; in their place for a new generation came a growth of pride on the one side and of resentment on the other.

III *British India*

The Company was not in the least responsible for these mistakes but it was the scapegoat. When the Mutiny was over and the mess had been cleared up, it was dissolved. The Home Government took over control represented now by a more splendid but less effective Viceroy with a more scrupulous, uncompromisingly British, administration. For behind him, soon connected by steamship and telegraph, stood a Secretary of State in London and a little later there rose up the mysterious majesty of an Empress. The commercial purpose was giving way to the divine mission and the divinity was not Hindu or Muslim but Christian and European.

So, after 1857, the atmosphere changed. The purpose of the new government was now peace and stability. And what was most needed for stability? Obviously the religion of the Brahmins and the power of the princes, both Hindu and Muslim. There was also the educational system conveying an understanding for the English language and a respect for British institutions. We may ask who paid for this system. According to the British Government it was paid for up to 1908 out of the profits of the sale of opium which they had, in the war of 1840, forced the Manchu Empire of China to accept. But long before 1908 it was tea that paid.

The Indian population, which for centuries before British rule, before 1800, had been stable at about 100 million, was now relieved from the restrictions of war and pestilence and partly also, owing to the spreading railways, of famine. It multiplied within India to 400 million; and millions of Indians, with the blessing of the British Government, but in defiance of Hindu law, now overflowed. They went wherever in the Empire the manual industry of some (Coolies and Tamils) or the mercantile and technical skill of others (Gujeratis and Punjabis) could profitably fill a gap in its apparently unlimited economy. Notably in Ceylon, Burma, Malaya, East Africa, Natal, Mauritius, Trinidad, Guyana, and Fiji, Indian colonies, both Muslim and Hindu, were settled. This overflow continues today, but no longer unopposed.

The consequence of Indian expansion was a pressure to find work for unskilled labour, to feed the factories which, as in Britain, prospered on the overcrowding and squalor of the great cities, something unforgettable to those who have seen it, unbelievable to those who have not. The mills of Bombay led the way in developing the conditions which have become universal in the industrial cities of the tropics, conditions with which native and colonial governments, whatever their professed beliefs, have proved equally powerless to cope.

One decisive change came with the Suez Canal in 1869. Its effect was felt at once in the two layers of the governing class. For the British it meant that Indian mistresses were set aside and British wives took their place. Since caste in India is *varna* or colour, the British became more distinctly a caste or, to use the Afrikaner word, more distinctly *apart*.

On the other hand educated Indians, even of modest means like Gandhi, could come to England to complete their education. And those Brahmins who had grown rich in the service of their military masters, the Moguls and the Company, could now afford to have English governesses and to go to schools, universities, and military academies in England. Young men in this privileged position were well informed in a European sense. They were the middlemen between Britain and India, as the Company had been. They had learned about Hinduism, Buddhism, and Islam, translated in English books. They began to form a new caste of their own, a caste of interpreters now outnumbering the British in India. They stood between the British and the native masses making it unnecessary for either to speak the language of the other. When the British civil servant, Allan Octavian Hume, recalled the hopes of Warren Hastings and Macaulay for Indian unity and independence it was therefore also natural that this English-educated caste should begin to see themselves as an alternative government. From this inspiration of Hume the Indian National Congress, presided over by the Viceroy, began its career in 1885.

The fuel for this movement slowly piled up in the form of protest against the Government, above all the Government of Curzon as Viceroy. For Curzon recognized that European education was not producing the results that Macaulay had expected. The *babu* had become an object of ridicule to Europeans. Even the *pundit* was sometimes sceptically appraised. The degrees had become too easy to carry weight. Of the 1371 civil servants, even in 1915, still only 63 were Indian. Curzon therefore required that the system should be supervised by Europeans. And his decree was resented. The province of Bengal had a population of 70 million. It was unwieldy and bitterly divided between Hindus and Muslims. Curzon split it. So angry was the response that the next Viceroy united it again. Today as we shall see, at the cost of millions of lives, Curzon's division has been confirmed.

Other future events began to cast their shadows before them, above all when the Government tried to keep the peace between religious communities. Early in 1919, Europeans as well as Hindus and Muslims were murdered by rioters and an army of 200,000, only one-third European, seemed dangerously weak to deal with such violence in a population of 400 million. When a small detachment of troops, faced with a crowd of 15,000 demonstrators killed 400 in Amritsar, the panic and the massacres of the Mutiny were seen in reverse. It was nothing to what was to come later but Indian politicians did not foresee this. What they saw was naturally a political opportunity. Out of it the visionary Gandhi created the hope of self-rule, the movement for *swaraj*.

Gandhi, the Mahatma, was a man from the middle of the people and nearly from the middle of India. By caste he was a Vaisya; by profession he was a lawyer, well enough off to be trained in London, and seasoned by long service to the Indian emigrants in Natal. From this service he

Table 7.1 *India: The British Raj and After*

1600	Queen Elizabeth gives charter to East India Company
1644	Madras founded
1662	Bombay (Parsee refuge) taken over
1696	Calcutta founded
1757	Clive takes over Bengal
1767–9	Verelst, Governor of Bengal, founds Indian Civil Service (I.C.S.)
1773, 1784, 1793	India Acts restrict Company's authority, give it a standing army; and declare withdrawal to be the aim of British policy
1773–85	Warren Hastings, first Governor General (G.-G.)
1783	Sir William Jones founds Asiatic Society of Bengal
1786–98	Cornwallis, G.-G.: excludes Indians from I.C.S. and eliminates trading and corruption
1800–60	Survey of India begun by Lambton, completed by Everest
1813	Christian missionaries admitted to British India
1828–35	Bentinck, G.-G.: abolishes suttee, thuggee, and some female infanticide
1832	J. Prinsep deciphers Brahmin script and Ashoka's inscriptions
1834	Charter Act: Macaulay establishes Penal Code and European educational system
1848–56	Dalhousie, G.-G.: extends British rule at expense of princes. Introduces railways and posts, restores canals. Founds three universities: first medical training of Hindus
1851	Harappa discovered
1856	Mt. Everest named
1857–8	Indian Mutiny
1860–1940	Army ($\frac{1}{3}$ British, $\frac{2}{3}$ Native) established at 200,000, except 1914–18; plus native princes' forces (360,000)
1867	First Indian Census
1869	Archaeological Survey of N. India established
1873	Queen Victoria declared Empress of India
1885	Indian National Congress founded
1897	Ross discovers mosquito's part in malaria
1898, 1905	Curzon Viceroy: Universities Act to supervise education; Bengal divided (reunited 1910)
1906	All India Muslim League founded
1919	Riots and murders in the Punjab; Amritsar massacre
1920–42	Campaigns of Gandhi against (i) British rule, (ii) industrialization, (iii) caste privilege

1937	Congress forms representative governments in seven out of eleven provinces
1940	Aim of Pakistan adopted by Muslim League
1943	Famine in Bengal aggravated by loss of Burma
1946–7	Hindu–Muslim massacres in Bengal and Punjab
1947	Mountbatten, Viceroy, separates India from Pakistan, persuades 562 princes to accede to either side and accept annual pensions of £6 million
1947	India and Pakistan independent (15 August)
1948	Gandhi assassinated (30 January)
1947–9	1st Pakistan War: Muslim provinces (Kashmir, Hyderabad) annexed by India
1953–75	Nagaland in rebellion
1947–56	Indian States rearranged on linguistic and racial basis
1959	Elected Communist government in Kerala removed from office by Congress Party
1961	Goa (Portuguese, Christian) annexed by India
1962	Chinese invasion of Assam and Ladakh (October–November)
1965	2nd Pakistan War, August–September (Punjab) Indian Army (820,000 men), Pakistan Army (170,000)
1966	Indira Gandhi, Nehru's daughter, Prime Minister; nationalizes banks and repudiates princes' pensions
1971	East Pakistan in revolt (March–December), 3rd Pakistan War: Bangladesh liberated (November–December)
1974	Nuclear explosion achieved by India
1975	Sikkim (Buddhist, Border State) occupied by India
1975	Government by decree established; opposition imprisoned; 'State of Emergency' declared (26 June)

was led to combine the roles of a politician and a saint. Knowing the Indian peasants who were nine-tenths of the people, as the Brahmin politicians from the north did not, he set himself two great concurrent tasks. The first was to get rid of the British Government. The second was to show the Indian people how they should govern themselves.

In the first task he was embarrassed by his recognizing his own and India's debt to British rule, above all, to British education. He was also embarrassed by the terrible dangers of violence in an India deprived of British rule. He determined, no doubt, for these reasons to pursue his aim by a Tolstoyan policy of non-violence and non-cooperation. In this, after twenty-five years, he at once succeeded and failed.

In Gandhi's second task he was again embarrassed. On the one hand he set himself to break down the barriers of hatred and oppression, discrimination and privilege within India itself, barriers of caste and religion, region and language, which would endanger any independent government of India. On the other hand, the task he set himself was to resist the development of Western industrialism for which the British were responsible and to which they were economically and emotionally committed. These last two aims, each admirable in itself, were profoundly opposed to one another. For only Western understanding by its power could break down what Eastern character had created. Later events have shown the tragic truth of this opposition.

IV *India Liberated*

At the beginning of 1947 the British Government in London announced its intention of withdrawing from India and the announcement naturally led to a weakening of an authority already undermined by agitation and by war. The Government saw that disorder might soon engulf the whole country. There were two parties in India, the Congress Party, predominantly Hindu, and the purely sectarian Muslim League. They could not be persuaded to agree on any division of power or territory. Inevitably so, for while the lower orders of society were divided by their religious practices, the leaders, although mostly from the Punjab, were of contrasted social character: the Hindus were led by Brahmins eloquent in speech and literary in taste; the Muslims although led at first by a lawyer were soon being managed by landowners. So long as the British were in power these disparate classes might work together and even talk together—in English. Without the British all cooperation was bound to lapse.

The Government reluctantly decided as its last act to impose a division of territory between Hindu and Muslim succession states. Their 'Independence Bill' was described by the Prime Minister in Parliament on the 10 July as a 'fulfilment of Britain's mission in India'. He might better have said an abdication of that mission since unity of government had been Britain's greatest gift to India. In this aim Hindus, Buddhists, and Muslims had in more than two millennia successively failed; the British alone, first by force of arms, and then by government, law, and language, had succeeded.

Not only the country as a whole but each of the great provinces watered by the Indus and the Ganges: the Punjab and Bengal, was also split. The new Muslim state of Pakistan was itself split into two parts. There was the western province of the Indus valley colonized by the mass invasions of Muslims; and there was an eastern province beyond the Ganges which had been Islamized later by Muslim princes; that is to say, by conversion to Islam of their Hindu subjects, especially of the lower castes. This eastern half of Bengal, when the British arrived, had been a decapitated society, ruled by their Muslim conquerors. It was this province which Curzon had tried to separate from the western half in 1905.

Independence Day was to be on 15 August 1947. The auspicious moment was fixed by Nehru and the astrologers at midnight. But a month earlier disorder had broken out in Lahore and Calcutta, the capitals of the disputed provinces. Fear gripped the minorities on the wrong side of the new boundaries. As at the time of the Mutiny, rumours spread and panic took hold. Flight then began. During August and September 10 million crossed the frontiers in opposite directions; but about 1 million died from massacre, from cholera, and from other diseases. If no boundary had been made at all 10 million might have died. Meanwhile Kashmir was divided and Hyderabad annexed by force. Some 48 million Muslims remained in India.

In this way two states were established, each to be governed, it was said, by a democratic constitution on the British model. It turned out, however, as might have been expected, that both provinces of Pakistan were actually being ruled by the military landowning class of the western province. In their eastern colony or dependency, which contained more than half the wealth and the population, they were assisted by Muslim refugees from India, chiefly from Bihar, who provided the educated professional class in the new state.

In India, on the other hand, the democratic forms were for some time maintained. But the Prime Minister of the federation, Jawaharlal Nehru, as well as the chief ministers of all the states had been nominated by the Congress. All of them proved to be Brahmins. In effect Britain, which had taken India from warriors, had handed it back to clerks. Early in the new year, Gandhi, a non-Brahmin, was assassinated by a Hindu fanatic. The princely rulers, whom the British were wisely pledged to maintain, had been replaced by the new government to increase its centralized and of course democratic power. Thereafter, between the liberal words of the government directed to the world outside and their traditional acts directed to India, there arose a contradiction. The world heard that caste discrimination had been prohibited by law, untouchability was abolished, socialism was triumphant: democracy was supreme. But privilege was secure.

Soon, in deference to Hindu beliefs, the killing of cattle or their sale to Muslims had been universally forbidden and the sale of milk was condemned. Over 200 million of the sacred cattle infested with diseases now multiplied while 30 million every year starved and died to be consumed by pariah dogs and vultures. In times of food shortage, religious festivals, *yagnas*, were held on the banks of the Jumna, with food allotted by the government in the hope of warding off the effects of an unfavourable conjunction of the planets. But the practice of female infanticide which might have been helped continued to be illegal.

Meanwhile the soil of India had to be defended and was from time to time enlarged. The attempt to subject the Christian hill tribes, the Nagas and the Mizos, continued in the east for twenty-five years. The Portuguese colony of Goa, also Christian and undefended, was seized in December 1961. But within a year Chinese forces followed Nehru's example and, invading India at both ends, corrected the frontier in their favour.

A continuing threat to the future of India however lay in Pakistan. Instead of one army modestly equipped by the British, there were now two much larger armies more lavishly supplied by the new powers who felt they could rely on the opposition between India and Pakistan to advance their own interests. They were back where the British and French had been in India two centuries earlier.

Between the two states there were three wars. In the third war of 1971 the eastern province had been set up as an independent state of Bangladesh. Eight million Muslim refugees had retraced their steps into India and again about another million were massacred, but this time by their co-religionists. The new state was left bankrupt and the people starving. As in other colonial situations it is still not clear which part of Pakistan should be held to have been liberated from the other.

Behind these political adventures the great problem of India remained that of a population expanding on a soil which, owing to poor management, was effectively contracting. To rectify the consequent growth of poverty nothing could succeed but a harsh, intelligent or authoritarian discipline of the kind that had succeeded in Japan and perhaps in China. But what the government had been providing was a kind of petty socialism. Since the governing party existed by getting its democratic election funds from capitalist industry no serious equalization could be intended. Rather an immense output of printed paper was required for providing permits and licences. Discontent had resulted especially among the swollen populations of the cities. In 1975 riots were frequent and no one knew how many political protesters, dissidents or suspects, were in jail without trial.

We know in Europe under both capitalist and communist governments that the more centralized control we have the larger the army we need of officials who can be neither well educated nor well paid. Under purely Indian conditions, the scope for corruption was unlimited. In India the point had now passed where peaceable solutions were constitutionally possible. Thus within thirty years after *swaraj* there had returned to India the pre-colonial prospects of tyranny and chaos as well as fragmentation.

V *The Lessons of India*

The history of the attachment and detachment of Britain and India clearly has lessons of value beyond the interests of the two parties concerned. When Pandit Nehru addressed the General Assembly of the United Nations in November 1948, speaking in English he explained what they were:

> We in India, who have suffered all these evils of colonialism and imperial domination, have committed ourselves inevitably to the freedom of every other colonial country . . . . Countries like India who have passed out of that colonial stage do not conceive it possible that other countries should remain under the yoke of colonial rule.

So much for the yoke theory. Throughout history, however, states great and small, primitive and advanced, have been saved from disorder by a government imposed by what the anthropologist, Rivers, called 'the enterprising stranger'. Often the imposed government has been better than its natural subjects enjoyed at home. For in this way the people at the bottom of society can often be protected from their native exploiters. Gaul and Britain had a better government from the Romans than the Romans had at home. And when the Roman Government in the end became impossible at home, it was only by settling in its own colony of Constantinople that it could survive for another 1000 years. The case had much in common with that of the Phoenicians in Carthage and the Normans in England.

In India the best governments have been those of Ashoka, a quarter Greek, and Akbar, a kind of Mongol or a Turk. In the last 200 years it might be said that British government was also a good government. Owing particularly to its advantage in being foreign it was often more enlightened, and less oppressive and it soon became less corrupt than British government in England, Scotland, Wales or Ireland. Even the British Army was usually more efficient in India than at home: it had

Table 7.2 *The population of India: increasing with time and classified by religion* (after census reports and H. Tinker, 1966. Figures in millions)

	1800 (estimated)		*100*	
	1867–72 (first census)		*206*	
1921	Hindu	217	British India	247
	Sikh	3	Native States	72
	Jain	1		
	Muslim	69	*Totals* 1921	319
	Buddhist	12	1931	338
	Christian	5		
	Parsee	0·1		
	Tribal	10*		

	India	*Pakistan*		*Totals*
		West	*East*	
1951	357	34	42*	433
1961	434	45	51*	530
1971	550	57	75*	682
	Caste—470 Untouchables—70* Tribals—10*		(Bangladesh)	

* unreliable

to be if it was to survive. Similarly, as Kropotkin tells us, the Tsar's government was always better beyond Baikal. May we not now also admit that the despised Mussolini governed Abyssinia better than he governed Sicily? And better than its Emperor, before or afterwards, governed his hereditary empire?

The British government in India unified the country and brought its upper layers 1000 years forward into the modern world. It did so by an honesty of administration at the top such as few peoples in history have enjoyed. It accomplished its revolution partly by harnessing the educational impulse which is universal among people who have themselves benefited from it.

The means, to be sure, could be damaging to Indian, or at least Brahmin, self-esteem. They were also often damaging to the British who by force of character had to carry out their revolution. These men did not return to England as heroes. Clive, the first of them, after long harassment, committed suicide. Verelst, the second, was ruined and died in poverty in France. Warren Hastings, the third, suffered for seven years an outrageous trial by impeachment. Only Cornwallis, the fourth (who had suffered enough in the American war), had his great achievements in India recognized in his own time. The misfortunes of the others were the consequences of an attempt without precedent (made also concurrently and unsuccessfully in the American colonies) to govern a great country by legal principles and parliamentary processes from a distance half the world away.

For India it was not only separation by the sea; it was also separation by the native divisions of caste and religion on which the British ultimately and almost inevitably brought their own Christian attitudes to bear. All these in the end made the continuance of British rule impracticable. It was these conditions that had prevented hybridization and the genetic development of a new kind of society which could have created a new order in India.

The results of this failure were naturally inherited by the governments of independent India. Those who demanded independence, Gandhi or Nehru, did not know, or tried to forget what faced them. For India after the British presents problems of government formidable and accumulating beyond any that have existed in history. They are due to the combination of the successes and the failures of British rule. On the one hand there is the possession of a common language of education and government. On the other hand, there is the fact that this language is effectively spoken and written, not by a tenth of the population as may happen in Europe, but by no more than a hundredth. And the other ninety-nine-hundredths demand their separate regional and vernacular unities of communication. Again, on the one hand, there is a caste structure establishing orderly hierarchical government. But it is a caste structure resting on a solid basis of superstitition, nepotism and corruption.

As for the natural resources of India, whereas the British government might exploit them for its own advantage, it could take and did take a long view in doing so. It considered the environment and was able to protect it for posterity. Now the environment, as is common with self-government everywhere including Britain, belongs to everybody and to nobody. Or perhaps we should say in India it belongs to the cow, the goat, and the monkey.

It was easy for Ashoka to think of 'all living beings'. He was blessed with less than 70 million under his care. Today his successors are burdened with 700 million. In all overcrowded countries people seek to emigrate. Thirty years after colonial rule has ceased the numbers of British residents in India are unchanged. But the numbers of Indian residents in Britain are greatly increased. These are no longer all of them men from the bottom of society: many are professional men who have chosen to suffer under the imperial yoke rather than enjoy the sweets of self-government. They are a loss to India of those India can least afford to lose.

VI *The Expansion of Russia*

The history of Russia begins with the colonization of the Russian plain by two groups contrasted in race, in language, and in stage of evolution. These were the Paleolithic Finnish-speaking hunters and herdsmen and the Iron-Age Russian-speaking peasants. The city-making from which modern Russia grew, arose again from two contrasted colonizations: the civilized infiltration of the south by Greek traders over more than two millennia and the barbarous invasion of the north by Vikings over only three centuries. Modern Russia grew, as Western Europe had done, by the extension of power from the north and of civilization from the south.

The expansion of Moscow was, to be sure, in all directions but it was the southward expansion that mattered. It met three centuries of resistance from Tatars and from the Ottoman Empire, both of them Turkish-speaking and Muslim. But in the eighteenth century it gave the Russians the wheat growing land of the Ukraine, the 'border' country, within which appeared in the nineteenth century, with British help, the coal and iron of the Donetz Basin. The westward expansion was continued to the present day meeting even more prolonged resistance but usually weakened by the divisions of the European states. The eastward expansion was quite a different kind of enterprise. Its foundation was the conquest of Siberia which began in the sixteenth century. Its culmination was the arrival of the Russian ship *Juno* at San Francisco in April 1806, a few weeks after the American explorers Lewis and Clark had left the Pacific coast. On the Russian River in California the Russians built their fort in 1812 which they held until 1841.

In this last movement exploration and trade were the motives; the natives interfered with neither and military protection was at first hardly needed. In the end, however, these operations brought the Russians face to face with two other powers: Manchu China which agreed to a frontier in 1689; and Japan of the Shoguns which was able, through the eighteenth century, to keep the intruders at a distance.

These were the first moves in the continuing scramble for the control of Asia. The Russian part in this enterprise was to occupy, pacify, protect, and colonize three regions. In the 1850s, in campaigns of which Tolstoy has given us some glimpses, the Caucasus was subdued, and the ancient kingdoms of Georgia, and Armenia as well as the province of Azerbaijan, were wrested from the Turks and the Persians.

The next Russian expansion occupied the twenty years from 1864 to 1884. It took in the western part of the region which we may still know as Turkestan with the great Muslim cities of Bokhara, Tashkent, and Samarkand. The drier eastern half of this heartland of the Turkish speaking peoples, the Tarim Basin, had been claimed by the Chinese under the name of Sinkiang.

One result of this operation was to exterminate in large part the Turcomans, those picturesque horsemen described by the Comte de Gobineau in his *Nouvelles Asiatiques*. Another result was to eliminate what were (after the British had cleaned up India) the most odious tyrants left in the world, the little Khans who had inherited the middle fragments of Tamerlane's Empire. The object of this move, however, was neither civilization nor trade nor conversion. It was simply to keep out anyone else, not the Chinese so much as the British, who indeed assumed that it was aimed at India. For had not the Huns, and Mahmūd of Ghazni, and Tamerlane, and his heirs the Moguls, all invaded India from this healthy highland breeding ground? Yet nothing happened. The country was not colonized. Apart from the army, the police, and the officials, all Russian-speaking, there was no immigration. The long sleep which had fallen on the country since the Mogul conquests was undisturbed.

Religion was not the motive force behind these advances but they might easily be seen as part of a general Christian assault on decaying Muslim Empires and kingdoms which was going on at the time all the way round from Senegal to Sarawak. The French indeed represented their attack on Algeria in 1830 as a crusade. Certainly, however, no such ideas guided the Tsar's ministers when in 1860 they took advantage of the Western dispute with Peking to relieve the Manchu Empire of a strip of territory on the Pacific, almost forgotten but as big as Norway. Here the port of Vladivostok was at once sited to become later the terminal of the Trans-Siberian railway.

This last great Tsarist enterprise, helped by French investors and French engineers, began in 1891. It was, however, reinforcing an old practice in colonization. Exile to Siberia, on foot, by horse and by coach, had begun already under Boris Godunov and its earliest victims included the uncles of the first Romanov Tsar. Slowly the prison camps (which Semyonov has described) and the mines had been pushed further east and beyond Lake Baikal. Now the industry and the settlement could be conveniently enlarged. Prisoners, like Lenin in 1897, could travel comfortably by train. Already in 1893 the railways were taking the first colonies of peasants into the new territory. But when the Japanese, in 1904, saw that the connection round Lake Baikal would soon be completed, without warning they attacked the Russian outpost of Port Arthur, and the Tsarist Empire met its one decisive reverse. Russian history and world history would have taken a different course if that connection had been made in time.

In conclusion we must note one profoundly important characteristic of Tsarist colonization in Asia. Like the British, and unlike the self-centred Chinese, the Russians had the European characteristic of encouraging inquisitive scientific exploration for its own sake often with the help of Westerners among whom Alexander von Humboldt was the most famous. In this way half of Asia, its plants and animals, its rocks, its peoples and their languages, was opened to the whole world. The last of these great explorers was the plant geographer and evolutionist, Nikolai Vavilov, whose imprisonment and death in 1941 marked the end of the epoch of Russian colonial enlightenment. All this was in contrast not only to the long record of Imperial China but also to the shorter record of Russian communism which we can now examine.

VII *The Communist Takeover*

The Tsarist Empire in its last years before 1917 presented to the world a compact unit absolutely controlled from the centre and dominated by a Russian-officered army, administration, and police. The bulwark of the régime was the landowning class which had arisen from three main interbreeding sources: Muscovite, Baltic German, and Swedish, and the chiefly caste of certain conquered peoples, notably Tatars and Georgians. Outside these circles of influence was an educated and intelligent professional class derived from the many racial groups classified by language in the first Russian census of 1897: not only Russians but also Finns and Armenians, Jews, Volga Germans, and Tatars both of the Volga and the Crimea (Table 7.3).

The technically and intellectually progressive movements in Russian society, including all the political agitators and communist and other conspirators had been derived from the mixture of these peoples in Russian cities with a flow of educated immigrants from Western Europe, a flow which ceased only with the Revolution in 1917. Lenin, born in 1870, offers us the plainest example of this mixing process for his pedigree (overlooked by communist literature) shows that his four grandparents were Lutheran, Jewish, Orthodox, and Buddhist.

Outside these governing and educated classes lay the vast body of the Russian, Ukrainian, and Polish peasantry. Beyond them were the urban and pastoral Muslims of the Turkish provinces, the pastoral Buddhist Mongols, the tribes of the Caucasus and of Siberia.

In approaching their subject peoples the Tsars had, like most imperial rulers, shown great respect for religion unless it promoted pacifism or dissent. Christians whom they could not subject to their own orthodoxy they merely expelled, Muslims with too many kinsmen over the border they had not dared to offend. Jews, on the other hand, were notorious dissenters with no friends anywhere and the Jews they had increasingly persecuted.

In this, as in other policies Tsarist governments were following the successful practice of most Christian rulers in the Middle Ages: they were setting up the Jews as targets so that the peasants and working classes could enjoy racial violence under the disguise of moral indignation. Hence the large emigration of Jews to the West for thirty years. Over the same period Jews had acquired a dominant position in the Communist Party. When Lenin seized power therefore he had to compromise at once between conflicting religious, racial, and political interests. The Communist Party was dedicated to destroying all religion —the opium of the people—except its own. It was also dedicated to removing all race and class distinctions, all disabilities of subject peoples. But its ablest leaders apart from Lenin belonged to a detested racial and religious minority. And Lenin needed a strong central government with which to impose his rule on the subject peoples of this empire. Hence his devious course.

In the six years that he was in power (1918–1924) he had to extricate himself from war with Germany, Poland, and the Western allies, and also from civil war with Denikin, Kolchak, and Wrangel. He had gained control by promising power to the workers, land to the peasants, and freedom to the subject peoples. He therefore addressed himself to the aspiring nationalities of the Tsarist Empire, now breathing, as they thought, the air of freedom for the first time in their history. Word went out that Russia was no longer to be a 'prison of peoples', all were now to be free. Capital punishment was abolished—for a short while. The press was to be free—for two days. The trade unions could elect their own committees, their 'soviets', to assert the supposed rights of the workers. The Tsarist practice, since Peter the Great, of controlling movements by an internal passport, a *propiska*, was abolished. The separate sister republics were now 'autonomous'. Each could speak its own language, choose its own alphabet, build its own university, elect its own government. Subject, however, to the condition that all punish-

Table 7.3 *Population of the Russian dominions as classified by census* (figures in millions)

Tsarist Empire First Census, 1897, by race and in 40 language groups			*Soviet Union Census, 1971, by provinces in order of conquest*			*by religion*
ARYAN	Russians[1]	55·7	*Russian Republic*			
	———		with Siberia		130·7	*Christian*
	Ukrainians[2]	22·4	*Ukraine* (1654–1783)		47·5	*Jewish*
	White Russians	5·9	*White Russia* (1667–1792)		9·1	*Buddhist*
	Poles etc. (3)	7·9	*Western* (1940–45)			increasing
	Lithuanians	3·1	Estonia	1·4		at 1%
	Germans	1·8	Latvia	2·4	10·6	per annum[9]
	Rumanians[3]	1·1	Lithuania	3·2		
	other Europeans (4)	0·4	Moldavia	3·6		
	———		*Caucasian* (1783–1854)			
	Iranians[4] (4)	2·0	Georgia	4·7		
	Gypsies	0·03	Armenia	2·5	12·4	
			Azerbaidjan	5·2		
CAUCASIAN	Georgians[5] (2)	2·5	*Turkestan*			*Muslim*
			Kazakhstan	13·2		increasing
SEMITIC	Jews	5·1	Uzbekistan	12·1		at
URO-	Tatars[6] (2)	5·2	Kirghizia	3·0	33·5	3–5% per
ALTAIC	Kirghiz	4·1	Tadjikistan	3·0		annum
	other Turki Muslims[7] (5)	4·0	Turkmenistan	2·2		
	Mongols[8] (2)	0·5				
	Finns (4)	3·4				
	in Finland	3·5				
Various	Chinese etc. (4)	0·7				
TOTALS		129·4			243·9	

1 Russians include 4·4 million in Siberia, mostly since 1893; also 1·8 million in Caucasia and 0·6 million in Central Asia.
2 'Little Russians' in Tsarist terminology.
3 Bessarabians, now 'Moldavians'.
4 Armenians, Kurds and (in Central Asia) Tadjiks.
5 Including Circasians, the favourite source of Turkish slaves.
6 Tatars in Crimea, North Caucasus, and Volga basin.
7 Uzbegs number only 0·7 million in 1897 (*cf.* 1971).
8 Buddhists, chiefly on Chinese border.
9 Non-increase of Russians in large cities due to deficient housing and to birth control, not by contraception, but by abortion (Kaiser, 1976).

General. The Russian census of 1897 was the most far-reaching and important census ever made apart from the British censuses in India. It classified the peoples in each province in forty linguistic and racial groups. These groups were to be mixed, deported, and partly destroyed under the Soviet Régime.

In the period before 1914, migration on a large scale had been permitted in and out of Russia. Net figures for 1856–1888 are: emigration of Russians, 1·15 million, nearly all Jews owing to persecution; immigration of foreigners, nearly all skilled Western Europeans 2·3 million. Illegal migration, without passports, at that time was numerically unimportant although politically momentous. Data from Siberian Railway Guide, 1900; EB. 1911; Intourist Guide 1931; Whitaker 1974.

N.B. The numbers in the table in parentheses refer to classes which have been combined in groups from the more detailed Tsarist census.

ments, all associations, all languages and publications, all strikes, all passports, and all journeys, could be permitted only by the proper authority. That is by the Communist Party which in order to preserve freedom and abolish privilege established branches in every district or community, with a soviet appointed and managed through a well-educated Russian-speaking Secretary by the Nationalities Bureau of the Central Committee in Moscow.

It dawned slowly on the peoples of the Union or Empire, and still more slowly on the peoples outside, that leaders were not elected from below, they were nominated from above, indeed from the top. And at the top was, not a committee or bureau but one individual, Lenin, and in due course his successors. Further, the system worked under rules which were being continually improved.

The Lenin rules had a diverse ancestry and a long evolution. Their two immediate parents are unmistakable. One was Tsarism: the practices and institutions of the Tsars, their method of government by *ukase* and their body of police, the *ochrana*. The other was Conspiracy: the practices and institutions engendered by the working of Tsarism and elaborated over a period of ten generations. In particular they are seen laid out, as Virginia Cowles has pointed out, in Nechayev's *Catechism of a Revolutionary*. From this work Lenin learned how to use a cell organization, a programme of bogus demonstrations and rigged elections, a penal system reinforced by torture, blackmail, and betrayal. Lenin had indeed discovered how to put the Borgias and the Jacobins, the Inquisitors of Rome and of Venice, all to work, without acknowledgement, for the Marxist system. The product of this cultural synthesis was the *apparatus* of his successors, Stalin and the rest, perfectly adapted to its traditional environment.

The apparatus worked and still works in secret but its origins are plainly to be seen since Dostoevsky described them in *The Possessed*. The harvest it has yielded is also to be measured years later from Solzhenitsyn's *Gulag Archipelago*. Its example has now been followed throughout the Communist World. And it has also gradually generated imitators throughout the anti-Communist World.

Stalin's collectivization of agriculture in 1932–4 and the ensuing purges had their coercive effects in all parts of the Soviet Empire. But the experimental aspects of the Soviet system of government are less well known. At the outset, on 27 December 1932, Stalin decreed that internal passports were to be issued once more. His intention was to use them in restricting the movements of urban populations (*Times*, 24 July 1975). But today the Soviet Government characteristically puts a different face on its policy. It represents the passport as a means, not of restricting, but of facilitating movement. It generously proposes to extend the internal passport as a privilege to the peasants that, is to 46 million collective farm workers. For since the Revolution, they now acknowledge, the peasants have never been allowed to move at all. Except as conscripts or deportees they have been more severely restricted than they were under Tsarist serfdom before 1861: the Russian peasant remains a serf.

Let us beware, however, of taking any announcement by the Soviet authorities at its face value. Soviet decrees have more unknown dimensions than the ukases of the Tsars. They may be published generally or locally, or they may be secret and confidential. And if they are published it may be for information abroad or for enforcement at home. And if for enforcement it may be retrospective or prospective. This decree inaugurating internal passports proposes to issue the 46 million documents between 1976 and 1981. In the future, therefore, we may discover whether the new passport is to be used to prevent movement, or to facilitate deportation, or both; we may even learn that it never took effect at all, that it was merely a gesture of encouragement to the world at large (*Times*, 27 December 1974).

VIII *The Soviet Empire*

So much for the method of Soviet government at home. Its method of dealing with the subject peoples outside Europe for the first twenty years was to make sure that the agents it appointed in the provinces could be relied upon to do what Moscow wanted. This meant a practice of subjection which led to revolts in one province after another: in Tashkent in 1920, in Armenia in 1921, in Georgia in 1924, in Azerbaidjan in 1929, and in the Kazakh 'Republic' intermittently for twenty years.

The treatment has varied with the conditions of each frontier province. On the one hand the former Chinese province of Outer Mongolia was seized by Russian communists in 1921 and by 1924 all rival leaders had been exterminated. Since the sparse pastoral population fears the Chinese who are close more than the Russians who are far away, they were allowed a formal independence. On the other hand, Azerbaidjan has a large population whose agriculture remains today as poor and as primitive as any in Asia. But on its edge is the oil field of Baku. Here Kirov, Stalin's right hand man, established in 1929 the harshest rule in the whole Empire. (No wonder that in that year it took me six months to get a visa for this area.)

Much depends on the character of the proconsul who is sent to govern a province. When an ambitious member of the Supreme Soviet in Moscow like Leonid Ilyitch Brezhnev is appointed in 1945 First Secretary of the Central Committee of the Communist Party in the newly annexed 'Republic' of Moldavia it is not because the Moldavians have heard of his reputation and demand his services: it is because the Kremlin thinks he will keep the province in order. When in 1954 the same energetic agent finds himself in Kazakhstan in the same position it again means that plans are being contemplated for the development of that country to which I will return in a moment.

Religion had seemed to Marx and to Lenin to be the weightiest obstacle to a communist revolution and for this reason religious institutions and beliefs had been, next to property, the first target of communist attack in Christian Russia. It might have been expected that the same aim would have dominated policy among the Muslim peoples of Asia. But prudence suggested another course. After all, Islam had never taught respect for a Christian Tsar. Moreover the Muslim peoples of Turkestan and Azerbaidjan spoke Turkish languages. They were closely bound to their warlike kinsmen over the border in Anatolia, in north Persia, and in Sinkiang. To inflame them, and indeed all the Muslim world, with an attack on Islam might lead to a violent response. The obvious course was to drop the Marxist principle intended for Christian Europe, to keep quiet about religion and to aim first at breaking the other part of the connection, the linguistic and cultural bond. The first step in this policy was taken under Kirov in Azerbaidjan in 1929, by establishing the Russian alphabet as the basis of education and publication in the Turkish languages. A monument to twenty-six Russian commissars assassinated in Baku in 1938 commemorates the prolonged resistance to this measure by the subject people.

Another step which Stalin had already taken in dealing with the Turkish peoples was to carve them up; to assign them to five provinces claiming that the division was popular and spontaneous, and then handle each province according to the strategic needs of Moscow. So, in 1924, the inhabitants of the cities of Bokhara, Tashkent, and Samarkand who could trace their history beyond Alexander learned that they were to be given the name of an illiterate pastoral tribe who had been converted to Islam by a Turkish chieftain named Uz Beg in the fourteenth century (Table 7.3).

This radical policy allowed Stalin to take the vast innermost region of the steppes stretching from the Caspian to the Chinese frontier and call it Kazakh, a name cognate with Cossack and applied to many nomadic horse-breeding Turkish tribes. To this new province he decided to give what we may call the full colonial treatment. The work and with it a state of war, began in 1931. It continued until 1951. By this time the numbers of the people and of their cattle and sheep were much reduced. When resistance was finally broken, a large body of Kazakhs, men, women, and children, escaped across the Chinese frontier and the Takla Makan desert to Kashmir. Two thousand survivors eventually found a home in Turkey in 1954, and it is owing to their survival outside Russia that we know the story (told to Godfrey Lias) of their unparalleled journey.

The Soviet pacification of the province meant that more than half the 13 million 'Kazakhs' were now Russian immigrants and the way was open to full colonization. Here were the Virgin Lands which the new Soviet leader, Krushchev, was able to offer to the pioneers of the Russian frontier in 1956.

Apparently Krushchev hoped his colonists would grow wheat on the dry steppes which had formerly supported the grazing of the Kazakh herds. He could not take sound advice because Stalin and he had eliminated Vavilov and other scientists who might have advised them. The programme failed and neither the colonists nor the Kazakhs have been shown to foreign visitors. These errors derive from the origin of the European Communist Parties. They are town parties and their political theory is a town theory. Hence the war in Russia and its colonies between the Party and the peasants. Hence the endless food shortage. And hence the saying in those colonies that there are four enemies of socialist agriculture: spring, summer, autumn, and winter.

Such were the Soviet experiences with what we may call the *external* colonies of their inherited empire. In dealing with the *internal* colonies which had grown up under Tsarist rule the Soviet Government had professed the utmost benevolence. Inside as well as outside European Russia, 'Autonomous Republics', 'Autonomous Provinces', and 'National districts' sprang up by the dozen in the early years of the Revolution. As Stalin took over, however, step by step, each group of people discovered that its privileges had lapsed. After 1933 it was as though Stalin and Hitler had been watching one another across the frontier or the battle-line which separated them, each quick to copy and eager to improve on the methods of his enemy.

In the first place the overthrow of the Tsarist Government had made no difference to the popular hatred of the Jews in Russia. For this reason Lenin had prudently excluded all Jews, apart from Trotsky, from his original cabinet. This attitude has never abated and it helped to extinguish the original Jewish communist leaders.

Already in 1928 an autonomous republic named Birobidjan was specially created by Stalin for the Jews in a strip of eastern Siberia facing the Chinese frontier on the Amur River, and 25,000 Jews (together with 160,000 Russians) have been induced to occupy this desolate region (*Observer*, 27 June 1976). But since Stalin's death the communist attitude towards Jews has been reinforced by the success of the state of Israel. Its very existence presents Jews in Russia with an interest, a racial and religious, historical and intellectual interest, independent of Russia and therefore intolerable to the Soviet Government. Whence come their frantic efforts to suppress those who reveal this interest.

The problem of the Jews in Russia is quite different from that of the other internal colonies. Of these there were three main groups whose fate has been carefully described by Ann Sheehy. One was that of the Volga Germans imported by Catherine the Great, herself a German, to improve the primitive agriculture of the Volga basin. Another consisted of the communities of Crimean Tatars, Muslims now numbering one and a half million, for whom Catherine had built mosques. A third were a group of four tribes with picturesque costumes and dances on the north side of the Caucasus: like the Basques who are probably related to them, they had proved highly resistant to bureaucratic control both before and after the Revolution.

For all these communities numbering several million the war brought destruction. After the German invasion was repelled it was easy to claim that they had collaborated with the invaders. All of them, men, women, and children, were seized and deported to prison camps chiefly in Uzbekistan in 1943 and 1944. Solzhenitsyn has described the procedure. Their lands and goods were also seized by the Government and the peoples themselves have disappeared. This was Stalin's final solution.

There are many aspects, some ephemeral, some enduring, of this reversal of Tsarist policy towards minority and subject peoples. Instead of the incorporation of foreign and alien elements in Russian society, we now have their rejection. Instead of the immigration of foreigners and emigration of Russians we now have the prohibition of both. Instead of intermarriage with foreigners we now have its condemnation as treason. A system of social assimilation by which, as I have previously shown, Russian society developed and diversified over the centuries has been abandoned. The evolution of a vast human society has been crushed into the mould required by the needs of the new governing apparatus determined to break the civilizing connection with Western Europe, the connection established by Peter the Great.

In its general character the Soviet Empire has certain points in common with all previous empires. The government is imposed on heterogeneous backward peoples by a compact governing caste. But its techniques of production, communication, and administration, whether advanced or primitive, are not its own: it has inherited them from predecessors whom it attempts to disown.

Again, although the Soviet Empire was acquired by force, it was taken over by fraud. The fraud consisted in a series of confidence tricks by which the conspirators, under cover of a new religion disguised as science and philosophy devoted to the service of the people, have transferred power to themselves. Then they have quietly dismantled what they did not need of this new religion. The result has been that from the beginning the Government has been concerned, like its Tsarist predecessor, with preserving its power, but with greater intensity than any other empire in history. A further result has been that the Soviet Government does not now know how to proceed. It cannot turn back. It cannot dismount. Having shut the gates against the rest of the world it does not know how to open them again. It is even at a disadvantage in copying what happens abroad. It can struggle only to go forward since it operates under the compulsions of a theory of progress which it derives from its capitalist enemies.

These difficulties the Soviet Government shares with many others. But it has a peculiar difficulty which does not spring from its being an imperial, colonial, and communist Government, or an unrepresentative and undemocratic Government. It springs from its double inheritance: the Marxist demoralization of (as Solzhenitsyn has told us) the whole of the world we live in; and the Tsarist use of the police to preserve power by preventing the movement of people and ideas.

In this respect the Soviet Empire stands at the opposite pole from the British Empire. Being founded on trade and for trade (as Adam Smith and Napoleon Bonaparte pointed out), the British always attempted to govern with the least expense and the greatest profit. Increase of power was often unprofitable and their greatest mistakes were due to parsimony. But the British hated to restrict any movements of people which might be useful to them; it is a policy which they still vainly attempt to maintain in a world with too many people and no empire to put them.

IX *Chinese Colonization*

Migration and colonization appear in China in four stages. The first two were the colonization of the heartland of China and its colonization of the outer provinces to make the Han Empire and also the present Republic or Empire of China.

The third stage was the subjection of the Chinese themselves by several alien races of military rulers. There were the Mongols in the fourteenth century who drove the Thai into Siam and the Shan into Burma and even led the Chinese themselves to attack Japan and Java. Next there were the Manchu who in the seventeenth century, drove out their defeated enemies into Taiwan and Indonesia. Then there were the Europeans and the Japanese. It was their assault which, beginning with the British attack in 1840, the Opium War, compelled the Manchu to admit foreign trade and eventually drove out the Manchu themselves in 1911. Finally there was the abortive attempt of the Japanese between 1934 and 1945 to occupy the whole heartland of China.

These last two operations were brought to an end by revolutions each of which had to deal with problems of colonization. This they did in different ways.

First came the revolution of 1912 in which Sun Yat-sen, genuinely believing in liberal and international principles, proclaimed his Chinese Republic as a federation of free peoples. The new national flag no longer displayed the dragon of a single authority. It showed five bars representing the equal rights and aspirations of the Chinese (the Han) and the four peripheral peoples, the Manchus, Mongolians, Muslims (of Sinkiang), and Tibetans. Second came the revolution of Mao Tse-tung in 1949. Here was a communist who was in the first place a nationalist who had lived only in China; and in the second place, not a townsman but a countryman, the son of what the Russians would have called a Kulak. Mao made no international or fraternal gesture. He didn't need to. His aim was what he called 'decolonization'. This meant taking back all the provinces the Russians and Japanese had occupied and then taking over all the peoples in them, the former subject peoples of the Manchu Empire. In fact a re-colonization.

In detail the first step was to fix the boundaries of Manchuria, Mongolia, and Sinkiang with Russia. The two states agreed cordially on one point, that the Turkish-speaking Muslims in old Turkestan on either side of their frontier should not speak loudly enough for Turks or Muslims elsewhere to hear. On each of these territories they therefore planted their own Russian or Chinese speaking officials and farmers. It was what the Romans had done in Gaul and the English in Ireland.

Then there were the Russian and American protectorates, as we may call them, in North and South Korea and in Taiwan, the old Portuguese and Japanese Formosa, now for the third time receiving its colony of Chinese exiles. These Communist China let alone. Tibet, on the other hand, they occupied in 1959, the priestly autocrat, the Dalai Lama, escaping to India. And the frontier with India they pushed back by force in 1965.

One other important colonial question remained in suspense, that of Hong Kong, the colony which, under pressure, had been ceded to Britain in 1841. In 1949 Mao Tse-tung judiciously conceded the existence of the colony, having foreseen its convenience. It continues as a British colony because the arrangement suits China and Britain as well as its residents. It is to the advantage of all to have this clearing-house, this commercial embassy, not within but just outside China's jurisdiction. It is outside China in four senses: territorially, administratively, linguistically, economically. But it is inside China historically and in the racial character of its population. Yet this is a selected population which has chosen to live under a compromise between British and Chinese conditions: a stratified compromise that has grown up since 1841 and is now little dependent on the opium trade.

Thus 4 million Chinese live under British rule enjoying by their skill and industry a prosperity, except in Japan and Singapore, otherwise unknown in Asia. It vibrates, as Jan Morris says, with pride, greed, energy, and success. It also repeats what has happened again and again in the last 6000 years but notably in the Phoenician and Greek colonies in the Mediterranean and the Hansa Towns in the Baltic: the association in a sea port by colonization and stratification or segregation for their mutual advantage of peoples of contrasted race and culture having different ways of life, instincts and morals, beliefs and aptitudes, and consequently making different contributions to the well-being of the whole community.

Consider, however, how this situation differs from the one where the differences are smaller, intermarriage is frequent and integration gradually blurs the racial although not the class distinctions. The difference is that in Hong Kong the governing class chooses to accept the moral outlook of the governed. It accepts the world-wide outlook of the proletarian and the plutocrat which is that present security is more important than future prospects. Welfare, insurance, and education can be left to those who want them. And beyond all these, the governors of Hong Kong may claim to rule one of the few spots left in Asia which is not quite a police state.

The occupation of Hong Kong for the Chinese, like the occupation of Gibraltar for Spain, may be seen as an infringement of national integrity, a flagrant demonstration of colonialism. But the communist Government of China recognizes that here, like the Japanese Shoguns with the Dutch in their port of Nagasaki, it can get the best of both worlds. It can take the profits of free enterprise without itself suffering this foreign infection. Moreover culturally, Hong Kong is for China what New York used to be for the United States or what Pera and Galata used to be for the Ottoman Empire. It is a place where East meets West, where the people of the mainland mix with another world. It is a half-way house where, not women perhaps, but ideas and money can be exchanged. And in the matter of money Hong Kong is also a half-way house between China and the Chinese overseas.

Migration overseas is the third aspect of Chinese colonization, migration largely southwards and from the south, into countries outside the rule of Peking in the north. There they appeared, and still remain, except in Singapore, as subject minorities. In space this has been a vast movement for it embraces the whole of the Pacific and all the great ports of the world. In time it reaches back into the southward expansion of pre-history. Its documentation begins with navigators of the fifteenth century under the Ming Dynasty whose voyages reached East Africa and settled as far afield as Bantam in Java. But its great impulse came when European colonial government provided the shield which capriciously protected Chinese living overseas. For a period under the Manchu this migration was illegal and therefore largely confined to men. After 1840 women again began to emigrate and Chinese communities again began to multiply so that they now number perhaps as many as 30 million.

Everywhere the Chinese went they throve through having a special value to the societies they entered. This value was broadly of three kinds. There was the mental skill of the trader, the manual skill of the artisan, and the reliable diligence of the rough labourer or, to use the Indian caste term, coolie. Let us now look at the world they colonized.

X *The Partition of South-East Asia*

The first colonization of tropical Asia filled it with dark people who remain in the south of India and in the upland and inland parts of most of South-East Asia. But already during the last Ice Age the paler Mongolian peoples pushed down into the plains and coasts of what are now Indo-China, Thailand, and Burma; smaller groups trickled over into India. Between the Indian and Mongolian worlds there remained, however, a line of cleavage which Coon had called the Movius Line. This is a division made by barriers to migration. It separates races of men just as the Wallace Line between Asia and Australasia separates species and genera of animals.

Into the world so divided came, about the end of the fourth millennium B.C., the innovation of grain-growing, on the Indian side in the Indus Valley, and on the Mongolian side in the valley of the Yellow River. Each slowly expanded, transforming itself as it grew. On the

Indian side the Aryan invasion in the second millennium swept the wheat growers into the Ganges Valley where rice took the place of wheat as millet did in Africa and rye in Russia. On this double basis of wheat and rice Hindu caste society developed with black aboriginal populations subjected to a government of still illiterate warriors and priests. At the same time a thin stream of barbarian cultivators must have carried rice cultivation eastward through Burma and through the islands as far as the south of China.

Meanwhile on the Yellow River the Shang conquerors had brought wheat and bronze and developed a standard form of writing. On these foundations a literate Mandarin caste and, after 1000 years a Confucian society, expanded southwards until it met and absorbed the rice growers in the south. The geographical lines of this expansion are still today visible in agriculture and audible in speech. For the Chinese Mandarin dialect, their wheat language, spread easily over the poor and primitive populations of the western mountains but it dissolved into a dozen diverse dialects when it broke into the south.

This Chinese expansion reached its first climax in the second century B.C. with the Han Empire now stretching to Manchuria in the north, Sinkiang in the east and Vietnam in the south. At the same time India also, having picked up writing from the Persians and the Greeks, had attained its first unification. There were therefore two unified literate Eastern empires and both were briefly in contact with the third, the Roman Empire in the West. This was the culmination of the world's Iron Age.

The unity of India had, however, been attained by a revolution: the teaching of a warrior ruler, the Buddha, had undermined the Hindu caste system. But the attack on their supremacy had been resisted by the priestly Brahmins. In due course they defeated Buddhism, the political unity it had given was dissolved and the social unity of caste was restored.

Buddhism, however, had a future elsewhere. With the help of the device of monasticism it could travel in all directions and it soon proved (as Arthur Waley has shown) capable of adapting itself over a whole millennium to the needs of all Eastern peoples. It proved itself to be Hinduism trimmed for export to the East much as, at the same time, Christianity proved itself to be Judaism trimmed for export to the West.

The expulsion of Buddhism from India meant the spread eastwards of a connected body of people bringing a wave of Indian civilization into several Mongolian worlds which had previously received only a trickle of Indian cultivators. The new migrants who broke through the Movius barrier clearly owed their success to the cooperation of their warriors with the smiths who made their weapons, the priests who made their laws and their rituals, and the masons who built their huge temples in Burma, Indo-China, and Java.

Thus at the beginning of the Christian Era, we see South-East Asia occupied by peoples who had become civilized, like the Europeans by immigration at several removes from S.W. Asia. Into this great region adjoining its racial and cultural parents, India and China, broke an Islamic invasion in the tenth century. For over half a millennium its southern half, Malaysia and Indonesia, was then subjected to the government of Muslim sultans of Arab origin.

The modern phase in the colonization of South-East Asia was a parallel immigration of Chinese and Indians largely under European protection. First the Portuguese and the Spaniards in the sixteenth century, then the British, Dutch, and French in the nineteenth century, opened the whole region to a simultaneous Chinese and Indian occupation of its culturally empty spaces, its free ecological niches.

How then did they divide the region between them? The boundary of their earlier spheres of expansion, as we have seen, has shifted over the last two millennia. Rice had taken over the whole cultivable area of S.E. Asia, stopping short only of New Guinea. Hinduism and Buddhism had covered the whole area with a second layer stopping short of the Philippines. Islam had then covered the whole of the southern part, Malaysia and Indonesia and the southern Philippines with a third layer stopping short only of Luzon and Bali.

Then, with the establishment of Portuguese stations and government, the Chinese began to settle in what had been the Indian sphere east of the Straits of Malacca. But their special opportunity came when Sir Stamford Raffles in 1819 set up an East India Company station which became Singapore. It was the Chinese who in the end mainly built up this colony into a Chinese style of Hansa Town, parallel with Hong Kong. Today the two main races in Singapore are balanced, Chinese and Indian as 77 to 14, while the Malays and Europeans are as 7 to 2.

Singapore seceded from independent Malaysia in 1965. It is the only Chinese-ruled state outside China and Taiwan. The four official languages are now Mandarin Chinese, Malay, Tamil, and English, representing the four racial groups. For 150 years the British minority ruled Singapore; now it is ruled by the Chinese majority, a diverse community speaking half a dozen dialects from the rice-growing south. The result is the only former British colony which, though a police state, may claim to be better governed than it was by the British.

In the region as a whole we must distinguish between the two main zones of Chinese immigration. The Buddhist countries of Thailand and

Indo-China were geographically and racially closest to the Chinese and therefore most congenial to them. The Muslim Malay peoples who stretched from Java to the Philippines were racially more different. They were also temperamentally more aggressive and more intolerant. Here from the first the Chinese had trouble.

In the Philippines under Spanish rule they were attacked again and again. In Batavia under Dutch rule in October 1741, 10,000 Chinese were massacred. Their trouble became worse when the colonial powers left. In Java in 1959 some 100,000 Chinese were driven out of their village shops and some returned to China. In October 1965 greater numbers were massacred on the excuse of being communists. In Malaysia independence came in 1957, and at the first elections in May 1969, 2000 Chinese were killed in Kuala Lumpur.

Facing these dangers in Indonesia, the Chinese, who had been recognizable by their names, speech, and dress, have lately tried to disappear into the population. Taking local wives and local names they have, like the Jews of Christian Europe, been increasingly assimilated. The pressure was of course strongest on Chinese indentured labourers who were taken to New Guinea and elsewhere without their own women.

In Malaysia the government and the civil service is four-fifths Malay: peasants and fishermen are all Malay; but the middle class, the technical professions and traders are Chinese with a few Indians. The Chinese thus remain conspicuous by their abilities and the advanced educational system inevitably emphasizes their distinction. To avoid this effect, to improve the social and economic prospects of the majority races, both the Malaysian and the Indonesian governments have introduced racial and linguistic discrimination notably in the universities. The methods used are quotas in proportion to the population in Malaysia. In Indonesia genuine exclusion of the Chinese has been tried. Since, to avoid this disability many have changed their names, candidates for admission have been required to provide photographs.

This kind of practice reminds us of the exclusion of Jews in Nazi Germany, the *numerus clausus* introduced in Hungary in 1925, and the quotas for Jews in Tsarist and Soviet Russia. In all these cases the proportion of Jews was higher inside than outside the universities and the object was to achieve 'social justice' by excluding the more intelligent race. The same object underlies the converse American legislation designed to raise the proportion of the Negro minority in responsible positions. Such methods may be said to reverse the general class-based education of a stratified society. But in the end we find that social justice for one man achieves social injustice for another.

XI *Indo-China*

The centre of the cleavage of S.E. Asia is where Annam or Vietnam, Cambodia, Laos, and Thailand meet, the rich and accessible region once known to Europeans as Indo-China, a good name.

Already in the third century B.C. the Indian movement represented by a people known as the Chams encountered in Annam the expanding Chin or Chinese Empire which imposed its suzerainty on the northern part of the country. Tongking indeed paid tribute to the Chinese Emperor, off and on, until 1862. The suzerainty was nominal and shifting but it had the enduring effect of an intrusion into the country by rulers who spoke Chinese, wrote in Chinese characters, and obeyed the Confucian conventions of China. They differed, however, from the southern Chinese mandarins, in one serious respect. They were not appointed by the Chinese Imperial Examination Board; consequently they were not regularly interchangeable on the Chinese imperial circuit. They came to be genetically isolated from China.

After this early overland expansion came, as we saw, many more general later emigrations and expulsions of southern Chinese overseas, and from the interpenetrations of Indian and Chinese races, classes, and cultures which followed, several lines across Asia may be drawn separating Indian and Chinese spheres of influence, religious or political. But if we take race to be the important differential we find the sharpest line of cleavage between the Indian and the Chinese where the plain of the Ganges meets the foothills of the Himalayas. Another cleavage, less sharp but most significant, divides the Chinese and Confucian north from the Buddhist south of Annam. So it was when the European navigators reached Annam in the sixteenth century.

One of the first fruits of their coming proved to be the most beneficial. It was the invention by a French missionary about 1627 of a romanized alphabet known as *quoc ngu* for the writing of the Annamese language. This device, slowly replacing the Chinese ideograms, separated Indo-China from its former homeland, tenuously but irrevocably attaching it to Europe. In the next century the attachment began to acquire a political framework. The French, displaced from India by the British, resourcefully turned to Annam and gained a concession for trade on an island (Pulo Condore) and a port (Tourane). Much later they were able to contest the suzerainty of the Manchu Empire and in the end had established themselves in the whole country dividing it between 1862 and 1893 into a colony and four protectorates.

The effect of this rule was the introduction to a growing population of the French language together with, not only soldiers, traders, and administrators, but also Catholic missionaries who effected considerable conversion. Their success was in the south, in the Saigon district, where Indian influence and the Buddhist religion had been strongest. In the north they took a different course, founding in 1899 the 'École Française d'Extrême Orient' which became in 1907 the University of Hanoi. From this centre the French rediscovered and restored the forgotten wonders of Indo-China's past, the stupendous temples and palaces of Angkor Wat and Angkor Thom.

The separate coastal provinces of Cochin China, Annam, and Tonkin, being linguistically akin, were later united by the French as a single unit of Vietnam. Between 1942 and 1945 the whole of S.E. Asia including Indo-China (now with a population approaching 50 million) was occupied by Japanese forces. When they withdrew and the French returned, the northern Tonkin province rebelled. It now became clear that the urban and literate people in the Chinese north and in the Indian south of the French colony had in fifty years been learning a great deal from their French protectors. But they had been learning different things. What the north had learned was shown by its communist political leader, Ho-Chi-Minh and by his military commander, General Giap. In an attempt to confine the communist rule a boundary was fixed between north and south by a conference in Geneva in 1954. But the expansion of the communists in the north continued. Finally, in spite of U.S. support and a nominal truce in 1972, the whole of the south was conquered (or liberated) in 1975.

In the Vietnam War between 1950 and 1975 North Vietnam was the aggressor. The Communist Government of Ho-Chi-Minh attacked South Vietnam in order to displace its ruling class which it believed to be corrupt and incompetent and a danger to its own safety. It had a similar justification to the Norman Conquest of England. The difference between the two governments did not, however, spring from their modes of administration, capitalist or communist, nor from their religions, Buddhist and Catholic as against Confucian and Marxist. Beneath all these, it sprang from the racial origins of all classes but especially of the governing classes of the two halves of Vietnam. Ho-Chi-Minh was the son of a Mandarin. The North was derived from China and the South from India and the line between them is the racial and therefore also cultural division which stretches from the Pamirs to the Pacific. The victory of the North was not a game of dominoes. It was a step in a southward advance which has been going on for nearly 20,000 years.

XII *Japan*

At opposite ends of the Eurasian continent stand the scattered islands of Japan and Britain, utterly remote but unmistakably parallel. Both of them were peopled and also civilized by wave after wave of colonization from the adjoining mainland. To Japan the colonists came by three routes. Entering from eastern Siberia probably before the last Ice Age the Ainu, hairy white hunters, were the sparse Paleolithic population. Then by way of the Ryukyu Islands came the first Mongolian colonists, originally from south China in the first millennium B.C. bringing with them their language, seamanship, and cultivation of rice. They pushed the native people northwards, rarely crossing with them, until the pure Ainu were left after 1000 years only in the cold northern island of Hokkaido.

Last of all, from Korea came a stream of Chinese and Koreans beginning in the second century B.C. and continuing up to the present day. It was these who brought Chinese civilization, first, with bronze, iron, and wheat, then in the fifth century A.D., with writing, Confucianism and Buddhism. These origins are fairly clear. Two inscrutable mysteries remain: no one knows how the untouchable Eta caste arrived in Japan; and no one knows who made the Jomon pottery thousands of years, it is said, before the Japanese arrived.

By the seventeenth century of our era the Japanese had for 800 years accepted a double system of government. An hereditary emperor was reduced to a sacred role while his chief minister held the effective power as an hereditary commander or Shogun. It was a polarity of government which has been seen in many forms in modern Europe and India as well as in the Ancient World. In 1600 the Tokugawa family had established themselves as Shoguns. They had gained their centralized power by breaking down the castle-towns and guilds of the earlier feudal society and they were preparing to set the country on a course of peaceful non-development. At this very moment, however, the new government found not only its plans but the whole structure of Japanese life threatened. European traders and missionaries were entering the country, people dedicated to economic growth and religious conversion.

In 1637 the Shogun took what he deemed to be the necessary steps to preserve his and his country's independence. He laid down certain drastic Rules of Exclusion. He banned the Christian religion massacring Christian converts. And, except for the perpetually immigrating and familiar Chinese, who could not be certainly recognized and were not feared, and the Dutch who were confined to a trading station, he expelled all foreigners from the country. Further he prohibited all foreign travel and the building of all ocean-going ships to Japanese; those trading abroad were thus exiled. He also prohibited the teaching of the Japanese language to the Ainu people.

Thus Japan, which had been almost fully abreast of the times, was suddenly cut off from the rest of the world. For 230 years Japan became a prison, the first prison society. At least such was the purpose of the Shogun's edict and his successors' policies.

In this way Japan was given a breathing space after tremendous struggles in the previous century. Peace prevailed with prosperity in the towns. In the country the population was stabilized by intermittent famines and the peasants' remedies of infanticide, abortion, and the selling of female children, Chinese-style, to the brothels in the towns.

The system, however, was imperfect—as the corresponding Russian system is today. One spy-hole had been left and one loop-hole was soon to be discovered. The Shoguns themselves had to know what dangers might arise for them abroad. So they had made it possible for their agents to see and to translate Dutch books. That was the spy-hole. The loop-hole was through the north. Before the century was out the Russians had occupied Kamtchatka. Soon Japanese ships were being wrecked and castaways were falling into Russian hands. Later still Russian explorers were moving down the Kurile islands and meeting the Ainu tribesmen. These things did not shift the Shogun, but they aroused a ferment of curiosity among Japanese scholars. So arose the strange paradox (noted by Donald Keene) that the Shogunate had done more than any country outside Europe to keep its people in the dark about Europe. Yet by 1800 they actually knew more, far more, about Europe than any other of the native peoples of Asia, Arabs or Persians, Indians or Chinese.

It was these inquisitive people who learned of the British humiliation of the Manchu Empire in the Opium War. Naturally therefore, when the United States demanded through Commander Perry in 1853 that civilized relations should be established, the Shogun's policy collapsed. In 1854 foreign consuls arrived.

After this surrender fourteen years of confusion followed. At last in 1868 the divine Emperor, a boy of 16 emerged from the shadows to take over the Government from the last Shogun. He did so as the figurehead for a group of Western nobles who had been excluded from the Shogun's Eastern junta. It was a revolution, a double break with a tribal ruling class and with the principles of a prison state. For the masses the reverence for China and Confucian doctrine was skilfully transferred to the older nationalism and superstition of Shintoism. But for the professional classes, European people, ideas, and above all science and technology, were to be admitted and indeed embraced. Once again Japanese could and did trade and travel. Now the whole world was open to them.

The native intelligence of the Japanese might have failed to develop if their society had had the class-bound character which superficial study has given it. We are told that the landowners, the Daimyo, were kept in order through their hostage families being held in Yedo (Tokyo as it now is); that the craftsmen and traders were strictly registered by the sumptuary laws; and that the farmers were all attached to the land by taxation. In practice, however, there were three leakages between these classes.

In the first place, in a country kept in peace, the unattached samurai had had no choice but to be assimilated in the lower orders of society. In the second place, adoption from these lower orders was an established practice of these samurai. In the third place the Shoguns themselves were polygamous and the most notable of them (Tsunayoshi, 1680–1709) as has happened in most long dynasties, was the son of a lower class mother. Indeed the gradation is worth noting here between the weak emperor who had for most of seven centuries been compelled to marry a woman of the Shogun's choice, often his daughter, while the strong Shogun bred as he pleased.

The new enterprising Japanese people came from the mixture of dispossessed landowners, peasants, and craftsmen who had developed trade and small-scale industry, and acquired skill, education, and wealth. It was the character of these people, of which the innovators were confident, which ensured their success. When in 1868 the Emperor displaced the last Shogun, the new Government at once admitted Western traders and abolished the restraints of feudal society. The result was a transformation which has been vividly described by Pat Barr. The enthusiasm of the people for the foreign inventions was without parallel in history. Already in 1872 the British had built the first Japanese railway from Yokohama to Tokyo. This was what they had been doing all over the world for forty years. But nowhere with such effect. By 1880 the Japanese had built their own railway over rougher country from Kyoto to Otsu—without foreign help. This was only the beginning.

How did the Japanese do these things? Organizing ability and discipline we know they had. Energy and industry they also had. But how did they pick up the skills so quickly? Skills which, as later experience showed, most other peoples never succeed in picking up at all. No one in Japan doubts that the racial character of the Japanese was responsible for this ability to assimilate with success one part of Western civilization; and that it was also responsible for their rejection of other parts.

The last century has seen tremendous social strains and political conflicts which have accompanied the adoption and rejection of different elements of Western culture by the various governments and the different social classes of China as well as of Japan. The next century will see many more.

Meanwhile let us notice that Yokohama was added to the great windows of Bombay and Calcutta, Singapore, Shanghai and Hong Kong by which Europeans (in contrast to the inland Russians) had let light and movement into the dark unchanging world of Asia. They were windows through which Asia and the world could see one another. But what is less easily realized (unless we visit, for example, an arts festival in Hong Kong) is that they are windows through which Asia can, for the first time, actually see itself.

The fruit of this opportunity, still no doubt far from mature, is an achievement that we can see only in Japan. For, alone among the states of Asia, Japan now shows us a legally established representative Government with freedom of speech and the press. It is, as in Europe, a fragile achievement. But it is connected with the racial character and cultural continuity of the Japanese people, above all of their professional classes.

Chapter 8

The Opening of Africa

I *African Evolution*

The Egyptians and the Greeks divided the earth into three continents inhabited by different peoples. In our minds the division has changed its shape but we still see Africa and the great land of the Negroes as standing by itself. Famine and war, poverty, slavery, cruelty, and crime, are common to the history of all three continents. But in Europe and Asia, after a lapse of a million years, we can see also the reward of an achievement, impressive even when it is disastrous, which is lacking in Negro Africa. Why is this? To find the answer we must go back once again to the beginning.

Man arose in tropical Africa, a region populated by his closest relatives and competitors, most of whom he seems to have been able to destroy, but a region also infested by their diseases, none of which he was able to destroy. These diseases, beginning with malaria and yellow fever, became more dangerous to him as he increased in numbers. There were two ways of escape open to him. One was to colonize other lands: here he succeeded. He moved out of the tropics, away from snails and worms, flies and lice, as well as from the jackals and antelopes, all of which lived around him in Africa, carrying his parasites. The other way was by genetic change, by acquiring resistance to the most destructive of his parasites: here also he succeeded notably by sorting out the hundreds of mutations in haemoglobin and its attached blood groups which have been arising throughout the evolution of the vertebrates.

Some of these mutations, as we saw, protect the carrier from death by infection but they often do so at the expense of his physical and mental vigour and his fertility. Hence the struggle between man and his parasites which (as Lambrecht and others have suggested) has played a crucial role in the history of man in Africa. The effects of disease for the last 30,000 years or so have evidently been to stop the Negro leaving Africa. He did not even reach the Canaries or Madagascar on his own.

They also stopped the people of Asia and Europe returning to colonize Africa. They could not break the barrier of African diseases to which they had no genetic resistance. They could raid the coasts and the desert edges (the Sahel) of tropical Africa. They could take the black man out of Africa but they could not themselves settle in his country.

There was one gap in the curtain of disease which secluded prehistoric Africa. It was opened by the highlands of Abyssinia and the long ridge which connects them with the Cape. Through this gap the Hamitic cattle people, who were later to be known as Hottentots, made their way to South Africa over 3000 years ago. And through it later Semitic people bringing grain and horses were able to establish themselves on the table land of Abyssinia from which later still grain-growing spread by migration to the Negroes. And also, as I have shown, the practices of mining and the art of building in stone whose traces we see at and around Zimbabwe. Both these gaps were later partly sealed again by disease, notably by sleeping sickness. As the populations of cattle increased they probably raised the barrier against themselves; they stopped horses and their riders ever getting through to the south. For these reasons also the invention of bronze failed to penetrate Negro Africa until after the fourth century when the iron-workers dispersed from Meroë as travelling castes of blacksmiths.

Two other severe handicaps blocked the entrance of civilization into Negro Africa. Termites destroyed all writing on wood or paper. In Cambodia and Java the same hazard existed but the stone inscriptions which have now been recovered could sustain cultural continuity. In Africa there is evidence of attempts to preserve the Hebrew scriptures. But the Falasha in Abyssinia, and even the Balemba in the Transvaal, show us that the scriptures were lost; and with them the basis of what civilization had penetrated Africa.

Yet another handicap, derived from disease, has to be added, one which Negro Africa shares with the Melanesian peoples of the New Guinea region. It is a universal development of witchcraft both for curing and for killing. The prevalence of infectious disease has maintained every possible fraud as a means of curing it. The profession of witch-doctor dominates Negro life in Africa, creating a religion whose redeeming features we seek in vain. For sorcery instead of remedying disease reinforces its causes, notably through the contamination of water by faeces. And the propagation of smallpox has been a special department of the witch-doctors' science. The rational systems of science, religion, and the law which Europe owes chiefly to the Jews and the Greeks could not make, and still have not made, headway against an invisible alliance of sorcery, disease and also crime in Africa.

In short, the lowered level of enterprise noticed in Negro Africa by the most observant Europeans, like Elspeth Huxley, is to be understood as the age-long effect of disease, the genetic and cultural responses to the endemic parasites of man in Africa. In addition the interactions between disease, superstitition, and isolation cut the African off from the opportunities of civilization and the momentum of racial evolution which arises from civilization. By keeping out the white man as a ruler inside Africa they exposed the Negro in the end to the rule of the white man outside Africa, a rule imposed in two stages, slavery and colonization.

II *Negro Slavery*

The dispersal of iron-workers over Africa put the means of war and enslavement in the hands of chieftains who now become kings all over tropical Africa. African Negroes however failed to discover how to employ their slaves otherwise than (like their cattle and their wives) as symbols of status. In West and Central Africa captured enemies were variously devoted to ceremonial killing, torturing, and eating. These customs were described by explorers between John Hawkins in 1568 and Richard Burton in 1864. They were still in full swing when the British occupied Kumasi in 1896 and Benin, the City of Blood, in 1897. Only in the east do the stone monuments of the Zimbabwe region suggest that slaves were used for a constructive purpose but it was a purpose probably controlled, between the fourth and fourteenth century A.D., by Amharic or Arab invaders from the north. An external impulse to the capture of slaves had come, however, much earlier in the trade with the Carthaginians across the Sahara. In the fourth century B.C. the Numidians, the original nomads of Berber race, known to the Romans as Gaetuli and to us as the veiled Tuareg, took up the camel. They discovered that with its help and their iron weapons they could carry, first salt, then gold and ivory, and finally slaves, across the desert to a Mediterranean market.

The developing Roman Empire, however, like its Egyptian, Persian, and Hellenistic predecessors, was not greatly interested in Negro slaves. The big development came with Islam. Arab conquests north of the Sahara, the Fulani advance south of the Sahara to the Niger, Muslim encroachment in Abyssinia, and the Arab slave depots of Zanzibar and Khartoum; all these made slavery the main form of social organization and the slave-trade the main form of commerce.

This was a remarkable Muslim achievement of which the 'Black Muslims' in the U.S. were unaware when, on his pilgrimage to Mecca in 1964, their leader Malcolm X, met the Emir Faisal. It reached a climax in the nineteenth century by which time many millions of Negroes had been enslaved by white Muslims. What happened to them all? Small Negro colonies exist in the Yemen and the Hejaz and near Jericho. Signs of Negro ancestry are seen in the Balkans. Negro slaves also remain in Timbuctoo and the Muslim fringe of the Sahel. But for the most part they have disappeared. Male castration and female infanticide have almost destroyed the traces of this massive deportation. In Africa, their removal merely sufficed with war, massacre, and disease to keep the population in equilibrium and to avert famine.

Meanwhile a different scene was presented by the west coast of Africa, when it offered itself to Christian Europe. Here the advancing Portuguese found to their surprise that Negro slaves were a commodity of exchange. They could be bought and sold from ships. Soon (in 1440) they discovered that they could sell the surplus to Spanish dealers. It was the grandchildren of these who were dispatched as slaves to Hispaniola by Columbus in 1502. Today their liberated descendants make up the Caribbean populations.

Columbus recognized that the native Amerindian populations were neither willing to labour on the land, often preferring to fight, nor able to survive contact with them and their diseases. The Negroes were able to do both. So the Christian slave trade began. As with the Muslims the slaves were mostly male and the population therefore scarcely maintained itself. So the trade continually increased. The Portuguese in Angola and in Brazil were the main sources of supply and of demand. But the chief operators were soon the English.

The total number of slaves transported from Africa to America between 1502 and 1850 has been estimated by Fage as about 9 million, an additional 1 or 2 million being lost on the way—about the same proportion as with white migrants from Europe. They were distributed over the whole lowlands of the east side of the Americas from the Potomac to the River Plate. The conditions and consequences of their slavery in America are described in my previous book. It is now their emancipation which concerns me.

At the beginning of the nineteenth century the position in Africa was simply definable. Muslim peoples, derived from the Islamic conquests, assisted by horses and camels, by hybridization and religious conversion, were settled in the north. Christians, Dutch and Portuguese, also assisted by hybridization and religious conversion, were settled in the south. In the east Muslim traders were engaged in the hybridization and conversion of Negro tribes and also in the capture of Negroes for transport to the slave markets of the Turkish Empire. And in the west

Christian traders, Spanish, Portuguese, and British were engaged in the capture or purchase of Negroes for transport to America.

The total consequences are clear. First, Africa was in process of being divided into a Muslim half and a Christian half. The balance was early shifted in favour of the Muslims by the British suppression of the slave-trade in the Atlantic. Later, however, the Arab trade also was suppressed. Secondly, the Negro slaves captured by the Muslims, as we saw, disappeared. Thirdly, the Christian half has multiplied several times in America and recently in Europe. Lastly, the population of Negro Africa is certainly today greater than it would have been in the absence of the slave-trade and the colonial government which followed it.

The motives of the people in Britain and the U.S. in suppressing, first the slave-trade, then slavery itself, like those of the Russian Government in abolishing serfdom, were mixed. The British activity had two main aspects. On the one hand, the Royal Navy, which would otherwise have been largely idle after Waterloo, was for forty years actively policing the seas with a little moral support from the Christian powers. On the other hand, large sums had to be paid in compensation to British slave owners (like Mr Gladstone's father) and to the Spanish and Portuguese Governments who complained bitterly of the injustice that was being done to them.

Meanwhile, however, profitable transactions continued. The Lancashire cotton industry, which Engels has described, was based on wage labour in England and on slave labour in the U.S. The two were ruthless in different ways. The slave owner incurred responsibility for employment and maintenance. The factory owner incurred no such responsibility. And in due course when the British needed labour to develop agriculture in the West Indies, or railways in Africa, they had to restore a system of indentured labour for Indians and Chinese (described by Tinker). This might yield a greater profit to the employer and it bore a prettier name than slavery. As Marx pointed out, we must not take at their face value labels for the different kinds of exploitation of labour.

III *Emancipation in America*

The North American colonies, both the English in Virginia and the Dutch in New Amsterdam, already in the 1640s took up the Spanish habit of importing Negro slaves, first from the West Indies and then directly from Africa. Boston carried them; Charleston bought them. The institution of slavery, however (as Fogel, Genovese, and others have shown), took a different form from that developing in the Caribbean and Brazil. There were no wars between colonies. The plantations were smaller. The relations of owner and slave were personal since there was no caste of Mulatto or Creole overseers between the white and the black. And, although the Negro religious rituals and witchcraft persisted, they were restrained by the Christian or European behaviour of the masters.

This system of plantation slavery grew very naturally out of the paternalistic, rural, and feudal society in England from which the southern planters sprang. But in the northern states there were societies of an urban, industrial, and puritanical origin of different cast of mind. Between the two a racial and cultural divergence had been clear from the beginning. But it had been suppressed during the movement for independence.

How was this done? The Declaration of Independence with its assertion of human equality had an effect in creating the modern world as great as that of the Communist Manifesto. And for both the effect was due as much to its falsehood as to its truth. For of the fifty-five signatories in Philadelphia twenty-two were slave owners. In the matter of slavery the price of their signatures has been exacted over the two centuries which have followed.

The principle that all men were created equal was a basis for getting the working classes to fight in 1776. But when ten years later the war was won, the principle had to be put into practice. A different phrase was now used in Philadelphia. The constitution of 1787 spoke of 'the rights of free men'. There were other men 'held to service' who might escape from it. They were to be returned to any party who claimed them. They were the Negro slaves. The word *slave*, some would have spelt out. The constitution deleted it. Southern planters and Northern traders had their way.

The sequel to the American Revolution was the French Declaration of the Rights of Man which foretold the end of the monarch who had intervened to save the U.S. It also suggested that Negro slaves in France and her colonies should be set free. But by March 1790 Paris like Philadelphia had discovered that the Rights of Man did not apply to Negro slaves, not at least in Haiti. There followed the bitter revolts, the British interventions, the Black Emperors, the Napoleonic betrayals, the breaks and reunions with France which ended in 1825, to be continued by a succession of bloody revolutions and interventions until today.

What had happened in France had set the ball rolling, as we can see from the sequence of events (Table 8.1). The driving force in the

Table 8.1 *The decline of slavery*

1772	Lord Mansfield rules that slave status is illegal in England
1776, 1789	U.S. and French Declarations of Principle
1792	Denmark agrees to end slave trade in 1802
1794	U.S. limits slave trade
1802	Bonaparte revokes French abolition of slavery
1807, 1811	U.K. makes slave-trade, first a civil, then a criminal offence
1808	U.S. stops importation of slaves
1813–29	Spanish American states abolish slavery on independence
1814	Congress of Vienna hopes the trade will stop. U.S. and U.K. agree to stop it
1815	France abolishes trade (Louis XVIII not Napoleon)
1815	Portugal stops its trade North of Equator (i.e. except from Angola to Brazil)
1820, 1830	U.K. pays £400,000 to Spain and £300,000 to Portugal to stop trade completely
1850	Brazil ends trade
1814–30	U.K. navy's blockade causes: (i) over-crowding of slave-running ships (ii) over-working of reduced slave communities
1833	Abolition of slavery throughout British Empire. £20 million compensation to owners
1833–8	British attempts to bridge transition to freedom by indenture fail
1835–8	Boer farmers trek from Cape Colony to escape control
1861–5	Civil War in U.S. to avert secession of slave states
1863–5	Emancipation of slaves in U.S.
1873–88	Brazil liberates slaves
1861–3	Serfdom abolished in Russia
1907	Slave-market abolished in Constantinople
1962	Slaves in Arabia (0·25 million) declared free by King Faisal

Note: see also Fogel and Engerman's *Chronology of Emancipation*.

movement for abolition however came from Britain. This country had for two centuries provided the men, ships, and capital which kept the slave-trade going. But now she was employing her navy in scouring the Atlantic and Indian Oceans of Christian and Muslim slave traders alike. This abrupt reversal of policy was made by a new class which came into power after 1832 and saw its own Industrial Revolution as a more effective means of exploiting the resources of the earth than the employment of slaves. Free labour was more profitable. It was free to move; free to work and, unlike the slave, free also to be out of work. The meaning of this other revolution emerged gradually during the nineteenth and twentieth centuries. It emerged in three great fields of activity and conflict, in America, especially the U.S., in Africa, and lastly and unexpectedly in Europe itself.

Consider first the United States. The early presidents took a temperate view of racial equality. Four of the first six were Virginian slave-owners, notably enlightened as indeed most of them were. The next nine were perhaps less enlightened for under them the native Indians were largely expelled from their homelands. But the less guilt they felt about the red men who were dead, the more they felt about the black men who were alive and visible. The issue of slavery became a focus of cleavage. Not that the attitude of the white to the black was sharply different on the two sides of the Mason–Dixon line. Slavery remained legal in New York until 1820; everywhere the Negro was despised and intermarriage was condemned or prohibited.

The war of 1861 to 1865 was the first civil war with conscription on both sides—for the whites. Over half a million white men were killed in trying to solve the problem of the black men which had been evaded in 1776 and 1787. When the war was won, a 13th Amendment to the Constitution was passed: 'Neither slavery nor involuntary servitude . . . shall exist in the U.S.' It might then have been thought that the knot was untied. Unfortunately, however, the knot was tighter than had appeared.

The emancipation of white serfs in Europe had taken 500 years of strife. It is far from complete today. Could the emancipation of black slaves come in the U.S. by the stroke of a pen? During the war the 4 million Negro slaves in the South continued to labour for their masters. Only the craftsmen slipped away when the Yankee armies approached. There were race riots in New York, not in Charleston. In the North, where there were a million free Negroes they offered to fight, and nearly 200,000 joined the Union Army; but the Negro regiments were segregated and paid at a lower rate than white men. The white men it now appeared were fighting not to establish equality between the races or to remove the barriers between them, but rather for the right to exploit the Negro as a free man. The paradox was recognized by Trollope on the spot in 1862. 'The Negro', he wrote, 'is not the white man's equal by nature. But to the free Negro in the northern States this inequality is increased by the white man's hardness to him.'

The first conflict was between President and Congress. Lincoln's successor, Andrew Johnson, was a Southerner. In May he proclaimed an Amnesty and Home Rule for the South. In December Southern delegates to Congress appeared in Washington. They were all white. They had already established for the freed Negroes the segregated, deprived, voteless status they thought proper for the black man. Congress retorted by trying to impeach the President, by refusing to admit the Southerners, by voting the 14th Amendment which asserted that all Negroes (unlike the Indians) were citizens, and all citizens, irrespective of property, could vote. Northern military governments were set up for three years in the South and the Southern delegates then reappeared in Washington including twenty-eight black men. To make doubly sure a 15th Amendment (in 1870) required that no man should be denied the vote 'on grounds of Race, Colour or previous servitude'.

All this was of no avail. Northern politicians had moved in to take over the responsibilities and profits of the South 'with both arms round the Negro's neck and both hands in his pocket'. The Negroes had had five years to go to school. Four thousand public schools and one university had been set up but the Negro literacy rate had increased only from 10 to 20 per cent. The rapture of the Abolitionists was giving way to disenchantment, largely due to an abundant capacity and determination among the Southern whites to recover control of their states.

The recovery was both legal and illegal. Legally they excluded the Negro from voting and jury service by a literacy test. They segregated him in public life and education by gang intimidation of the Ku Klux Klan, by the constant threat—not only in the South—of lynching. And finally they had him back in economic servitude. How did this happen?

When Britain ended slavery and Russia ended serfdom they compensated the owners. Lincoln would have done the same but his successors, remembering their dead, felt no other price need be paid. The slave owners, however, were in a position to demand a price. They held the land. They could employ their former slaves as wage-earners or share-croppers. The Negroes took the brunt of the impoverishment the war had brought to those lands which, a short time before, had seemed to be the richest States in the Union.

Meanwhile, Negroes in the South who sought work in the towns found themselves shut out of white trade unions. The first violent Negro response came with racial riots when the military occupation ended. The Federal Government turned sour. 'The whole public', President Grant declared in 1875, 'are tired out with these annual autumnal outbreaks in the South'. Two years earlier the Supreme Court, noting the trend of opinion, had begun to rule against interfering with the white man's South.

What then was the position of the former slaves? The majority preferred to work where they had always worked as tenants now of the master they already knew. They had not sought freedom. But now they were free they could be unemployed. They were no longer the capital protected by the white planter: they were the labour competing with the white worker. They began to move north as the escaping slaves had done for 200 years, but now by rail instead of by road. The movement was from southern fields to northern cities. At first it was a movement of the 'talented tenth'. The census of 1860 had scored 12 per cent of Southern Negroes as 'Mulatto' and the migrants were the enterprising products of hybridization who believed themselves capable of coping with the problems of white city life.

From the free Negroes of the North and these early migrants after emancipation have sprung the middle or professional class of Negroes in the United States. Its record is less distinguished than that of the impoverished European immigrants, notably the Jewish refugees from Russia, who were arriving in New York at the same time. But it made its own creditable contribution to American life. Some started as caterers and entertainers, notably the Creole musicians from New Orleans. Others were teachers like the admirable Booker Washington. He has told us his own unforgettable history. Other stories were those derived from the lower end of the spectrum. And it is the whole spectrum that we have to follow into the American cities.

The diversity of the Negro community did not help to break down the barrier to mixing with the whites. Its size, as one-tenth of the whole population of the United States, probably strengthened the white fear of interbreeding. How then should social relations be regulated? The form of the American problem was inevitably legal and the crucial issue was inevitably education. Three important steps were taken.

The first was the 14th Amendment to the Constitution in 1868 which declared that all races were legally and politically equal. At this time, however, there was no public schooling in the South. When the schools appeared the Supreme Court had to decide what equality meant. In public schools it decided in 1890 that black and white should be 'separate but equal'. But after sixty years it became clear that separate could not be equal: the white pupils would always get the better teachers. Hence, in 1954, the judgement was reversed. Separation was discovered to have become 'unconstitutional'. Here again a practical difficulty arose. If communities were separated the children would have to be artificially and compulsorily scrambled. In the end, however, two great social lessons have been learned. The first is that education (as we have seen) has to begin at home and equality is therefore never attainable in a society organized by families. The second is that forced integration, which is intended to remove conflict, often succeeds in arousing it.

IV *The Free Negro*

About 1890 a second movement of Negroes began in the U.S. It was a mass movement of what the earlier migrants felt to be the southern relics, the lower orders, of Negro society, those born since emancipation. The end of the plantation system had ruined both the planters and the Negroes. Now its ruin was driving out the surplus Negro population. To be sure, they believed that the streets of New York were paved with gold, as indeed they were, for a few. The Southern States tried to stop the drain of manual labour but the Supreme Court in 1911, observing that serfdom was replacing slavery in the South, and valuing the free Negro in the North, vetoed the stoppage. By this time West Indian Negroes had joined the stream. They formed settlements, first, in the more decayed parts of lower Manhattan which were now being deserted by Jewish and Italian immigrants. The chief of these, San Juan Hill, was a field of battle between the Negroes and the Irish. And the police were Irish for before 1911 there were no Negro patrolmen.

About 1900 the scene again changed. A light-skinned Negro, Philip A. Payton, found that if a single house in the respectable white suburb of Harlem was bought and let to a Negro family, the white neighbours would quickly sell their properties at reduced prices. These houses could then be let to Negro families who, living at a much higher density would pay an enhanced rent. In this way the block would soon be transferred from white to Negro occupation at great profit to the realtor.

Payton's method of 'block-busting' made him the father of the Negro ghetto. Between 1920 and 1930, 119,000 whites moved out of Harlem and 164,000 Negroes moved in. In 1926 there were 336 people per acre in the Negro area and the rents had doubled. Negro landlords fleeced both races without discrimination but (as Osofsky puts it) the Negro was having to pay in rent for the depreciation his presence induced in the value of the property.

The two World Wars speeded up the transformation of New York and other northern cities. The sudden rise in demand for manual labour was short-lived but when it fell the ghettos were established. The Negro's emergency value and his northward migration had fixed him in a new niche to which he was even less well adapted than the white urban proletariat. He was fixed most securely by a rate of reproduction from which the African restraints of war and disease, and the plantation restraint of controlled marriage, had both been removed.

A new hybrid civilization, if that is the right word, had been created. By 1928 the brothels in Harlem numbered sixty-one and all but six were white-owned. The churches however numbered over 140 and they all belonged to Negroes. Of these eighty-six were 'storefront' conventicles improvised by such sects as 'The Metaphysical Church of the Divine Investigation' or 'The Sanctified Sons of the Holy Ghost'. The congregations were gullible. The noise was terrific.

This atmosphere with its witch-doctors, its faith-healers and diviners, its sellers of amulets and cockroach rum, made Harlem something new, a solid African city, in a framework of American wealth and technology. With prohibition in 1918 Harlem soon became the citadel of law-breaking. To gambling, prostitution, and liquor, the trade in narcotics was conveniently added. And there it is today, the world centre of the heroin traffic where pushers and addicts assemble. In due course, from New York and other cities, addiction to drugs spread from blacks to whites and from town to country. Meanwhile, murder, a rare event on the plantations, and now chiefly of black by black, reached a world climax in New York and Detroit. These were the first of the *no-go areas* which were to follow the Negro into the white man's cities.

The industrial expansion of the United States attracted to its northern cities not only the Negro but a variety of no less impoverished Europeans. Before the Civil War there had been the Irish refugees from famine after 1846, and the German refugees from oppression after 1848. Afterwards came the Jewish refugees from pogroms in Russia, and southern Italians and Greeks escaping from over-population. Nearly all these immigrants arrived in New York destitute and unable to speak the language. Although none of them fared so ill as the Negro at first they presented a lamentable picture. The prosperous Anglo-Saxon natives felt (as Robertson puts it) that they were being dispossessed. Their prosperity they were being asked to share with people who seemed alien to them. They were not troubled by the Negro. He was apart: segregated socially and racially, separate in school, in church, and in the graveyard. But about these other breeds they were sorely troubled.

Hence, following the pause in immigration for the first World War, came the Immigration Quotas. They were established by the U.S. in 1920 and 1924. In order to preserve the Anglo-Saxon predominance in the country (without giving too much offence) the proportions of each nationality to be admitted were to agree with those estimated as already settled in that crucial year 1890.

These quota rules have been the chief factor determining the quantity and the quality of the United States population today. They might of course be said to have locked the stable door after the colt was stolen. They might also be said to have locked the wrong door. This was inevitable when rough rules are made for private reasons by public compromise among ill-informed legislators. The British and French quotas were largely filled by Negroes from the West Indies who moved into Harlem. Jews escaping from Nazi Germany found themselves under the United States quota for Poland which did not exist in 1890, so they had to go to South America instead of the North. Meanwhile the most dangerous operators from Sicily or Corsica found no difficulty in entering a country where their kindred were already ensconced along with their potential victims, the Negroes.

The fate of the Negro carried as a slave to the plantations of Virginia and moving of his own free will to the city of New York followed a pattern which we can see repeated a little later, after 1940, in South America and with suitable variations in Europe and Asia. In the great cities of Rio de Janeiro, Caracas and Santiago, wealth, derived from technical industry and the operations of skilled European enterprise, has given the opportunity for unskilled employment to the impoverished Negro, Mulatto, and Mestizo peasant populations of South America. All these with Catholic encouragement have propagated beyond their capacity for well-rewarded employment. They have been drawn into the cities. In these tropical climates they have not needed the massive houses required in New York. They have set themselves up in shanty towns which city governments eager for their labour and not needing to pay well for it, allowed them to build. Hence the *favelas*. They did not demand that their health or education should be provided for. All they sought or could seek was survival. And what they got in addition was a propagation which has guaranteed their continued destitution.

V *White Serf, Black Slave*

The black slaves of the United States and the white serfs of Russia, after as long as 400 years of bondage, were freed at almost the same time. The time that has elapsed since these historic acts of liberation allows us to compare the hopes that attended them and the disappointments that have followed them.

In the first place we see that, between serf and slave, the distinction is traditional rather than practical. With both the master had power of life and death, of buying and selling, of marriage and breeding. The servant's treatment depended on the character of the master and the judgement of his society. Russian serfs were on the whole worse treated than Negro slaves in the U.S.A. before liberation; and better treated afterwards. The difference is reflected in the accounts of Kropotkin, Fogel and Engerman and many others; and also in what we know of the earlier insurrections rare in the U.S.A., but frequent and terribly suppressed in Russia.

In other respects the two experiences show us significant parallels. In both an enterprising and often hybrid fraction of the liberated people moved off the land into the cities. In Russia they gave an impetus to social and industrial revolution and after 1917 they may be said to have contributed to a new but hardly improved governing class. But in both countries the majority who remained on the land suffered grave disappointment. In Russia this was due to oppressive taxation by the Tsars and to effective re-enserfment by the Soviets followed by the extermination of the Kulaks: we can see the errors of policy in all their cumulative effects. With the bulk of the Negroes, on the other hand, the tale of woe finds its source, not in what happened after liberation, or during slavery, but to the fact that in freedom the technical and urban development of the white majority in the United States did not offer them a helpful environment. If liberation had been selective and gradual, as it was in Western Europe, its results would have been happier in both Russia and the United States. That was something which was rendered impossible by the political character and the sudden development of both countries forced on them from outside by the Industrial Revolution.

VI *The Struggle in Africa*

In imagination we have all seen the dramatic episode when Henry Stanley met David Livingstone at the Arab slave depot of Ujiji in 1871. But its meaning changes with the passage of time. Now we may see it as the encounter between the contrasted European interests in the land and in the peoples of Africa; between the urge to put something into Africa and the urge to get something out; between the desire to teach, reform and convert, and the desire to plunder, to exploit or to govern.

These European motives and the tension between them have proved to be the creative force in Africa during the century which has followed.

The climax of African exploration, and indeed of African history, came six years later when Stanley crossed the continent from Zanzibar to Boma and sorted out the geography of the Nile and Congo basins. European planning and technology, mapping and medicine, and European heroism made this achievement possible.

Stanley's discoveries and his administration enabled King Leopold of the Belgians to establish the 'Congo Free State' in 1885 as a private corporation for ransacking the country. But his venture was terminated in 1908 after the British consul in Boma, the tragic Roger Casement, had exposed its atrocities to the sight of Europe. The King's initiative had in fact awakened Europe to both the opportunities and the dangers of Africa. It led to the Berlin Congress which agreed to divide Africa into colonies where each European power, Portugal and Spain, Britain and France, Germany, Italy, and Belgium would give what it wished and take what it could.

How much was to be given and taken was debated in each European country for the next thirty years. In both France and England there had long been parties for and against colonization. How much of Mozambique Portugal offered to Britain for 3 million pounds in 1897 is debatable but the pro-colonial interests of each power had no doubts of their own purpose: it was predatory.

They proceeded to get out the minerals and to fell the timber. Then they turned to agriculture and developed cocoa and coffee, cotton and rubber, for export. Following the French example in Algeria, the British took some of the best, but previously uncultivated, land in Rhodesia and Kenya for their own settlement; in consequence the population of these colonies, African as well as European, began to grow. But it did so only with the help of immigrant skills. The government, surveying, engineering, and medicine, were European. The workers who built the roads and railways were Indian. The traders were Indian, Syrian, Greek and Armenian. The human apparatus of European technology and world commerce began to be assembled. The closed tribal societies which had been governed for 2000 years by massacre and mutilation, sorcery and slavery, were opened to the light. For the first time the world began to see Africa and Africa began to see the world.

The same illumination had come a century earlier to Asia. But now the effect was more startling. In the course of sixty years, from 1885 to 1945, war was almost eliminated—not in Europe but in Africa. Disease was mapped and reduced. Locusts were tracked and controlled. Game animals, at first slaughtered, began to be preserved and protected.

The Arab slave trade was curtailed. Human sacrifice and cannibalism were forced into the background. But other African habits proved profoundly resistant to European influence. The tribe seemed to decay but was still supreme. For cultivators, slash and burn agriculture was still the method. And for herdsmen, wives, slaves, and cattle were still the symbols of wealth. The practices of trade were resented and resisted. The ways remained open for the destruction of the land. The possibilities of improving health and agriculture and avoiding famine were obstructed everywhere by superstition.

Meanwhile missionaries had taught their pupils European languages opening the way to colonial employment. A thousand Negro tribes could be recognized, everyone differing in character and ability from its neighbours. In the Congo it was the Baluba who ran the civil service and in French West Africa the Dahomeyans. In Nigeria the Ibo were unpopular but indispensable. In Kenya, already in 1903, the destiny of the wily Kikuyu was foreseen by Meinertzhagen. And when a university was set up in Blantyre it was the tribes in the north of Malawi that took all the honours. Universities and military schools however had their decisive effect, not in science, scholarship, or commerce, but in the natural fields of African effort which are, in all combinations, eloquence, politics, and warfare.

Eloquence and politics came first for in demanding *uhuru*, or 'majority rule', African politicians found a sympathetic echo in the Governments of the U.S.A. and the U.S.S.R. The leaders of the new superpowers of 1945, believing in freedom for all parties, wished to see Africa opened, as India had been, to the teaching, the trade, and the protection which they could now afford. Also, for the U.S.A., there were openings for capital investment and mineral exploitation. There followed, from 1958 to 1976, an epoch of decolonization and the emergence of forty black Republics.

The governments of the new states, whose boundaries were mainly those laid down by the Berlin Congress, were set up by the leading exponents of liberation in each. Constitutions were adopted to preserve human rights, establish representative government, and enforce the law. The Charter of the United Nations was accepted with enthusiasm, and delegates were appointed to its organizations and agencies. Missions were sent to industrial capitals and the World Bank to obtain loans for the purchase of equipment and the arms which would be needed to settle external disputes and to assert internal authority.

The results of these activities had certain characteristics in common. Any ruler who survived did so by making himself head of a disciplined party connected with a police and military establishment and having a tribal or racial basis. Then, with the opposition in jail, and himself as President for Life, he could make the laws as he needed them. It was soon clear (in 1964 to Elspeth Huxley) that no Negro Head of State would ever resign. In fact none has done so although many have been assassinated or deposed. Insurgency has usually failed against the army's equipment. But in the Congo, the mines, and in Nigeria and Angola, the oil, were too important to be left to chance and the powers took a hand. Rebellion also has torn Sudan, Chad, and Abyssinia. There have been five years of massacre in Uganda and fifteen in Ruanda.

Behind this new life of Africa, black and white governments, white corporations, and modern versions of the pre-colonial interloper, are all extracting the assets of the continent. The general pattern is familiar. It follows the lines of what has been described in Latin America since 1908 as 'dollar diplomacy'. Now it has the additional interest of a competition for military bases between capitalist and communist powers. For the people of Africa, however, operations at a lower level have had a different kind of effect which was already clear from Hunter's map of Africa in 1969: the dispersal of refugees between thirty of the new African states. This map showed the results of tribal conflicts among Negroes, as well as of political expedients among their rulers.

In Ghana, the cocoa industry established by the British had attracted some 2 million immigrants, mostly Africans, who had contributed to the prosperity of the people and the colony. Most of these, half of them children, were expelled at two weeks notice (*Times*, 17 December 1969). By contrast with these inhumanities the refusal of the Tanzanian government to employ non-Tanzanians seems the extremity of moderation.

The expulsions of non-Negro minorities are better known since they were the people who, having introduced administration, industry, agriculture, and trading, had prospered under colonial rule. The Europeans went first. Then the Indians of East Africa. These were expelled over the years from Kenya and all in one year, 1972, from Uganda. Next were the people in West Africa with Syrian and Lebanese passports who were, in race and religion, of Greek and Armenian origin. These were expelled suddenly from Nigeria by a decree of March 1972.

The short-term purpose of expulsion was to confiscate the property of strangers for the benefit of the native government. But the long term effect on each African state is that it destroys the cooperation of people of different tribes and races by which the African colonies had developed and by which indeed all social, cultural, and of course racial, improvement depends. We have already seen how unpopular are alien groups who are noticeably prosperous, like Jews in Christian countries or Chinese in Muslim countries, when they live apart from the natives. For this reason the British had restricted Indian immigration into the Sudan in the 1930s. The constructive method of discrimination is, of course, not by race but by work, not by expulsion but by taxation. In this colonial governments could succeed but African governments, having begun by expelling their colonial administrators, were defeated.

The outward forms of Negro governments vary widely. At one end we see the Muslim Amin of Uganda. He repeats the violence of his pagan predecessor; the Kabaka Mutesa we may recall burnt his seventeen catamites alive on their conversion to Christianity in 1864. Or there is Marshal Bokassa of the Central African Republic, known as Papa Boc from his use of execution squads for public flogging to death on Haitian lines (*Times*, 2 August 1972). This ruler was converted to Islam on 19 October 1976, and declared himself Emperor on 5 December of that year. At the other end we see the Liberian oligarchy now completing 150 years of dominion with aboriginal serfdom in the background and the U.S. rubber industry in close support. Behind this political variety there is one continuous pattern: the police state with a concentration of wealth in the hands of a few individuals and families dividing the profit with foreign interests, a pattern familiar to us in Latin America and now characteristic of the Third World.

Naturally, in these circumstances, proposals for federation made by the colonial powers have all been repudiated by the Negro successor states. They all subscribe to the United Nations but the responsibilities of cooperation have proved to be as intolerable between the states as between parties within the states. Today it might therefore seem that there is only one Negro state which can present honesty in the process or decency in the results of government, namely the Republic of Cuba which is known to have dispatched a Negro army for the liberation of Angola in 1975. This, however, would be a misunderstanding for Cuba has a predominantly white population. And when the communist dictator, Dr Fidel Castro, seized power in 1959 he was in fact, after sixty-one years, restoring the rule of a native Spaniard to the former island colony. And he now has 6000 (white) Russian advisers.

A question now arises: what preserves governments in Negro Africa which do so little good to the majority of Africans? Their first safeguard is tribalism in the absence of a professional class. Their next safeguard is the double fence of debts to foreign interests and the arms provided in return which enable the dictator to say to his subjects: 'I have the Maxim gun: you have not'. And the third safeguard is the inability of the powers to agree on what might take the place of these independent governments—which applies also to the one state in

Africa which has for a long time known how to run its own affairs. That is the Republic of South Africa.

VII *South Africa*

In South Africa and in Rhodesia European minorities control the state by excluding the Negro or Bantu majorities, and also the hybrid or 'coloured' and Indian minorities, from any part in government, by segregating them in special townships or 'homelands', and also by prohibiting interbreeding. How did this come about?

The British took over the Dutch settlement in Cape Colony in 1807 and began to settle the country themselves. When they prohibited slave-owning in 1835, those Dutch or Afrikaner farmers who were most offended, all members of the fundamentalist Dutch Reformed Church, migrated and set up the Boer Republics of the Orange Free State and the Transvaal. This 'Great Trek' was the first of several heroic episodes in their history. Forty years later their farming lands were found to include the richest diamond and gold fields in the world. The discovery was the work of foreign prospectors just as it was with the Arab oil wells. The wars which followed may be seen as a struggle to control these mines. The strength of the whole British Empire was needed in three years fighting to crush the little Boer Republics in 1901.

Five years after this struggle a Liberal government in Britain reversed this colonial policy. In 1910 (excluding three British-protected Negro territories) it established the Union of South Africa as a self-governing dominion. This act of liberation was as naive as any, for it meant that the Afrikaners had a slight but resolute majority within the white minority. They were in a position to take over control of the whole country from which they had earlier separated themselves and to remove the British safeguards for native peoples.

They were in a position to reverse the effects, not only of their defeat in 1901, but also of their exile in 1835. This reversal by two parallel moves they skilfully proceeded to undertake. Their first move was to establish their principles of white supremacy, principles which were uncompromising both in a religious and in an economic sense. They required racial segregation in land, in employment, in education, and in sexual relations. This policy was given its extreme form by a Dutch immigrant, Hendrik Verwoerd. He called it *apartheid.*

Here was a method of organizing a society of many races in a way known throughout history and best seen at work today in India under the name of *caste*. In South Africa, *apartheid* has been imposed by a small minority of the population through changes in law over a period of fifty years. In India, on the contrary, caste has developed as a relation between many layers of society by consent of all and as part of the evolution of custom and of social structure over a period of 3000 years. It is a system which law has never imposed and has recently failed to remove.

The second Afrikaner move was to break the detested British connection which stood in the way of the first part of their programme. Success was achieved by Verwoerd with a well-planned referendum in 1961. The Union seceded from the British Commonwealth and the way was open to establish a new order of a kind which was not unlike that appearing at the same time throughout black Africa; it proved to be indeed a tribal government in charge of a police state.

South Africa became in this way the only legally stratified society in the world today based on unchangeable hereditary servitude. It is of a kind foreshadowed in the Pentateuch since 4 million whites (2 million being Afrikaners) rule and exploit 17 million blacks and 3 million mixed or coloured and Indian people. It also became a superb example of the efficiency, administrative, technical, and legal, of a small determined and coherent European community, with only a slight Negro admixture (about 7 per cent) in its ruling class. Progress and profit, with law and order, were its calvinistically ordained aims. Or, as Americans used to say, its Manifest Destiny.

Rhodesia like the Transvaal is based on a white expedition of settlement and conquest from Cape Town. It began in 1889. In two wars between 1893 and 1898 the followers or emissaries of Cecil Rhodes, the Cape Colony Prime Minister, subdued the Matabele and the Mashona and set up a capital named Salisbury after the British Prime Minister. It was *à propos* of this campaign that Belloc wrote: 'We have the Maxim gun: they have not.'

In Rhodesia, as in South Africa, however, European methods in agriculture sustained an increasing African as well as European population. But it existed side by side with a primitive farming compatible with native tradition and witchcraft (*Times*, 29 Jan. 1976). Consequently, when threatened by the British Government in 1965, this colony made a Unilateral Declaration of Independence resembling those made earlier by the United States of America and the Union of South Africa. It was also largely for the same reason since what they all wanted was freedom to treat the native peoples and their lands as their own property.

The Rhodesians had approached their problem also in their traditional way. In 1903 they had made sexual intercourse between black and white a criminal offence, as it now is in South Africa, but with this difference that, as formerly in the Southern United States, only the black male can be an offender. And after Independence they were able to introduce all the controls by which 'parity' is established. This means that the land is equally divided between the 5 million Africans and 250,000 Europeans. Likewise the funds for education. It may be thought that for the whites here, as for the Indians in East Africa, the object is to get all they can out of the country for themselves as quickly as possible. But we must remember that the black rulers in black Africa (although they begin with the promise of majority rule) want just the same thing: they are merely, in general, less effective in getting it.

Here then is a paradox of exploitation. The Europeans have deprived the Bantu population of any political rights and subjected them to the same control over movement that is used in communist countries for the whole population. By doing so the two white governments have given their Indian immigrants (who have not been expelled) and the Bantu a standard of living and housing and even of education that has for seventy years attracted their kinsmen from outside their frontiers. Their conditions are worse than those of migrant workers who move legally into northern Europe; but better than those of vagrant workers who move into the shanty towns of South America; or indeed the normal resident majority of inhabitants in Calcutta or Jakarta. To these advantages of urban South Africa may be added a certain freedom from witchcraft and ritual murder, recurrent warfare and corrupt administration.

The price exacted for these benefits has been the policy of apartheid: a policy which has become worse than the slavery it superseded because, as elsewhere, it has replaced agriculture by industry and personal partnership by corporate exploitation. It has been followed by the coexistence of whites with overwhelming numbers of black populations who have become something between enemies and slaves. But it also grew out of the need of those black populations who, under white rule and by white rule, have been caught in the universal industrial treadmill. They have multiplied beyond their own unaided capacity to feed and employ themselves. And every year this need and this incapacity, as we shall see, are growing greater.

VIII *Colonization in Reverse*

With the Independence of India in 1947 the U.K. Government had to consider the rights of movement within an Empire whose future political prospects were uncertain. Inasmuch as the relationship was being dissolved, not by force, but ostensibly by amicable arrangement, the Home Government wished to preserve the simulacrum of Empire. This it did by offering the privilege of British nationality to all former subjects who chose to accept it. Under the British Nationality Act of 1948 they received passports as citizens of 'U.K. and Colonies'. The inhabitants of the British Isles only slowly discovered the unforeseen consequences of this momentous step. They found that they had abandoned the right, which they had successfully defended for 900 years against a succession of European assaults, one of them quite recent, of keeping their small over-populated islands for themselves.

This last imperial gesture was seen in various lights by the rulers of the newly liberated colonies and their subject peoples. African states issued their own passports. Their Indian minorities (now described as Asian) foresaw trouble. They usually chose to take British passports. Since their enterprise in trade had made the Indians the richest members of the African communities amongst which they lived, the Governments of Kenya and Uganda soon realized, as we have seen, what economic assets they would gain by stripping and expelling them. Soon every former colony, discovering the population problem which Western medical science had bequeathed to it, began, first to exclude, and then to expel citizens of the other colonies, often at the point of a gun. The India of Mr Nehru rejected all Indian emigrants with British passports. From 1963 therefore the Indian and Pakistani minorities were laid on the British doorstep.

Meanwhile, however, another train of events had been set in motion in Jamaica. In 1948 a former German ship, the *Empire Windrush*, arrived there advertising cheap passages to England. It docked at Tilbury, loaded with men having British passports but few other resources, qualifications or invitations. This will never happen again, declared the astonished Colonial Secretary. But it did. In due course they were followed by a million others, dependants and kinsmen. The West Indian immigrants collected tightly in the over-populated industrial towns. Soon Brixton became the London counterpart of Harlem or indeed of Kingston in Jamaica. The supply of cheap unskilled labour was welcome to employers at the time. British Railways, now a nationalized industry, advertised for more. Nor did the trade unions object to an invasion of men who would do the worst paid work and would be the first to be laid off in the unlikely event of a return of unemployment.

The British Treasury, for its part, perhaps knowing of the Negro's use in strike-breaking in New York, reckoned on a 'counter-inflationary' effect. Soon a new population had been bred with claims for accommodation, education, health, and welfare for themselves and for their posterity; these claims had been fixed in the U.K. in 1948, the year the immigration began. The young men competed with the natives for housing, women, and jobs. Some riots followed. This was colonization in reverse.

After fifteen years it had become clear that the flow must be checked. There was no idea of any plan, quantitative or qualitative. The possibility of any population policy was too unfamiliar to be considered. But coloured immigration somehow or other must be slowed down. Immigration Acts on the lines of an American Quota were therefore passed in 1962, 1969, and 1971. These proved ineffective owing to the unlimited number of dependants who were not excluded. And in 1965, the Government, having tried to cover up its discrimination against immigrants on grounds of race, promoted the first of several Race Relations Acts, fiercely denouncing any native citizen who might do the same.

Owing to the skill of the great trade unions, and the lack of skill of the management, the industrial expansion in Britain fortunately began to slow down in 1962. But in Europe it was otherwise. The formation of the Common Market, coinciding with the rapid expansion of oil supply, inaugurated an American-style period long desired by capitalists and communists alike of what they lovingly call 'economic growth'. And, as in the U.S., it inaugurated an unprecedented migration northward into the industrial cities: a movement to meet—if not create—the millennium.

The movement, which had long been known within Italy and Spain, was now international. France, hesitant at first even to accept her own *pieds noirs*, the Christian exiles from Algeria, now eagerly welcomed Muslims from Algeria, Morocco, Tunis, and Senegal as well as Christians from Portugal and Spain. Not quite eagerly enough, however, for soon (as with the Mexican chicanos in U.S., the Koreans in Japan, or the Indonesians in Singapore) the smuggling of illegal immigrants by ship, plane, and sealed van became an industry, a new kind of slave trade, profitable and also demoralizing. The same shanty towns known outside Lima or Colombo, now appeared in France under the name of *bidonvilles* (*Times*, 5 February 1973).

In exploiting this situation the Germans felt they could be more prudent and less scrupulous than the former guilty colonial powers. They refused to allow their indentured *Gastarbeiter* to bring in women and children. Nor did they allow them to vote or to stay without limit. Greeks, Turks, and Croats obediently returned home to their neglected fields laden with the showy fruits of Western technology. But they returned home without any mortgage on the future of Germany. Here we see the closest parallel with *apartheid* in South Africa. For a part of the Afrikaner policy is to use the blacks, to separate them from their women, to restrict their breeding, and to return them, modestly rewarded, to their 'homelands'.

The most instructive situation is that of Holland, a rich but very crowded country. The Dutch wished to be independent of their last colony, Dutch Guiana or Surinam, thereby escaping both the odium and the obligations of colonial rule. They fixed the date at 25 November 1975. The Negro ex-slave population were generally pleased with this prospect which they took to imply Negro rule. But the Hindus and the Amerindians foresaw disaster. And the propertied Negroes (or 'Creoles') hurried to escape to Holland. Coming into Britain the immigrants from tropical colonies were equally diverse. They were the West Indian Christian Negroes, the Indians who were mainly Sikhs by religion and by race, and the Muslims who were either western Punjabis or eastern Bengalis (who were later to meet and fight in Bradford).

Each European country has thus received its own variety of ex-colonial immigrants. Each has had its hopes of advantage and exploitation. But each has been trapped, even in the short summer of prosperity, by the conflicts their governments, distracted by the pursuit of immediate wealth, were unable to foresee.

IX *Mankind on the Move*

In every migration we easily notice the sudden effects, good or bad, at the receiving end. We easily miss the slow effects, more often bad, at the giving end. One British gift to India was Western medicine. But in India today there is a greater dearth of medical care than anywhere in the world. Why? Because Indian governments are willing to lose medical skill by emigration to the U.K. and the U.S. Another kind of brain drain by the action of governments empties Africa of commercial skill. The painful principle declares itself that people will go where they are most valued; that good workers will go where there is good government; that bad workers will go anywhere to get fed. Every attempt at equalization, at homogenization, is frustrated by the natural variation in human character. Whatever governments may do, we find that men who have judgement and discrimination will use them in their own interests. How else could such men have survived?

We may deplore the result and label it as exploitation or colonialism, racialism or élitism, or even in athletics olympism. All our past evolution, we know, has been based on the action of our competitive instincts. But their action, we observe, at the present speed of invention, communication, and movement, now threatens to overwhelm us.

In these circumstances we naturally look at the example of the communist states working under the control of the Soviet Union. They have made the greatest efforts ostensibly to suppress competition by equalization. In doing so they have also had to suppress immigration and emigration, and all the initiative behind them. Even so, in the country the Soviet Government needs every man it can get but in the cities it cannot cope with overcrowding. Hence their need once more for internal passports. After sixty years of communism the Soviet Empire has 37 million farmers raising less than 200 million metric tons of grain per annum while the U.S.A. has 4·3 million farmers raising over 200 million tons (*Times*, August 1975). The Tsarist Empire exported grain. The Soviet Empire has to import it. Inefficiency gives a slowness of change with advantages which I shall consider in the next chapter. But they are not the advantages that the Soviet Government (or the Russian people) have been struggling to achieve.

The lessons to be learnt from colonization and decolonization under capitalist and communist management concern all human societies. In less than a century what has happened in the relations of advanced and primitive races and classes has recapitulated what happened millennia ago in the origins of society. But now both colonization and decolonization have come with such speed to people so ignorant of their own history, or so distorted in their imagination of it, that they (and their governments) have less notion than ever of the causes and consequences of what they are doing.

There are both real and imaginary histories of colonization. Marxist and also liberal theorists tell us that colonial powers are parasitic on their colonies. But in fact they were often giving as much as they took. Consequently as soon as they relinquished their colonies in Africa and elsewhere, the colonial peoples hurried to reverse their colonization. They hastened to fix again on their necks the yoke from which their leaders had been agitating to liberate them.

These political terms are of course fraudulent. The genuine historical process has been that the skilled and literate elements of society, scholars, traders, and craftsmen, have been moving northwards in Europe for 2000 years creating cities and creating employment within them for the surplus rural populations around them, surplus and impoverished by over-propagation. Now under the sudden stress of industrial expansion and sudden ease of communication they have drawn northwards even the surplus impoverished rural populations of the south including Hindu, Muslim and Negro Africa, and Asia.

The state of affairs which I have visualized at the beginning of the Agricultural or Neolithic Revolution, thus repeats itself before our eyes, but in reverse. Now agricultural immigrants are being drawn into the industrial countries, whereas six, seven and eight thousand years ago industrial immigrants were drawn into the agricultural Nuclear Zone: both by the prospect of being fed.

The distinction between the industrially developed countries and those agricultural countries whose governments want them to 'develop' into industrial countries remains, for it is an inborn human distinction. And we find little evidence that they are developing, except to their own lasting disadvantage. For they are still being exploited by the industrial countries who alone can provide the technical enterprise that industry needs. It is not merely that the people who do the developing expect to be paid for it, just as they did when they represented colonial powers. They also expect to take whatever it suits them to take. The effect is therefore still exploitation. But it is less efficient, more corrupt, and even more destructive of the environment and the natural resources of the earth.

On these grounds we must, for a moment, forego the luxury of thinking of the world as a place where groups of men, large and small, pursue their narrow interests from year to year. We must make the effort to stand back and think of mankind as a whole and the earth as a whole, with a past and a future. When we do so we find that our past evolution can now tell us something very clear about our future. And this knowledge compels us to ask a question altogether without precedent, namely how long do we expect that future to be? This is a problem of economics in evolution.

Chapter 9

Economics in Evolution

I *Man and Nature*

The hundred different ways of looking at the history of man are easy to separate but once separated, they are harder to put together again. The historical and archaeological evidences, the agricultural and industrial techniques, the principles of heredity and the problems of disease, the measurement of intelligence and the transmission of culture, the development of religious ideas and political institutions, all of these we need to put together in understanding the whole. But there is no part of our knowledge of man that is, or needs to be, so closely connected with all the rest as his housekeeping, his economics.

When man is seen in terms of individuals and groups whose services are of value to one another in arranging the work that will keep them alive, the values concerned cover the complete range in time and space between the immediate individual and the past and future of all mankind and of all the planet. Yet there is no part that has been so readily separated and subdivided. Economists speaking of 'economic activity' come to believe that there are some kinds of human activity, some personal relationships or non-pecuniary advantages, that are not economic and can therefore be disregarded, a familiar simplification whenever statistical method takes a grip on science. The imponderables must be omitted.

We need to look at the parts of our economics, as the founders of the science did, both separately and together. We have to remember also one thing they did not know, namely that man has inhabited this planet for 5 million years in the past and his descendants may also inhabit it for 5 million years in the future: or as much of this as we can bear to include in our little universe.

In putting man's problems together what strikes us most now is that in our evolution we have acquired two connected but opposed faculties: an understanding of how to control nature and an understanding of ourselves as part of nature. The first has transformed and is transforming our relations with nature and with one another. The second has so far had very little effect at all.

The reason for this contrast is that taking control over nature has separated civilized men from their primitive ancestors and contemporaries and from their fears of nature. And in taking control civilized man has come to look upon himself as the Lord of Creation. His GOD, deserving capital letters, is a reflection of himself and his authority. The world has been made for him to enjoy, to dominate, and to exploit. And who can say him nay? This is especially a Jewish, a Christian, and a Muslim idea but it has been the belief of all rising aristocracies.

Man's understanding of himself as part of nature, to be sure, has always been there. Worldly men have often said *noblesse oblige*. Misgivings about nature have been voiced by mystics and they could be heard in the Old Testament. Not in the New Testament, nor through Christian teaching, however. For only through biological and evolutionary heresy in the last century, have they acquired a rational and a practical meaning. What is this heresy? It is that man today is not the end-all and be-all of creation. He is a part of an immense process of immeasurable duration. He is not the landlord but the tenant of the earth. He has obligations before he has rights. He has to justify himself, not on the Day of Judgement, but in the course of duty, as a good tenant or a bad tenant.

This idea of man as a trustee does not commend itself to the mass of mankind. It has not appeared in the manifestos of political parties whether capitalist or communist. Disaster may of course lead to a new insight, a religious conversion. The opposition between those who care too little and those who care too much may sometime dissolve. Meanwhile, however, we need to clear our minds on the issues. We need to give economics back the evolutionary dimension it demands.

The problems of economics, we can now see, have arisen in an evolutionary sequence; they have a natural history in which each step has conditioned what was to follow:

1. Nature and its resources, which were there before man and will be there in part after man.

2. Man and his populations, their numbers, multiplying in quantity and competing in quality, and demanding expansion of territory in an apparently unlimited world.

3. Man's inventions and discoveries; his tools for opening nature to his agriculture and his extraction of energy with its own evolutionary sequences; his weapons for making war; all increasing and diversifying his means of employment.

4. Man's production and consumption of goods, his interest in the hoarding of property which he is able to create, acquire, and preserve.

5. Man's practices of trade, barter, and exchange leading to the combination of societies as well as the notion of supply and demand; the genetic differentiation of producers and consumers in castes and classes, hence the division of labour and the pursuit of monopoly.

6. Man's bartering of work against maintenance with or without protection of the worker from unemployment, so that employment may be taken for life or a year or a day, organized as slave or serf, tenant or employee, or free man.

7. Man's invention of money, wages for work, income from capital, usury and investment, credit and debt, profit and profitability; and of spending as against saving.

8. Finally, taxes and subsidies, tariffs and tolls, civic and national income and debt, balance of trade and liquidity, ending up with a World Bank, and the pretended separation of politics, economics, and scientific understanding.

These elements appear in their numbered order. Numbers 1 and 2 are the object of study of the natural or experimental sciences; number 3 is the object of study of the historians of science and technology; numbers 4–8 have been the field of economics. They are all causally connected but their connections obey unusual rules. In the early stages of man's history the connections were almost wholly forward. Numbers 1 and 2 had great effects on number 3 and so on down the line. The resources of nature conditioned the survival and increase. Only later were the resources of nature seen to limit the feeding, the employment, and the survival of men.

II *Malthus*

The earliest men, like all other animals, were supporting themselves from the produce of a limited territory and were multiplying beyond the limits that that territory could support. Their physical and mental faculties, developed by selection and competition, enabled them to expand into a wider territory until they had occupied all the continents. The resources of these continents they discovered how to exploit by two main types of activity, namely agriculture and industry.

Only in the eighteenth century did overcrowding bring home the limits of these developments. The great naturalist Linnaeus for example noted that 'where population increases too much, envy and malignancy towards neighbours abound'. Twenty years later Malthus broached the problem in general and far-reaching terms: he explained (although he did not use these words) that the possibilities of multiplying men are infinite; the possibilities of feeding them on the earth are finite. When limits have apparently been reached during history, numbers have been curtailed by three methods: the public controls of war, famine, and pestilence, the private control by vice, and the private virtue of self-restraint when people like himself postponed marriage until they could afford to support the children that resulted.

It has taken the six generations of men who have followed the appearance of Malthus's statement to understand the spreading implications of his argument. First, we may ask, are the resources of the earth indeed limited? The expansion of man over new continents and their exploitation has been enlarged since Malthus by endless invention and enterprise. At the expense of primitive peoples, hereditary skills, and civilized customs, this exploitation has proceeded with a power which is now approaching a climax. It has also proceeded at the expense of the earth itself and in disregard of the future needs or claims of posterity. Why? Because men assumed that their descendants would always have reason to be grateful to them for what they had done: they were in credit.

This expansion and exploitation seemed for optimists to make nonsense of Malthus's limitation, of his day of reckoning. But now, after nearly two centuries, we know that his principles have a cogency beyond anything he could have realized. We can see how man's populations always expand to fit themselves into the space available to them. For example the populations of Europe and Africa were not diminished by 500 years of emigration to America. They were just what they would have been or a little more. The increased population of the New World today is thus a windfall or bonanza for the peoples migrating, free or slave, from the Old World.

Today, therefore, we can enter into Malthus's argument with a knowledge of the past that was beyond his ken. We know the limits of the earth. Engels might condemn Malthus's 'vile and infamous theory', and ask what is impossible for science? But now we know that not only the earth but science itself has its limitations. We also know how dependent the parts of life on the earth are on one another; how utterly we depend on plant life; that if plants disappeared all animals would fade away. Looking back we know that 10,000 years ago man had no cultivated plants or domesticated animals. And we know that without these things the human population would be quickly reduced to a hundredth part of its present numbers, fully employed but earning a poor and sordid living. And looking forward we know that one day our conditions will decay and life will become extinct. But we must wish to decay under our own control rather than by careless catastrophe. Thus our new knowledge gives an inexorable reality to Malthus's view of the future.

In successive editions of his book over the following thirty years Malthus argued the issues he had raised over a wide field of natural science, human experience and, to tidy matters up, divine revelation. The first thing we notice is that he relates human fertility with that of animals and plants. It is always excessive. And the checks to survival are always discriminating. 'The powers of selection, combination, and transmutation which every seed shows are truly miraculous. Who can imagine that these wonderful faculties are contained in these little bits of matter?' Darwin and Mendel, and their successors in the following century and a half, used almost the same phrases to refer to the experiments from which our present knowledge of evolution and genetics is derived. Further, foreshadowing Galton, Malthus adds: 'by an attention to breed, a certain degree of improvement, similar to that among animals, might take place among men'. The problem of quantity implied a problem of quality.

Malthus then takes these ideas and applies them to society. He refers to 'the want of frugality observable among the poor' so different from 'the petty tradesmen and small farmers'. He adds: 'Their present wants employ their whole attention, and they seldom think of the future. Even when they have an opportunity of saving, they seldom exercise it.'

Here Malthus is making a distinction between two social classes which, as he puts it, is 'transmissible' or to use a later term, hereditary. Thirty years later he returns to the same point: the difference between the lower classes who are 'unable or unwilling to reason from the past to the future' and the higher classes who 'look before and after'. The distinction he is making evidently comes to what we call intelligence.

How is such a regrettable difference of character to be remedied? In 1798, he agrees that marrying the milkmaid might mend the 'constitution' of the squire's family; that is, he is accepting ordinary Darwinian assumptions and proverbial wisdom. But he shies at the principle of selection: the human race 'could not be improved in this way without condemning all the bad specimens to celibacy'. In 1830, four years before he died, yielding to his critics, he eases out of the whole evolutionary and eugenic dilemma (just as Darwin did in his old age) by slipping in the environment: the lower type comes from the action of 'despotism, oppression, and ignorance'; the higher type from 'civil and political liberty and education'. National education, he feels may be the remedy.

Malthus here is quietly letting go his primary doctrine that it is indiscriminate charity which distorts the evolution of society. But that is only an afterthought. It is strict genetics that he applies to his policy for 'the future improvement of society'. His checks operate on different individuals or classes according to their different hereditary characters, mental, physical, and moral. The relief of distress offered for two centuries by the poor laws of England (and not elsewhere in Europe) had thus served to propagate people who were not otherwise able to raise families. Their incapacity could only be multiplied by heredity and in geometrical progression. Thus public assistance, unless controlled with severe discrimination, had the effect of postponing and enlarging the suffering it was designed to remedy.

During the two centuries that it had been operating there was, however, one consequence of this poor law policy of which the governing class in England was perhaps unaware. Public assistance had sustained a poor population from which the nation had drawn a supply of cheap labour. They provided the material for its press gangs. They kept the navy and the army going. They populated the colonies. And as industry developed, reinforced by the immigration of Irish navvies, they moved from the country into the towns to form the new working class. These refugees from famine, whom all Europe as well as Britain now knows, created the life described by Engels in Manchester in 1844.

Between Malthus and his critics there was from the beginning a misunderstanding. His principles by their intellectual and abstract character have cast a light (or a shadow, as they would say) on all the biology and economics that have followed them. What he could not face were the practical problems of the terrible world which was growing up around him. For that we had to wait almost until our own time, notably for the insight of the Hammonds, to describe what Malthus could only partly grasp as he grew old. For that time was the crisis when the rulers of England were coping well enough with the problems of Europe and India if not of America. But they were baffled by the problems created at home, by their own people, people who were in the throes of making an agonizing revolution; they were exchanging rural serfdom for an industrial bondage with which we ourselves have still not come to terms.

III *The Malthusians*

As soon as Malthus was dead, in 1834, the greatest political advantage was taken of his opinions. The 'pinch-pauper' Poor Law was a charter for those who wished to exploit cheap manual labour in building industrial Britain. Dickens, Engels, and Mayhew tell those of us who are too young to remember what they need to know of that world. But first look at the unintended channels along which Malthus's ideas flowed.

It was Malthus's statement that opened the windows of our minds to both the possibilities and the limitations of time, space, and number. And it was his biological attitude to the problems of economics that led, first Darwin and Wallace, and then Galton if not Mendel, to the study of evolution and the understanding of genetics. What is less well known is the bearing of this later understanding on Malthus's own assumptions. All organisms multiply, if unchecked, in geometrical progression; most of them as Wallace says, ten or ten thousand times as fast as man. Without this margin for selection to work upon, their 'combinations and transmutations' would have destroyed them instead of diversifying and adapting them.

Malthus is therefore right in concluding that the 'sexual passions' will not wither away. Not because they are 'constant' as he supposed, for they are the most variable of all hereditary properties; but rather because they are constantly preserved by their selective survival. Malthus is also right in arguing that there will always have to be selective checks on multiplication. But he failed to foresee the possibilities of industrial exploitation and he also failed to foresee the implications that the following century would endow with the word 'Malthusian'.

Already in his lifetime Malthus was shown an unwelcome way out of his problem of checks to propagation. A certain Francis Place, an apprenticed leather breeches maker who became a friend of Jeremy Bentham and James Mill, and the founding father of the trade union movement, was a disciple of Malthus. In 1822 he made the practical suggestion that physical impediments designed to circumvent disease might also be used by married couples to prevent conception. Birth control would at one blow cut out the need for Malthus's checks of vice and misery, famine and moral restraint. This shocking proposal was advanced by devoted lines of advocates and spread slowly over the world. Assisted by a great range of scientific invention it has after 150 years transposed the problem envisaged by Malthus.

In the first stage of this revolution, improvements in housing and communications, hygiene and education, were necessary preliminaries. All these changes, beginning near the top, moved slowly downwards in industrial societies. The result was a sharp disequilibrium in rates of reproduction of educated and uneducated classes as there still is between educated and uneducated nations.

The differential effect of birth control coming at a time of improved public hygiene, had two contrasted effects on society. First, the working classes in Britain expanding in the period 1830 to 1880 moved from the country into the towns where they were able to survive but became the victims of industrial exploitation. Secondly, the reduced expansion of the educated classes between 1880 and 1930 led to the fears on which Galton, as we have seen, based the eugenics movement, a genuine continuation of the ideas of Malthus. We can now look at these ideas in their total evolutionary perspective.

IV *Birth and Death Control*

The problems of mankind would be simplified and the problems of social justice would be quickly solved if men and women varied in their ability or willingness to propagate in proportion to the survival value of their offspring under the conditions of the society in which they would have to live. What a preposterous suggestion! Yet apart from man and his domesticated and dependent animals, such a reproductive restraint is a most widespread property. A vast range of physiological devices and instinctive responses are known which lead mammals, birds, and insects (as well as plants) to stop breeding when they are uncomfortable or short of food; when indeed they suspect that they are economically at risk.

These systems of control are themselves genetically controlled. They avoid overcrowding, reduce bullying, and generally maintain a state of peace and justice. They are also a first stop in all the stops of natural selection. Provisionally we may regard them as the primary system of population control in animals. And for man they can be seen as the first and most primitive of a long sequence of stages in his reproductive evolution, all of this sequence being represented in peoples and practices that are living today.

One element in the genetic control of man's reproduction, as we have already seen, is his development of an incest taboo. This is particularly interesting because it is an exception to the general course of human evolution with its displacement of instinct by reason, judgement and intelligence. The second stage of man's evolution, his unparalleled expansion, demanded the removal of all other instinctive checks to his propagation. It demanded competition and even conflict, and the evolution of a reproductive habit as prolific as his increasingly slow development would allow. Only in this way could man have multiplied his numbers a million times and colonized the whole earth in a mere twenty or thirty thousand generations.

In the last phase of this expansion came a third stage of man's reproductive evolution, the use of intelligent checks on propagation. What Malthus knew as 'unnatural passions and improper arts' were perversions, abortion, infanticide, and human sacrifice. These practices included cannibalism or, as we may say, the recycling of human flesh, and also the equivalents of euthanasia. They were assisted by warfare, sporadic, seasonal or ceremonial. All of them served to prevent overcrowding and famine: in the human emergency reason was called upon to do what instinct had earlier done to limit population.

This was the state of mankind when agriculture changed the prospects, economic and evolutionary, of the cultivating peoples. In this fourth stage the earth was opened to them and within fifty or a hundred generations the advantages of propagation were multiplied. Children again became an asset. Full employment and the necessary nutrition could be guaranteed. The Old Testament records and Christian teaching confirms the dawn of a new way of life. The restriction of population began to be condemned. What had been the Nuclear Zone for agriculture became the Nuclear Zone for Judaism, Christianity, and Islam, with human life and human propagation becoming sacred. All this was rational and calculable for it was both economically profitable and racially eugenic. The world, in terms of agricultural exploitation, had become once again underpopulated.

When, after agriculture, societies became stratified, labour divided and the land occupied, we may speak of yet a fifth stage in the evolution of human breeding. For now the advantages of propagation were different for different social classes. On Malthus's view they were also differently understood. The name of proletariat suggests that those least in demand, least capable of looking after themselves, and most easily exploited, have usually been the most prolific. Is it true that those with a capacity for forethought, restraint, and responsibility are also more intelligent and likely to find more useful employment? And that their capacities are hereditary? There can be no doubt that the connections are there and that their absence will give what sociologists call the 'deprivation cycle'. It is this cycle which Jesus had in mind when he said 'the poor you have always with you' (Matthew, 26.11). It is the cycle of social injustice which will always arise when resources are limited, men compete, and chromosomes pair and separate to show that one is better than the other.

Into this fifth stage of population control the nineteenth century brought the effects of the Scientific and Industrial Revolutions transforming the population process as it had existed since Neolithic times. The limitation of war, famine, and pestilence, went with the growth of birth control. Each new step began in Europe and spread over the world. Medicine subdued in turn the contact diseases like smallpox and syphilis, the water-borne diseases like typhoid and cholera, and the parasite-borne diseases like typhus, malaria, yellow fever, and sleeping sickness. The European empires spread these life-saving inventions; and, side-by-side with them, the death-dealing inventions which introduced their rule to Asia, Africa, and America.

When the Europeans relinquished their tropical colonies in Africa and Asia they left behind them the medical means of increasing population, as well as the military means of reducing it. They also left behind an appetite for the European activity of industrial development. Unfortunately, they could not leave behind the racial and hereditary skills and instincts, the education or the educability, which would enable the inhabitants of these tropical countries to develop agriculture, to organize industry, or to practise the birth control necessary to avoid an explosion of population. The primitive agricultural peoples of the tropics had been given the recipe for creating poverty perfected by the industrial nations without any of the safeguards which a colonial status might have established.

With industrial societies the problem is simpler. But it has two aspects. First the ruling classes (communist or capitalist) have to be converted. Ever since King David numbered the people, rulers have generally liked to have large and increasing populations under their control. They are now learning that stability of numbers is safer. Some of them, as we have seen, have already learned to restrict immigration and have expelled immigrants.

Another method open to rulers is to remove those laws which have been enacted under the rules of the fourth stage in order to encourage propagation. This has already been done. First there was the Japanese Eugenics Law of 1948. Then came the reforms in the industrial countries with a Christian tradition in northern Europe. The two most important fields are homosexuality and abortion. The persecution of homosexuals was derived from Jewish law and was calculated above all to discourage celibacy and encourage reproduction. It is out of place in a society which has reversed its aims. The prohibition of abortion had the same origin and the same purpose and is similarly out of place. The future child is replaceable: its future environment will not be. Since children are everywhere too numerous, women should not be compelled to have children they do not want. They should not even be required to pay for the abortion. Again, for the same reason, sterilization should be free for both men and women. Under these conditions there will be more room in society for children whose parents want to have them.

For the people as a whole the problem is different. Must they adjust themselves to a reversal of their instinctive and hereditary attitude to propagation? Not quite. The utmost pursuit of fertility inherited from the Neolithic stage promoted their development in numbers and in civilization. Today they need to restrict the fertility of the population as a whole. The question is can they do it without restricting the free choice of individuals? Owing to the heterogeneity of our societies individuals vary in the degree to which they want to have children. It is easy to vary by taxation the burden of having children so as to reduce the reproductive rate of the whole or a part of the population. This policy has often succeeded in raising the birth rate. It could be used with the opposite effect. But only, provided that parents are made, as they used to be, morally and economically responsible for their children.

V *The Evolution of Employment*

As men and women understood at the beginning of their existence and as the Book of Genesis later reminded them, the earth did not owe them or their offspring a living. By the curse of Adam they had to work for it. But, as time went on, by the inventions of some, all were able to improve the living they made and increase the numbers who made that living.

In terms of the several sciences, including economics, this exploitation rested on sequences of inventions changing man's relations with the earth by enabling him to get control of more and more energy. All this energy ultimately came from the sun. But man's skill and ingenuity made the earth yield it up by many different routes: plants and animals, wind and water. There were minerals, coal and oil, which came from plants and gave us the Industrial Revolution. There were also stone and metals, tools and weapons, the gift of the earth itself.

In the long evolutionary perspective these processes continually changed the character of men and the character of the earth they were exploiting. Successive inventions increased the efficiency and hence the scope of human employment since they provided for the food, clothing, and housing of an increasing human population. But in doing so they damaged the earth and depleted the resources on which they and their descendants were being made dependent, an earth and resources to which, for the most part, they saw no limit.

Now there is no food without employment and no employment without food. The limits of human employment and food were set by the resources of the earth and the skill with which they were used. To this skill and to its increase by invention, men, even the wisest men, again saw no limit. There was reason for this illusion. Every invention had bred its own class of specialists from which new inventions came. It had also created the profits and the capital from which larger and larger investments could be made as men proceeded from the flint industry to the computer industry. To be sure, increasingly rigid coordination between classes and industries led to each new invention causing dislocation and hence bankruptcy of investors and unemployment of workers. But those were merely interruption.

History shows us how particular inventions have led to cycles of activity of trade and of employment. The character and extent of these cycles were not and could not be foreseen by the inventors. The unemployment of well-equipped feudal armies in Europe was relieved by Pope Urban II with the device of sending them off on Crusades: it is a policy which still works. Overpopulation in Europe three centuries later was met by the invention of ocean-going ships with the ensuing great navigations and migrations. They were a Venetian invention which ruined the rich of Venice but not the poor who knew where they could do better.

The interactions of invention, employment, and migration were multiplied, extended, and accelerated when the Industrial Revolution seemed to restore the prospects of unlimited expansion enjoyed by earlier generations. Not only the earth and its resources, but the prospects for invention itself, promoted by the new organization of knowledge, seemed unlimited. If the socialist Engels asked: What is impossible for science? Samuel Smiles, speaking for the capitalists, would agree that nothing was impossible.

Prudence or pessimism, however, was not extinct. While Engels and Smiles were writing, man's responsibility for his environment and its future was prophetically defined by the American, George Perkins Marsh, in 1864. And the following year the English economist, William Stanley Jevons, was able to explain to Mr Gladstone that the mineral resources of the British Isles were finite.

During the two centuries since Malthus the relations between the numbers of men and the availability of resources to feed and employ them has been slowly reversed. Slowly states have decided that men may have a negative economic value. At least most men in most circumstances. The decay of slavery is not simply due to the growth of noble sentiments. It has been due also to the spreading recognition that slaves that have to be fed are not worth buying. With recurring unemployment free men were thought to be a better bargain. A demand for working men in time of war disappears when the damage has been repaired. Or when the shortage of natural resources makes itself felt.

The cities of the industrial world have seemed to be doing well when they could import men freely from the country who would have cost them £5000 to raise in the town. When the next generation appears the balance sheet begins to look different. As the empty spaces of the world have filled up, and as the food and energy supplies have fallen, resistance to legal immigration has grown. Hence, as we have seen, the increased rates and costs of illegal immigration. The numbers cannot be estimated, least of all into Britain where even the rate of legal immigration is officially unknown. Only in the communist states do we find an absence of all immigration, legal or illegal.

All over the world men are voting with their feet. They are trying to find food and employment in a world where both are becoming scarcer in relation to the numbers seeking them. And they are scarcest in countries where the necessary proportions of professional people capable of developing and exploiting invention are lacking. Fiscal devices, legislation, formal education, comprehensive welfare, capitalist or communist administration, none of these will make good the lack of the right numbers of the right people in the right jobs. And not too many of the wrong people.

In any country, we now learn, the level of productivity offered by the workers and management, the level of consumption in income and welfare demanded by workers and investors, and the cost of energy available from natural resources, enable it to support a certain population. Beyond this limit it suffers from what we may describe either as overpopulation or as underemployment. The whole world, industrial and primitive, capitalist and communist, has now passed beyond the limit of population it can carry at the standard of living it has enjoyed, other than by the exploitation of new sources of energy. Until this problem is solved all economic systems are at hazard. It is the cost of energy and the demands of income therefore that next need our study.

VI *The Energy Explosion*

The first step in the Industrial Revolution was the discovery in the eighteenth century that the energy of coal could multiply the effects of human and animal labour. Beginning with the steam engine a vast range of machinery exploited this discovery supported by a vast development of the scientific understanding we call technology. Already in 1865 Jevons explained that the use of the land might reach a limit, as Malthus said, but it need not destroy the land. The use of coal destroyed the coal. It was gone for ever. Mining of coal however still demanded heavy manual work. Quite a different scale of expenditure and profit, quite a different distribution of employment, and above all quite a different rate of depletion, arose from the discovery that mineral oil, drilled without drudgery, could do everything that coal did and a little more (Table 9.1).

Comparison of the oil revolution with its predecessors helps to show us what they all meant. Each discovery in succession, chemical, mechanical or geological, promoted a sequence of unprecedented developments. Each development was welcome because it offered new investments and profits and it promoted new employments on an ampler scale than those which it had displaced and destroyed. The fact that each development changed the sequences of use and led to alternate gluts and famines of the oil which fed the whole operation merely stimulated the alternating pursuit of new demands or new supplies. The fact that each development led to a local but spreading pollution could be ignored since the whole of society seemed to benefit from top to bottom. The consequent depletion of the oil and despoliation of all the other resources of the planet only rare individuals noticed or cared about. Moreover communists and capitalists alike claimed that natural resources were the property, not of mankind or of posterity, but of some state, corporation, or individual. Alike their profits would, they hoped, pay for the power increasingly needed to protect them, either from one another or from their own subjects.

These had been common attributes of mineral enterprise since their Neolithic beginnings. What was new with oil was that it was superimposed on the coal revolution. And the oil was so much easier to get out. It might cost 10 cents a barrel to put in the pipe and it could be sold for 10 dollars when it came out of the pipe. The profits of the oil were large, immediate, and miraculously expanding. Its uses multiplied and diversified. Hence supply generated demand in a way that Adam Smith had not foreseen; and for 120 years it was still doing so. While for our posterity, its loss will bring desolation, for us it seemed to bring infinite joy.

The oil revolution like its predecessors has diversely affected the classes and nations and races of men. On the communist side it has separated China from the Soviet Union. On the capitalist side it has separated the industrial states from OPEC and OPEC from the backward nations of Africa, Southern Asia, and South America.

The impulse, however, came from the capitalist and industrial states. It all started with drilling and refining in the U.S.A. Europe developed the petrol engine. Both promoted the motor and aircraft industries and the exploration for the world's oil. Agriculture was transformed by machinery and fertilizers, roads were built, and railways bankrupted.

Table 9.1 *Mineral oil exploited* (after Derry and Williams, Anthony Sampson, and others)

500 B.C.	Oil seepages used for fuel and caulking boats by Persians and Greeks and for ink by Chinese
A.D. 1500	Shale oil in England
1854	Benjamin Silliman Jr. of Yale (1816–1885) distils kerosene from petroleum
1858	Drilling and pumping in Pennsylvania
1860–5	Kerosene replaces whale oil for lamps in U.S.A.
1860–1945	U.S. is dominant oil producer in world: 700,000 wells in 70 years. Zig-zag of glut and famine: price 10c. to $20 per barrel of 42 U.S. gallons
1870	J. D. Rockefeller (1839–1937) unifies oil production and distribution in U.S. (Standard Oil, S.O., Esso, Exxon)
1873	Baku begins oil drilling (Gulbenkian); 1930 Urals; 1973 Siberia
1886	Daimler invents petrol engine (whence cars, tractors, aircraft)
1901	U.K. oil concession in Persia (1901–61, 16 per cent to Shah), 1908, oil struck (B.P.)
1902	Shell and R. Dutch combine (Deterding): Baku and Borneo
1911	S.O. split into 38 companies by law; remains united and begins foreign exploration
1919	U.S.S.R. nationalizes Russian oil and begins international export
1928	Secret foundation of the Oil Cartel: the Seven Sisters
1937–9	Oil, motor, and rubber companies begin to buy up and run down railways in North and South America
1938	Mexico nationalizes oil (S.O. etc.)
1948	Venezuela introduces 50/50 profit division but S.O. accounts adjusted
1951	Persia (Mussadeq) withdraws U.K. concession (B.P.)
1953	Persia ruined by oil boycott; C.I.A. intervenes; Oil Cartel takes over
1959	Gas found in North Sea
1960	Cartel restricts production, reduces price paid to lessor states. Five of these confront Cartel with OPEC union
1964	Continental Shelf Convention on oil rights
1966	U.S.S.R. suspends export of oil

1966	Cartel begins to support anti-communist parties in independent states of all continents
1967 (June)	3rd Arab-Israeli War: the Little (Arab) Embargo
1969	Revolution in Libya unhinges Oil Cartel by fixing prices
1969	Oil discovered in North Sea (U.K. and Norway); also in Canada, Alaska, Australia
1970	OPEC begins 'collusion' in Oil Cartel (instead of confiscation)
1971 (Feb.)	Teheran conference fixes annual dollar price increases at 2·5 per cent
1971 (Aug.)	U.S. dollar devalued
1973 (Oct.)	4th Arab-Israeli War: the Great Embargo. Cartel subjected to OPEC (13 states): price rises from \$3 to \$12 per barrel

Some cities were devastated in war, the rest were devastated in peace. Air and water and the ocean itself were poisoned and polluted. At the same time a large part of the crafts and the craftsmen inherited from the past of Europe were ruined, superannuated from society, and lost to civilization.

Meanwhile the wealth extracted from oil by the industrial states has had different effects on the formerly colonial societies of the backward or primitive world. These are described as the 'developing' countries which means that a donor country provides 'foreign aid' helping them to follow in the course which the industrial countries have shown them. This policy has two other (temporary) advantages. First, it provides employment in the donor country, especially in the armaments industry. Secondly, it also gives the donor country priority in stripping the assets, the timber and minerals, of the recipient.

These transactions appear for economists as money and loans, credits and debts. For politicians they appear as influence or power. For both they seem to be achievements. But for the next generation they will appear as energy wasted, resources depleted, employment misdirected, and governments corrupted. They will appear as populations uncontrollably expanding, disastrously misplaced, and increasingly conflicting. The conflicts will be between nations, and between races within nations, over the division of housing and goods, meat, grain, and fish. For even now they are being fed by an agriculture, notably in the U.S.A., which uses as much energy in the form of oil as it gets from its harvest in the form of grain.

And where did these populations come from? The expansion of

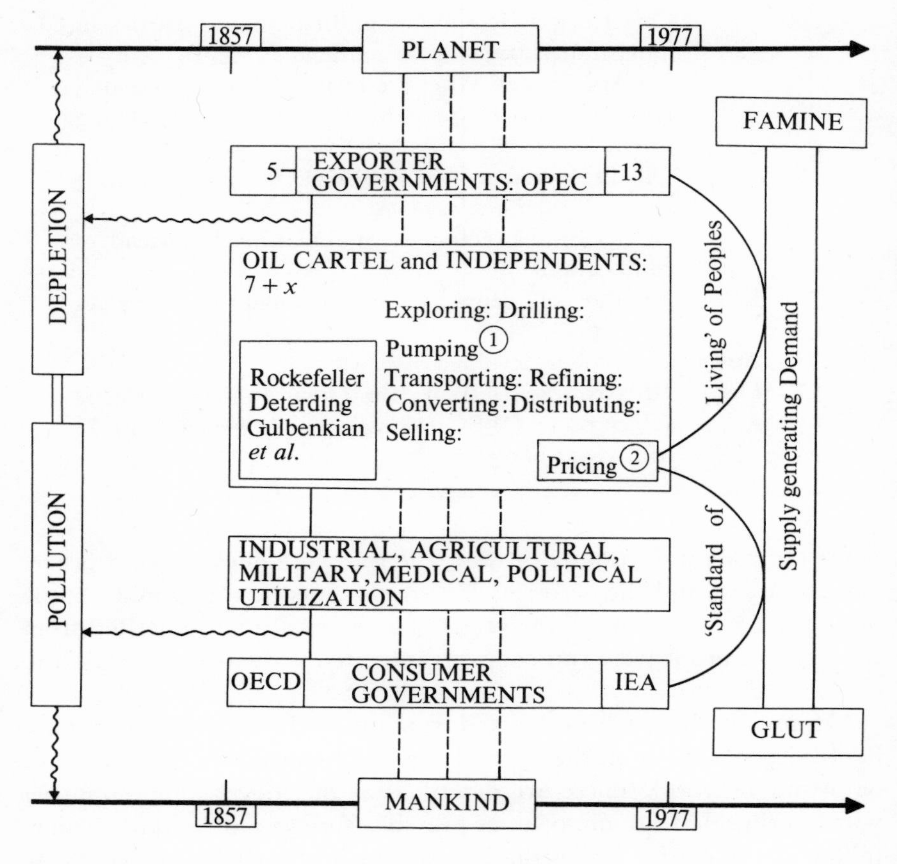

Fig. 9.1 Diagram showing the arrangements made for the exploration of the capitalist world's resources of mineral oil since 1857. Note that with man-made products demand generates supply; with natural resources supply can generate demand. OPEC, Organization of Petroleum Exporting Countries; IEA, International Energy Agency; OECD, Organization of Economic Cooperation and Development (after Anthony Sampson, 1975)

industry by oil had created an enormous demand for the use of unskilled labour by great corporations whose methods Schumacher has so effectively described. Birth control had slowed down the propagation of the working class (so much feared by the exponents of eugenics) in Europe and the U.S.A. The labour was therefore, as we have seen imported from the teeming populations of Africa, India, southern Europe, and southern U.S.A. By the energy of oil in ships and aircraft, the necessary people were cheaply and swiftly transported.

The great energy expansion gathered strength in the U.S.A. during the 1939–45 war. In Europe it developed with reconstruction. Its effect, like that of the original Industrial Revolution, was to make the world much richer. For most of the world that meant, once again, that it could breed faster and survive. For those who did not breed faster it meant a new plan of expenditure, divided into three fields. First, there was the higher 'standard of living' or competitively more conspicuous consumption. Secondly, there was the economic growth to cater for continuing this consumption carried out in disregard of the resulting pollution of man's environment. And, thirdly, there was the production of armaments for governments to be used for threatening or carrying out the destruction of wealth and people all over the world. This last item of expenditure competes with the first and also compensates for it. It has been reckoned (by Ruehl in 1976) to be at a world rate equivalent to a tax of one dollar per barrel on the world's oil production. A large part of it is paid for by loans from the I.M.F. and other government agencies.

The momentum of this expenditure is such that, like the oil flow itself, it could not be stopped without world-wide economic collapse. Yet this momentum at the same time promotes vast obligatory movements of people and consumption of irreplaceable natural resources. These are now being burnt up at about a million times the rate at which they were accumulated by growing plants from the sun's energy.

So overwhelming is this momentum first economically and then culturally that it is now compelling the great governments of the world to plunge headlong into the competitive replacement of the oil, whose disappearance threatens famine and unemployment, by the most dangerous of all human inventions, the fast breeder reactor producing plutonium.

Thus all the resources of the earth, human and natural, are being mobilized and exploited, scrambled and misused with short-term plans whose irresistible animal impulses are no longer rationally connected. The whole of mankind, governments and individuals, capitalist and communist, are thus trapped on a consumption–production treadmill from which none of them dares try to escape.

But what impulse has led powerful and apparently well-informed men to throw away all plan and premeditation? A number of factors have favoured this world-wide loss of judgement. The human population, the human consumption of energy, and the human standard of living that went with it, had all grown together. Surely they would, and should, and must, all go on growing together so long that no man need take heed for the morrow. This is the belief in 'progress'. It has been borne out by past experience. It seems to be a proper inference, a mere extrapolation from recorded history. And what other inference can we draw, given the optimism of instinct and temperament which has brought success to the most successful of our forebears, the men who made us what we are?

Scientific study confirms us in the view that all these achievements are due to the use of the sciences which are more powerful today than they have ever been. Moral considerations also demand that this power can, will, and must be used to secure social justice, security of employment, and the extension of the benefit of civilization to the unfavoured peoples. So it is that communists aim to catch up with capitalists, Europeans aim to catch up with Americans, and Africans aim to catch up with Europeans. Europe had evolved out of 5000 years of urban life, one might say, out of blood, sweat, and tears. But that belongs to the past. Surely now with the help of foreign science and foreign credit, both freely available, backward countries might develop more quickly—without any restriction of population or migration, and without any penalty of pollution or depletion.

These delusions have yielded enough spiritual comfort and profitable dividends to overturn the balance against past ages of traditional and religious beliefs. A genuine respect for society or nature and a spurious faith in the rewards and punishments of an after-life were equally rejected. Displacing these today is a vacant optimism which will continue until painful reality makes itself felt.

Let us turn now from the achievements and promises of science to the theories of economics which have been founded upon them.

VII *Hard Money and Easy Money*

A century before 1914, Britain and the other leading trading states issued currencies which they promised to exchange on demand with gold. This convention maintained a basis of agreement on trade and investment, on taxation and expenditure, on prices and wages, on capital values and rates of interest. Its success was partial. Its merit was that it depended on a multiplicity of accidents beyond the control of any one government. It did not maintain regular economic growth or full employment. On the contrary continual changes, due to inventions and discoveries, dislocated industry and agriculture and led to cycles of boom and slump in trade. No government, at least until Bismarck, made any provision for the effects of the slump. The recurring opportunities of migration and war seemed to be sufficient remedies.

When war came on a large scale in 1914, the system collapsed. European currencies ceased to be backed by gold. Each state established a separate means of exchange, a currency in which it claimed a monopoly for its own citizens. Each state moreover, optimistically counted on making good its losses from indemnities inflicted on its defeated enemies. But in the event all Europe proved to have been economically defeated. Russia, in revolution, repudiated its currency, and all its debts at home and abroad, keeping the industry, the building of which had incurred the debts. Germany did the same over the period 1914–24, so far as all formerly gold-backed debts were concerned, by unlimited printing of currency, that is inflation. France and Italy went half way on this course. These three countries had thus repudiated the debts of the governments and of their industries to their own citizens: they had wiped out the savings of the middle classes and had given their industries a fresh debt-free start. British governments, eager to maintain the credit of London as the banking capital of the world, resolved to repudiate no debts but to re-establish the gold standard.

This policy would have been practicable if the value of the pound sterling had been reduced in line with Britain's industrial competitors to, say, one-half of the 1914 value. But in 1925 the pound was restored to its full pre-war gold value of 4·84 dollars. Thus all the undepreciated pre-war debts, rents and royalties, were re-established in a country with the oldest industry in the world. It was an industry with continuity from its beginnings, in ownership and management, labour and education, all this unbroken by invasion, inflation or military defeat. The burden was one from which only another war might relieve it. The problem, it seems, had been foreseen and the correct remedy proposed by David Ricardo, in arguing the use of the gold standard, a hundred years earlier.

This crippling burden, lightened too little and too late by devaluation in 1931, was responsible for the high level of unemployment in Britain until 1940. But something else was responsible for the depression which struck world trade through both industry and agriculture in 1930. By this time the damage of the 1914 war, except in Britain, had been repaired. Consumption and demand had fallen and it was only in Germany that the forced draught of preparation for the next war seemed to restore full employment. In Britain and the U.S.A. it was only the war itself and its successors that could be said to have 'cured' unemployment.

In these circumstances when the second war was approaching its end new policies were prepared for dealing with the problems of unemployment on both the national and the international level. On these policies the views of John Maynard Keynes had a decisive influence. Keynes had first become known in November 1919, both for his contradiction of the official policy of the Allied Powers, and for his correct estimate of the possibilities of exacting indemnities from a defeated enemy. His opinion was based on the paradox that payment of debts between nations may damage the creditor as much as the debtor.

Depression and unemployment, Keynes argued, arose through deficient demand which is indisputable if we forget about population and resources, efficiency and competition. Further the deficiency could and should be corrected by increasing the expenditure of governments beyond their revenue. In due course, when boom followed slump, expenditure could be restricted and equilibrium restored. How this could be done is still unknown.

Keynes's policy has now been tested by many governments in several diverse situations. British governments rejected it altogether and disastrously following 1930. Germany and Hitler, on the other hand, adopted it. But the cure of unemployment from 1935 to 1939 depended on a total control of capital and labour, investment and wages, culminating in the war. In the U.S.A. in the same period, without these advantages, government spending was directed to removing unemployment but, even with concurrent preparations for war, it did not succeed.

Nevertheless, after the war, Keynes's prescriptions (without his reservations, for he died in 1946) were followed in Britain. Governments claimed to have assured prosperity by easy money, by inflation, by increasing expenditure beyond revenue and borrowing the difference. The currency was reduced by stages to less than a quarter of its value in terms of gold, or of the Swiss franc and the German mark.

The effect of devaluation in Britain was to lay a blanket of protection over an industry still partly trapped at the pre-1914 stage. In doing so it slackened the incentives of competition and, in the hands of weak governments, it did so progressively. But the purpose of protection gave it a more far-reaching effect. Its purpose was the creation of full employment without serious reservations, which meant not only full employment but overemployment. Not only manning but overmanning. Not only with home labour but with immigrant labour. And in addition should not the work be congenial? This was an aim which many employers had lost sight of. For it is a property of the most efficient large-scale industry with its cheap energy that it devalues the personal interests and skills found in small-scale industry. Congenial full employment had therefore become an impossible goal: as Schumacher (and Studs Terkel) have fully explained.

When full employment was seen to be the supreme end of both industrial and financial policy a stage was reached when it became independent of the quality or value of the work done. This was a possibility outside the visible spectrum of economic theory and trade union practice. How then could politicians or civil servants understand what was happening? They could not know that the value of work is invisibly measured in several ways, notably by the quality of the manager and the worker, and by the use of the goods they offer to society. In these values men take pride or feel shame. But pride and shame were being devalued along with the currency.

To these primary abuses others attached themselves as the years went by. The first was that the trade unions could now make the running and decide the rules. And success was so well assured that the employers could come to terms with the employed and with the government. Opposing parties could enter into collusion over inflation as easily as they were doing over immigration. The majority, for the time being, benefited. Only a minority could complain: some whose savings lent in trust were being dissipated; and others whose wages, through interest in their work and concern with its product, were not keeping pace. Only after twenty years was it seen that such people had stopped saving and investment was lacking.

For governments another primrose path led into the fields of foreign policy. There were the hungry people of the 'developing' countries. Their governments wanted money; some wanted food; all wanted arms, mainly to keep their own people in order. The industrial countries could provide them. Loans could be had at a low rate of interest. Repayment could be at the debtor's convenience. And for a tied loan the quality of goods was no longer arguable. Accordingly in thirty years the I.M.F. has lent over 60,000 million dollars to Third World states. The principle has been that the creditor, instead of demanding interest of the debtor, will pay interest to the debtor in the form of a new loan whenever he requires it. Why? To avert or postpone his bankruptcy or his conversion to communism (*Times*, 2 Sept. 1976).

In Britain, inflation set the scene for this rake's progress. In the United States, wars in Korea and Vietnam justified a similar debauch and postponed the day of reckoning. But throughout the capitalist world an unrecognized common agent was sustaining industry and supporting credit. This was the flood of oil: the discovery of new sources of oil in all six continents and under the ocean floors around them. This was extracted at first by the oil companies on long-term agreements from the territorial owners at a profit based on the claim that the demand was slight. But in the 1960s the owners of the land, the thirteen members of OPEC, discovered that their oil, which was ebbing away, had become vital to the industries of the consumers. It was vital at all levels of employment and investment, of food production and transport, of armament and war. They should increase four times the charges for their product. They could then reduce their rate of depletion, prolonging the life of their natural resources. In 1973 they did so. The industrial nations had enjoyed the first instalment of this treasure trove. OPEC would take its share of the second (Table 9.1).

This was a salutary discovery. Together with the end of the Vietnam War it led to a world-wide industrial recession. In doing so it exposed the fact that the prosperity of the industrial nations since 1945 had been promoted at the expense of an irreplaceable natural resource. The revenues of industrial companies and the wages of their workers had been paid in large part from the use of oil. And the oil would continue to rise in price as it approached exhaustion and came to be replaced by sources of nuclear energy which being more costly, and more dangerous, would also after a few accidents become less and less acceptable.

The discovery then was salutary because it warned all nations, industrial and non-industrial alike, albeit belatedly, that the pursuit of economic growth had gone too far. That is, not in the interests of any one nation, but of all mankind, or rather of the future of all mankind. As between nations the problem was different. The possession of natural resources and the price that can be asked for them is not a matter of justice: it is a lottery; a lottery held, to be sure, under solemn legal auspices. But when nationalization, ownership, and the price of oil were brought in question, by Persia in 1951, and by OPEC in 1973, the British (socialist) and the U.S. (non-socialist) governments retorted in the same way: with threats of force rather than arguments of principle.

There are principles, however, that we can discuss. Sparsely populated countries like the U.S.S.R. and U.S.A. draw well in the lottery of mineral wealth. So do the Arabs who were enriched by the accident of their having so destroyed the vegetation of their territories that they can divide this wealth (which they have not earned or even discovered) among the fewest possible beneficiaries. We may expect that they will squander this second instalment as fecklessly as the industrial nations have squandered the first. Meanwhile the industrial nations, on both sides of the Atlantic, will have to consider the problems of over-consumption, over-production, and over-population; they will also have to see what they can do to help the immigrants whom they have brought in to their cities to share their prosperity.

Meanwhile also the World Bank will no doubt decide how to help us out from the collapse of an economic policy with which it has been in collusion. A withdrawal from growth and a return to competitive management and competitive labour are the painful remedies which a number of economists, notably Hayek, have been trying to explain to us for a long time.

If we now compare our condition with that of the great communist experiment, we can learn something useful. The Soviet Union has the same economic goal as the capitalist states, industrial or otherwise. It wants wealth and power. And it wants them quickly. It has the necessary natural resources. It promises success to its people for it proclaims the cargo cult of science ('socialism plus electricity') brought by Lenin from the West. But its centralized power, its secrecy, its inefficiency, its inhumanity, and its sheer ignorance, have prevented it attaining its goal. Like the Western governments it has fed its people on great expectations which it cannot fulfil and many Russians, in spite of censorship, have long been aware of this failure—more so than the free democratic people of the West.

What now does the Soviet Government do to provide full employment for its people? There are many queues in Moscow but none for employment. Why is this? Because all employment, all residence, and all movement are directed, and all wages and prices are fixed, at a level ensuring that there can never be a surplus of goods that are wanted: there is always a shortage. Finally, as a long-stop there are the armed forces. They are elastic. That original socialist invention of military conscription ends with release from service. But the timing of release can always be planned by the government to suit the national interest, as Napoleon discovered, some time before going to Moscow.

VIII *The Welfare State*

At the same time that the industrial states of the capitalist world reached their climax of prosperity they were overtaken by what we may call compensatory movements, demands for social justice, arising from many sources. Imaginative men as diverse as Bismarck, Lloyd George, and Franklin Roosevelt had seen the need for relieving the inhumanities of industrialism. The new abundance brought feelings of guilt or compassion to some of the most conspicuous beneficiaries of exploitation. The threat to the rich, as well as the promise to the poor, presented by Marxism was now backed by the subversive power of the Soviet Union with its pretence of having put the workers on top through a revolution in which scientific method and socialist principles were said to be practically combined.

For those moved by these persuasions, whether of love or fear, the Keynesian proposal of maintaining consumption of all goods (including oil) by borrowing, by deficit budgeting, seemed to be the answer to every problem. The Common Market countries, to be sure, had suffered an inflation earlier and took steps to avoid its repetition. But the U.K. and U.S. which had not suffered this daunting experience proceeded with less restraint. All the more so since the U.K. had the habits of Empire and the U.S. was acquiring them. And no less so since they, especially the U.K., did it in the interests of the Welfare State. In the U.S. the welfare enterprise was primarily a local affair undertaken by the great cities, notably New York, supported by Federal agencies. In Britain, however, it was a national responsibility.

When it emerged, fully fledged, in the U.K. in 1948, the welfare legislation aimed at an equal uniform provision to secure education and health, allowances for unemployment and for children, and pensions for retirement, for the whole native population together with provision for foreign visitors and an unlimited admission of colonial immigrants from the dissolving Empire.

These were large commitments for a country financially insolvent and they could not have been carried out without a gift from the United States of Marshall Aid to the value of 6450 million dollars, which seemed a great deal at the time and was indeed greater than that bestowed on any other country. Even so the welfare programme had to be followed by inflation and later devaluation of the currency which sufficed to maintain full employment until the recession of 1973 when the price of oil was corrected by OPEC.

Meanwhile the economy had been further distorted by the evolution of the trade unions. What they had lost in brain, as we have seen, they had gained in brawn. Originally organized to provide security from distress, they could now devote themselves single-mindedly (as Paul Johnson has shown) to a new and more dignified purpose, to developing their political power, to securing a monopoly of employment by the 'closed shop' and thereby raising their wages, not in relation to the value of the work done, but as a means of destroying their own employers and the economy of the nation.

Thus welfare, plus full employment, plus wage-increase competition guaranteed inflation. The damaging effects of the three policies naturally enlarged one another. Government and people were united, again we may say in collusion, in their pursuit of high consumption and the indulgence of waste. Had not Keynes written in his great work 'consumption is the sole end and object of all economic activity'? How fortunate that the line of least resistance was scientifically correct! No party dare threaten the promised improvements in the style of life by a parsimonious restriction of borrowing. Hire purchase became a private virtue as well as a public policy. And did not the World Bank stand as a guarantor of economic rectitude?

Malthus however had pointed out that all societies with money include spenders and savers. The spenders fall in society, the savers rise and build up industry by investment. But in the inflationary Welfare State this was no longer true. The spenders could not fall. They spent and in doing so promoted inflation and protected themselves against it. The savers could not rise, for they trusted the government and lost their savings. Only the thrifty could fail to thrive.

All welfare systems developed to meet the needs of capitalist industrial states have proved insolvent in the last twenty years. In general terms their failure has arisen from the removal of the natural restraints of individual judgement and rational self-interest. In their place came national rules applied by remote officials, people who could never be wrong and, as with all nationally socialized concerns, increased in number by Parkinson's Law. Care of health and education was first delegated, then standardized, then demoralized. The medical and teaching professions, observing that personal relationships and private virtues had been devalued, undertook a dedication in reverse, a dedication to the official system. To pay for the costs of this system the government by inflation was cheating the public and the public was learning to cheat the government.

There is a particular defect inherent in any scheme for ensuring the health of a whole nation. The contract is bound to offer the medical profession all the funds it needs to protect and prolong without discrimination the lives of every man, woman, and child. It is to this principle that the profession is traditionally dedicated. But, as discerning physicians already knew, the application of this principle, the giving of this 'right' subject to legal interpretation, would incur unlimited cost. Every advance in medicine would multiply the burden on the community of saving, supporting or prolonging lives that would not previously have survived. In addition, as we have seen, many of these advances would add to the burden of hereditary debility and disease in future generations.

There is a defect, however, not just in the practical workings of the Welfare State, but also in its underlying assumptions. It springs from a principle we noticed at the beginning of our account of human evolution, the principle that the family is the indispensable basis of human society. The family came before religion. Its character is not the *result* of religious teaching, but rather the *cause* of it. The family is the product of the selective advantage it has had in protecting human society and its propagation.

Love of what is within the family and fear of what is outside it are bound together inseparably in maintaining it. Both the love and the fear are necessary and rational ingredients of human life. Or, as the saying was: fear of the Lord is the beginnning of wisdom. Against most human vagaries and material vicissitudes the family protects its members. It provides security: never complete security, for the individual must always do something for himself or herself. Indeed in face of the Industrial Revolution and modern urban society the family provided a less and less sufficient security and that is why the Welfare State came into being. But in removing, or pretending to remove, all need for the security of its members, the Welfare State has in effect knocked away one of the original and indispensable props from the family and from society. Although different races and classes are by their nature differently affected, it is to this innovation that we partly owe the breakdown of both family and social obligations in modern industrial societies.

Must we then, as some argue, dismantle the Welfare State? It partly sprang, as Milton Friedman has explained, from the desire to do good with somebody else's money: a laudable aim when some people obviously have much too much. But nobody spends other people's money as carefully as he spends his own. Especially if he doesn't know the giver or the receiver. The lesson is therefore that the Welfare State must be *devolved*. It must be returned to its source, the Guilds, the Trade Unions, and the Friendly Societies who could make it work because they knew the people who were doing the job. It is a principle which still works in certain ancient cities, for example, in Tuscany.

The grand formulae of the past have failed because their authorities treated people as statistical units. And the units retorted by claiming rights without duties. This turns out to be as demoralizing for human beings, as the imposition of duties without rights. The new assumption of equality and imposition of uniformity is in effect as demoralizing as the old wage and chattel slavery. The pretended rule of a majority becomes the rule of yet another minority, grasping its own privileges.

Now we see that the responsibilities of the State, the family, and the individual must always be balanced, reciprocal, and conditional. The impersonal State must be replaced by the voluntary and personal association. The society which fails to recognize the individuality of the people underneath will itself fail, for it is from the diversity and independence of individuals in body and mind, in education and work, that all open and free societies have sprung.

IX *The Environmental Equation*

The economic contrasts, crises, and even catastrophes of the present century have served to show mankind, that is ourselves, in a clearer evolutionary relationship with our environment than ever before. Earlier we had seen man expanding, in the words of Genesis, to subdue the earth, using to the limit of his skill every invention that would enable him to exploit this earth, this environment. Now we can see that, at every step in this process of increasing power, man unawares has been doing damage to the earth in proportion to the good he has been doing to himself.

To this rule we may acknowledge two riders acting mainly to the detriment of the earth. One is that while the good has often been short-lived and confined to the innovators and their heirs, the damage has generally been lasting and even irreversible. The other is that while some people have been peaceful, prudent, and thrifty, there have always been others who have behaved abominably at the same time both to the earth and to their fellow men. Indeed, it is so happening, as we know, more than ever today.

The good that men got from hoeing their crops and fencing their stock was slight at first and so was the damage they did. But when they cut down the forests and grazed down the prairies the damage appeared; not to them, of course, but to their descendants long after. When men began to mine the earth, still the damage was slight for it was done with the sweat of their brows. But when they used the power of the coal to mine the coal, the power and the benefit and the damage were all multiplied beyond imagination.

All this was trivial compared with the power, the benefit, and the damage that came from oil. The magnitude of these things and the speed of their release intoxicated the great men on top and demoralized the little people below. All of them felt that they deserved their rewards. God or Nature had at last done justice to them.

Fortunately, however, the damage that followed now came so swiftly that the connection between the power and the disasters which ensued was evident. The victims took courage and began to protest. Who could fail to see the connection between oil and economic growth and the degradation, pollution, and depletion of earth and water and air? Intelligent men could see that many of these effects had been foreseen. Others might have been foreseen in a less optimistic world. But there are always others that could not have been foreseen. How much more is this true of what will come after oil? Can we indeed imagine what kind of creatures will be creeping round our cities after a few more centuries of economic growth?

In these circumstances we have to enter into a new department of economics and of politics. We have in the past been concerned with the division of income and wealth among living men. From this preoccupation came the emotional disputes, trite and increasingly trivial, between the political right and left. Now we must be equally concerned with the division of wealth between ourselves and our descendants: or between mankind and the planet we have inherited and they may inherit. For this is the planet on which we must no longer assume that our activities always confer inestimable benefits.

In this new situation our guiding principle must be that a high level of consumption, a high standard of living, the great triumph of the Industrial Revolution and the capitalist world, not only damages our present environment, it also dissipates and impoverishes that future inheritance. Conversely the dependence of communist and other backward countries on human labour, their much deplored failure to develop an industrialized agriculture, is bound to protect these societies against the consequences of Western civilization with its efficient and skilful and hitherto irresistible exploitation of the earth.

This comparison of Past and Present as well as of East and West leads us to recognize a sequel to the principle of genetic control which we saw governing man's evolutionary relations with his environment. It may be expressed by the following crude but inexorable equation. The rate of damage and depletion suffered by man's environment (D) is connected with the number of people (P) and their standard of living or rate of consumption (S). As we may say: $PS = Dk$. In this equation P and S are the two primary values which decide what damage we do to our country and our planet. But if we apply the equation to separate countries or regions, D becomes divisible into damage at home and depletion abroad. And for separate peoples k includes many variable components such as intelligence and discipline, education and taxation.

The modes of government of different countries are therefore something we must examine. They are of concern to the future of the whole world in both a cooperative and a competitive sense.

X *The Divided Nations*

The nations of the world are connected by their need to trade with one another, and also by their organization of the United Nations whose charter explaining its aims and its 'faith in the dignity and worth of the human person' the allied founder members signed in 1945. The original fifty have expanded to one hundred and forty and have gradually fallen apart into groups whose political aims, economic systems, and military dispositions have increasingly diverged to become three separate worlds. Many of the member nations are in a state of tension or conflict. Most are in a state of evolution. Some are unstable in political structure and individual management. How in fact do they differ? And how may we expect them to behave in the future?

The First World consists of twenty states of N.W. Europe with their British, American, and Japanese associates. Their governments are in some sense responsible to those they govern. Although subject to corruption they are able to resist its domination. They claim to be democratic and free. This claim is based on a slow evolution of common political, judicial, and educational systems which they share and which have led to their economic and military alliances. To these Open States we may add Sweden, Finland, Iceland, and Israel since an individual freedom of economic activity, as well as of movement, expression, and belief, is common to all of them. It is a part of their culture which is taken for granted on account of its social and its racial foundations. It allows a wide range of economic organization in which capitalism and socialism are allowed to compete.

In all these respects the First World is utterly contrasted with some of the peoples and with all of the governments of the Second World. This is an alternative world which claims to be communist but also democratic although hardly free. Government works through disciplined parties which in turn discipline the whole of the populations under their control. The discipline proves to be no less corrupt than the absence of discipline in the capitalist world but it takes quite different forms. Their Marxist socialism is as much diversified as capitalist socialism since it has by secret processes produced Leninism, Stalinism and Maoism, Titoism and Castroism, Ho-chi-minism, Kimilsungism, and Khmer-rougism. Their internationalism has evidently given place to nationalism for not all of these are on speaking terms with one another.

The principle that unites these states is that government is heavily polarized: it is, as socialist government apparently must be, from the top downwards and from the centre outwards. Movement of opinion upwards is penally suppressed. Movement of people in or out is likewise penally regulated. These then are prison states which challenge the existence of all societies claiming to be independent of them.

Inevitably the smaller members of these two groups are attached to the greatest powers within each, the U.S.A. and the U.S.S.R. And the two great powers look to all unattached states for their support. These constitute a Third World of supposedly 'unaligned' states which first took shape in 1961 when thirty-five heads of state met at Belgrade. By 1976 at Colombo, their number had risen to eighty-five. If we take these states at their face value, most of them also claim to be demo-

Table 9.2 *The United Nations divided by modes of government*[1]

		Movement		*Government*					
Class	*Status*	*Emigration*	*Immigration*	*Executive*	*Legislature*	*Judiciary*	*Media*	*Individual Rights*	*Political Parties*
1st WORLD Open States *c.* 20	Industrial and Capitalist	free[2]	restricted for unskilled from 3rd World	by election from people or legislature	by election of representatives through alternative parties	independent after nomination	censored by owners, unions, libel, secrecy, and decency laws	free religious and political belief. Some taboos on expression.	depend for financial support on unions of employers or employees
3rd WORLD Police State (non-aligned etc.) *c.* 100[3]	Backward or Mixed or Oil-producing	free subject to detention and expulsion[4]	subject to negotiation	based publicly or secretly on legislature or army	elections subject to intimidation, corruption or suppression	subject to influence or dismissal by executive	controlled by executive directly or indirectly[5]	criticism of government punishable without trial	as 2nd World or replaced by police
2nd WORLD Prison-States *c.* 20	Communist	only by expulsion or defection	only by executive invitation with hostage control	nominated secretly within ruling party	spurious elections of party nominees	nominated and removable by executive	totally controlled by executive, bad news suppressed or delayed	none:[6] imprisonment, torture and execution: trials in special cases	single party organized and disciplined by executive through police

1. Governments all described as democratic.
2. For skilled artisans in Britain free only since 1825.
3. A majority of the United Nations: with about half a million 'prisoners of conscience' detained without trial.
4. Foreigners expelled as such or because too skilled.
5. By using foreign technicians retained under conditional permits.
6. Lenin rules forbid public discussion of religion, sex, race, and politics.

cratic. But if we look at their history, we see that they are mostly governed by individuals who gained power by force and will not relinquish it except to force. They are police states (Table 9.2).

Now we must not be too disparaging of the police state. The nations of our First World emerged painfully enough from the condition of police states only in the last two centuries. Their peoples have all been subject in their time to corruption and violence, to imprisonment and torture without trial. They are all of them today only precariously protected from these accidents by a vigilant and educated public opinion indispensably based on a professional class. They are now protected, not against feudal barons or royal tyrants but against the attacks of industrial corporations, trade unions, and government departments, against the assaults of both capitalism and socialism. A Department of the Environment can today destroy a country's environment just as treacherously as a House of Commons could, in the eighteenth century, destroy a country's common lands. We in the First World are not therefore by any means safe from the inversion of authority which has diminished or destroyed individual rights in the Second and Third Worlds. We know it is easy for us to go downhill. What we do not know is whether the states and peoples of these other worlds have any chance of climbing uphill.

It may be thought that states of the Third World, whether India or Brazil or Yugoslavia owe their limitations of government to their history as colonies of former imperial powers. And that therefore we may expect them to recover, to make their way back on to the path we have followed. But can we explain the 150 years of wars, oppressions, and insurrections of Latin America by the effects of earlier Spanish colonial misgovernment? Or can we attribute the brutal expulsion and massacre of the Chinese minority in Indonesia to the effects of Dutch oppression?

When we go around the globe to India and Africa we are forced to see that the responsibility rests largely with those who govern today. These are people who have taken power themselves by force and have divided the power and the profits of government in various proportions, not with their own people apart from a few friends, but with stronger and richer people outside, with corporations in the First World and governments in the Second World, with people who are engaged in stripping the local assets, oil, minerals, and timber. In return these people offer their own products to 'develop' the Third World.

The means of development, as we have seen, turn out to be largely the arms needed by governments to keep in power. The production of the arms is what the First or Second World powers need in order to maintain employment and industry at home and to threaten one another. This is the new colonial situation which turns out to be, for the people and for the earth, a little worse than the old colonial situation.

But why do the governments of the communist and capitalist worlds need to threaten one another? The pronouncements of the communist press we need not consider since they are intended for the people at home. The activities of the K.G.B., the C.I.A. and the F.B.I. are also in part internally generated. But what are we to make of the diplomatic contests, the wars fought by proxy, and behind them the armaments? These are genuine enough. Superimposed on them, however, are various words like coexistence and détente. These words seem to mean that the capitalist states provide credits which enable the U.S.S.R. to buy grain and also equipment without diverting its resources from an army and the making of arms, or a prison-state establishment which it dare not dismantle.

If this is so the U.S.S.R. has become economically and technically, industrially and agriculturally dependent on the West to maintain the military power which it uses to threaten the West. This in turn makes sense only if East and West are maintaining their economies, their employment systems, by producing arms and maintaining armies which they dare not dismantle or disband without endangering their internal network of credit and basis of power. They have created in collusion, scarcely knowing it, a World Superorganism with its own rules of behaviour and development. And they have done so because neither the capitalist nor the communist systems with the resources available to them can support their populations without this collusion at the standards of living they have established, standards which they do not dare to lower, since they have always promised to raise them higher. They cannot stop the treadmill. And they cannot get off it.

This collusion extends to the allied and associated powers on both sides. It operates however through a pattern at once labyrinthine and asymmetrical. For the communist governments work directly for their own advantage through their own hierarchies. But the capitalist governments work indirectly for or through sectional interests which have to be placated in accordance with their own constitutional processes. And the two opposed kinds of government are themselves endangered in different ways, personal or collective, by any failure of either their co-operation or their competition.

The two leading Russian critics of the Soviet Government, Andrei Sakharov and Alexander Solzhenitsyn, tell us that the Western governments have sacrificed their claim to moral respect by continuing this deliberate collusion without securing any relaxation of the torment which the Soviet Government inflicts on all independent opinion within the frontiers of its power—within its prison. They are right. But Western governments are not striving to gain moral respect. Rather, it is to be feared, they are looking forward to the next democratic election.

This is not all. Behind these transactions is a world-wide destruction of resources and pollution of nature which is involved equally in the making of guns and the growing of grain. For both, as we have seen, depend on the consumption of irreplaceable oil. The whole metabolism of our Superorganism depends on one connected digestive system. The whole of it works, East and West, for the benefit of people living today who are taught by a vast system of popular communication to think only for today. But tomorrow is not far away.

Chapter 10

The Problem and the Choice

In September 1925 the Soviet commissar, Gregory Zinoviev, addressed a gathering in Moscow celebrating the bicentenary of Peter the Great's Academy of Sciences. In a rhetorical passage he explained that 606 experiments had been needed to find a remedy for syphilis. But his government was prepared to try 6006 remedies to deliver the world from the disease of capitalism. His audience of capitalists thought this an idle fancy. I recall Bateson, who was present, saying that since the first of these experiments had cost the lives of one-quarter of the population, few would survive to enjoy the completion of the programme. We have, however, since the time of Zinoviev seen a number of experiments of this kind. He himself was killed in one of them. The prospect of a quarter of the population being repeatedly lost no longer seems so fantastic. There were indeed two serious ideas in his proposition. One was the idea that communism was a fallible experiment. The other was the idea that unless we make such experiments with a view to changing their character, impulse, and direction, all our societies, capitalist and communist alike, are capable of ruining themselves.

In the course of our survey of the field we have looked at such serious questions as crime and disease, education and eugenics. These, however, appear as domestic questions to be separately answered by different nations. They are all child's play compared with the economic problems of population and migration, production and consumption. For these are problems stretching over the whole world, problems where man's little universe is unmistakably one, connected both in its evolutionary origins, and in its future fate. Our several treadmills are all one treadmill. At the same time we recognize that they are problems of the individual. For as the teachings of Adam Smith and Robert Malthus, Karl Marx and Charles Darwin agree, the animal principle of the self-interest of individuals, often, as we know, enlightened and extended, is the only motive to be infallibly relied on in the conduct of human affairs.

This self-interest, as we have seen at all stages of our argument, is expressed in two impulses, those for competition and for cooperation. The expression of each is full of paradoxes. For their interactions or conflicts are variously adjusted to one another in relation to every need, whether of food, reproduction or power, and at every level whether of the individual, the family or the tribe, the class, the sect or the nation. But behind them all we now recognize the ever-pressing feedback effect of invention and discovery which Western science has taught the world to regard as progress, inevitable and hence indispensable progress.

Here it is that we are driven to seek the opportunities of bold experiment. But we have now found that our attempts to modify or divert, control or suppress, competition have led to few successes and many failures.

At the outset we see that, as soon as societies became stratified, people used them in competing to avoid competition. The royal dynasty and the industrial monopoly, the guild, the trade union and the closed shop are all symptoms of this secondary level of non-competition. When it succeeds it always carries the risk of failure so that the rise-and-fall of families, of industries, and of empires becomes to a great extent a measure of this dangerous success. It is not surprising therefore that socialism and communism succeed in avoiding competition only by shifting the sites of abuse, transposing the modes of corruption, and concealing the processes of conflict. And if by their inefficiency they have reduced the damage they do to nature they have at the same time increased the damage they do to man.

These experiments have been carried out internally, regionally or domestically. But while we are in the middle of them the world as a whole has been brought face to face with one common problem. The success of nations, the capitalist nations, separately pursuing their competitive courses, has confronted them all with the prospect of exhausting the whole world's resources. All nations together are trapped in pursuing the same end of expanding their separate and petty exploitations of the earth beyond any possibility of what the earth can bear. All of them have been making so much noise about it that they can never hear the earth's complaint.

There is, to be sure, the sharp contrast that we have seen between two groups. There are those who are trapped, whether through ignorance or superstition, incapacity or instinct, by their habit of multiplying their numbers without limit. And there are those who are trapped by their habit of enlarging their consumption of goods without limit, goods which they can produce only with the help of energy which in turn they have to take from the earth. And here the fatal sequence opens out before them: coal, oil, and then the infinitely dangerous plutonium.

From this rake's progress the peoples and governments of the world will not be easily restrained. Industrial governments with educated peoples may succeed in restricting the numbers of the population. But beyond this they have to restrict the competitive impulses of individuals at all levels of society. This is to ask them to abandon their only remaining faith, their belief in progress and their worship of success.

The industrial nations and their governments have been swept forward by the pressure of invention through a barrier they did not see into a world they have not yet understood. As the resources of the earth become more depleted and populations both more crowded and more deprived, the greater will be their effort to pass the problem on to the next generation. Self-deception will become more persuasive. Optimism will take hold. Those who remember 1914 and 1939 will also remember that these smaller calamities were produced by optimists but foreseen by pessimists. Indeed before these events an optimistic temperament had seemed to confer a permanent selective advantage in human evolution. It is not so now.

The remedy for our ills in theory, the pessimist's theory, is neither remote nor obscure. It is to recognize that the world is indebted to Europe for two great achievements which have transformed human life in the last 500 years. One is the control of nature which has led to our present crisis. The other is the understanding of nature and of man which is our means of escape from this crisis. How, you may ask, can these two things be separated? For Europe forced them together on America, Asia, and Africa.

In the first place let us imagine what would have happened without that rough intrusion. The condition of those continents could scarcely have changed in the last 500 years. China would still kow-tow to the Son of Heaven. Japan would still be shut up in the Shogun's cage. India would still be the prey to warring rajahs. And along the roads to Tripoli, Khartoum, and Zanzibar, Arabs would still profitably drive their caravans of castrated slaves. Cannibal flotillas would still block the cataracts of the Congo. And on their remote islands Maoris and Melanesians would still be consuming human flesh. No population problem would have disturbed any of these lands. Indeed it might never have disturbed them until genetic or ecological decay severally overtook them.

We must put aside our moral indignation about what the Europeans did and how and why they did it. What matters is the results. For the first result was a liberation of Asia and Africa. The way was opened, as we have seen, for processes of change favouring the growth and the unity of all human understanding. The second result was the subjugation of the whole world to the European idea of progress by the control and unlimited exploitation of nature.

This good and this evil having been done, can we assume that the rest of the world, enlightened by Europe, will accept the good and reject the evil? Hardly so! The evidence is that the rest of the world will not generally accept free speech, representative government, and human rights, as they are known in our Western world. But they will generally accept all the means that they can get for exploiting nature and destroying the resources of the earth. The problem therefore returns to us. Our chickens come home to roost. It remains for us to use our understanding of nature and of ourselves to control the dangerous power we have let loose on mankind.

If we look back on the last 500 years we see the Hebrew and Greek and Christian confidence in man as the master of nature meeting the diverse peoples of northern Europe and in that fertile soil creating the Protestant ethic of industry, ambition and self-reliance whose success especially in the New World has created the profligate societies we now know. These are the societies whose fraudulent promise the Third World so greedily accepts. The peoples, of course, know nothing of what is happening. But by the time their rulers have led them to disaster these rulers will be elsewhere. And the industrial nations will be having all they can do to save themselves without helping anyone else.

Our remedy then is to return a little way towards what we once believed. We must take up again that respect for nature which until recently guided and preserved so many of the peoples of the earth. Neither the practice of thrift nor the restraint of greed and self-indulgence need be too painful if we undertake it soon. But the longer we postpone it the more painful it will be. If we embark on our experiments with determination 6000 of them may not be required. But, if we don't embark on them at all, what Keynes, our late mentor, called the 'thin and precarious crust of civilisation' will be broken.

To any such reformation, any such changing of course, one grave obstacle at once appears. All the great industrial nations would have to change course together. And we know that each will believe it can do better than its neighbours—and will try to prove it. But in all these nations now there are a few people who take seriously the future of mankind, its quantity and its quality. They are people who know that our past evolution has been governed by the needs of future generations. They are people who recognize that the race or class or nation or species which rejects this principle is putting its own future at hazard. They are people who therefore ask themselves the practical question: do we want to expand, to multiply, and to consume the good things of the earth without limit and without regard either to the earth itself, or the children who will inherit it? Or are we willing to set ourselves a limit, to measure the capacity of the earth to support us and our descendants, and to fit ourselves, as our ancestors did, to that capacity?

The attempt to study the whole of our little universe, to understand its connectedness with the past and the future, to see the value of the knowledge collected over many generations by the devoted labours of our fellow men, will perhaps persuade our own generation to pause before it plunges into the abyss.

Notes

Chapter 3, IX, p. 75. *Disease resistance:* its connection with genetic polymorphism was discovered by E. B. Ford (see his *Genetics for Medical Students*, 7th ed. 1973). McNeill's *Plagues & Peoples* (1976) gives a valuable account of the historical evidence in Europe and Asia. My *Genetics and Man* (1964) and *Evolution of Man and Society* (1969) are concerned especially with its effect on the pre-historic and historic colonizations of Africa and America.

Chapter 3, X, p. 80. The production of a strict inter-racial F_2 offends, of course, against the incest taboo in man. In U.K. it is also prohibited by an Act of 1906 making incest a criminal offence. The nearest we can get to an F_2 is perhaps the hybrid population under the care of the Aboriginal Medical Service in Sydney, Australia. The group concerned numbers 6000 and suffers from six types of genetically significant disability often unhappily combined:- (i) physical malformations, (ii) parasitic infections, (iii) lactase deficiency, (iv) malnutrition, (v) alcoholism, (vi) prostitution; hence an inability to cope with conditions either in the cities of the whites or the bush of the blacks (*Times:* 12 August 1977).

Chapter 4, III, p. 85. Patterns of animal behaviour, particularly the building up and breaking down of instincts, have been elegantly described and illustrated by M. and R. Burton (1977: *Inside the Animal World*, Macmillan, London).

Chapter 4, V, p. 95. The Poulton inheritance unfortunately can not be investigated further. The father's brain preserved in the Hunterian Museum in London was destroyed by bombing in 1941. And the son's body, when he died in 1943, was cremated without the examination he wished. I am indebted to the family, the Museum and Professor Ford for this information.

Chapter 4, Table 4.1, p. 100. The extra Y in XYY males increases their maleness also in respect of tooth size (Alvesalo *et al.* 1975. *Am. J. Hum. Gen.* **27**: 53–61). The principle of genetic control of the speech mechanism discussed in *Evolution of Man and Society* (1969) and in Ch. 5 is thus reinforced.

Chapter 4, VIII, p. 114. The failure of later investigators to take note of the writings of Galton, whether they were confirming or rejecting them, is on a par with the failure of Bateson and Morgan to take note of the earlier writings on chromosomes on the basis of which the one rejected and the other supported the chromosome theory of heredity. It seems that, equally in psychology and genetics, and equally in Britain and America, the twentieth-century successors have disregarded whatever inconvenienced them in the writings of the nineteenth-century pioneers whose work they were developing or disputing. As I have pointed out elsewhere (*Proc. 6 Int. Chromosome Conf.* Helsinki, 1977: Elsevier, Amsterdam), from this habit of relying on hearsay, later errors and misunderstanding have copiously accumulated.

Chapter 5, V, p. 138. The parallel development and mutual dependence of flowering plants and mammals beginning in the Cretaceous was, it seems, so perfect that it brought to an end the accumulation of the fossil fuels which we are now so rapidly consuming (F. W. Went, 1974, on Air Pollution, *An. Rev. Pl. Physiol.* **25**: 1–26).

Chapter 6, I, p. 146. The evolution of literacy in Europe was selectively assisted by the law under Benefit of Clergy. In England from 1350 to 1531 even a layman convicted of rape or homicide could escape hanging by an ability to read in Latin the "neck verse" (Ps. 51, verse 1).

Chapter 6, II, p. 150. The contemporary violence and vandalism of youth in industrial cities must be in large part due to a lack of the opportunity and need for heavy manual work. While cheap oil lasts the young will no longer even need to walk (see Chapter 9).

Chapter 7, V, p. 182. Corruption in British India was conspicuous only at the top. Most Viceroys from Lytton (1876–80) to Willingdon (1931–36) accepted, and some sought, presents from Native Princes.

Chapter 8, IV, p. 219. Some striking racial differences in behaviour are not closely related to intelligence. For example the White and Non-White (in effect Negro) communities in the U.S.A. have quite different habits of killing, as shown by the frequencies of the victims. The White is evidently 3 times more inclined to suicide than the Negro, but the Negro is 8 times more inclined to homicide than the White. (U.S.: H.E.W., *Nat. Center Health Stat.* S20, 5; 1950–64).

Chapter 8, VI, p. 223. It has been said that Third World rulers are classifiable as prigs, crooks or monsters. How this works (and, with it, Majority Rule) may be illustrated by the evolution of Uganda. The country became independent in October 1962 with Dr. Milton Obote, a Christian of the Acholi tribe, as Prime Minister. He repudiated the federal constitution in February 1966, made himself President in April, deposed the Kabaka and suppressed his government in May. In 1971 he was in turn deposed by Idi Amin, a Muslim of the Kakwa tribe. The new dictator then expelled all Asians (Hindu and Muslim) and, according to Amnesty International, murdered 300,000 who must have belonged overwhelmingly to the great Christian majority.

Chapter 8, VI, p. 225. The urban population of Cuba is racially mixed. Genetic tests on the donors to the Blood Bank in Havana with nearly equal numbers of three groups arbitrarily classified by appearance showed: Whites with 5% Negro genes, Negroes with 13% White genes, and Mulattos or Intermediates with an equal average contribution (Gonzalez *et al*: 1976, *Am. J. Hum. Gen.* **28**, 6).

Chapter 9, II, p. 238. Before 1800 naturalists, economists and philosophers, all assumed an evolution of society. The evidence they took from Aristotle or Horace (*Sat.* 1, 3. 1. 99). With it, ignoring Lucretius, they assumed a soft heredity modifiable by the environment (e.g. Adam Smith, *Wealth of Nations*, 1, Ch. 2). Lamarck gave us the culmination of this view. After 1800 scientific assumptions slowly clarified. They did so in the direction of Lucretius. Malthus, Lawrence and Charles Darwin in succession adopted the hard heredity implied by natural selection. This scientific view was conclusively defined however only between 1865 and 1900 by Mendel, by Galton and ultimately by Weismann with the chromosome theory (see my *Genetics and Man* and *Darwin's Place in History*). Meanwhile a sociology and economics based on moral feeling and political aims favoured by a soft heredity grew out of the writings of Marx and Spencer. Their theories or sentiments have assumed that all men are good unless (with Marxism) they or their ancestors have held property or (with liberalism) they or their ancestors have been ill-treated by others – who were not good. The scientific and the sentimental views of man are thus still utterly opposed as they were already in the *Fable of the Bees*.

Chapter 9, IV, p. 241. The most elaborate and best understood of all population controls in mammals is that of the female kangaroo who can have concurrently offspring at three stages of dependence on her and her food supply: the uterine embryo, the pouch embryo, and the young-at-foot, the last two with different milk supplies from two teats (Dawson, T. J. 1977. *Sci. Am.* **237** (2) 78–89).

Chapter 9, IV, p. 243. To answer the wide question as to how far individuals can impose on society the economic consequences of their propagation, abortion will of course have to be connected with all the other factors in the control of population now left to chance in a Welfare State.

Chapter 9, V, p. 245. Propaganda in Britain in favour of Industrial Development or Economic Growth began seriously with the Society for the Diffusion of Useful Knowledge. Their Committee whose Chairman was the Lord Chancellor included 13 F.R.S.s. In 1830 it published an *Address to the Working Men of the United Kingdom* (216 pp. price one shilling) explaining, especially to the handloom weavers earning 7*s.* per week, that the results of machinery were to increase wealth and employment. From this early manifesto comes the view that industrialization will provide full employment for all people and power for all nations without limit and for ever. We now know however that it is true only for some people and some nations and so long as certain natural resources remain to be consumed. And only so long as demand for consumption is unsatisfied. Such demand can be guaranteed thanks to their high and accelerating rate of obsolescence only for the manufacture of arms. The driving force maintaining economic development today is therefore more and more the prospect of military conflict in preparing for which new and increasingly dangerous sources of energy must be extracted from the earth.

Chapter 9, Table 9.2, p. 264. In the U.K. free speech has long been curtailed by the prohibition of offences against the Deity known as blasphemy. Hitherto this has referred to the Christian Deity of established religion and majority opinion. Since the Race Relations Act of 1976, however, it must be taken to refer also to the immigrant deities of many or all minority groups. Offenders may, perhaps, try to shelter under Lord Mansfield's judgement of 1762 that "The Common Law of England knows no prosecution for mere opinions".

Chapter 10, p. 270. The contrast we can still make between understanding Nature and controlling Nature shows how well Bacon's distinction between Experiments of Light and of Fruit has borne the test of time (*Novum Organum*, Aph. 99).

References

List additional to those in the *Evolution of Man and Society* and *Genetics and Man*

GENERAL

Brierley, J. K., 1967. *Biology and the Social Crisis*. London (Heinemann).

Coon, C. S., 1965. *The Living Races of Man*. New York (Knopf).

Creed, E. R. (ed.), 1971. *Ecological Genetics and Evolution*. Oxford (Blackwell).

Derry, T. K. and Williams, T. I., 1960. *A Short History of Technology* (for Ch.2, IX). Oxford (University Press).

Ford, E. B., 1972. *Genetics for Medical Students*. London (Chapman & Hall). 7th edn.

Harrison, G. A. (ed.), 1961. *Genetical Variation in Human Populations*. Oxford (Pergamon).

Katz, S. H. (ed.), 1975. *Biological Anthropology. Sci. Am.* San Francisco (Freeman).

Race, R. R. and Sanger, R., 1975. *Blood Groups in Man* (Racial Distinctions). Oxford (Blackwell). 6th edn.

Roberts, J. A. F., 1973. *An Introduction to Medical Genetics*. Oxford (University Press). 6th edn.

Roe, A. and Simpson, G. G. (ed.), 1958. *Behaviour and Evolution*. Yale (University Press).

Whitehouse, D. and R., 1975. *Archaeological Atlas of the World*. London (Thames & Hudson).

CHAPTER 1. EVOLUTION

I *Genesis*

Campbell, B. C., 1972. Conceptual progress in physical anthropology: fossil man. *Ann. Rev. Anthrop*. I:27–54.

Clark, J. D., 1970. *The Prehistory of Africa*. London (Thames & Hudson).

Cleland, J., 1749. *Memoirs of a Woman of Pleasure: Fanny Hill*. P. Quennell (ed.), 1963. New York (Putnam).

Coon, C. S., 1962. *The Origin of Races*. New York (Knopf).

Goodall, J. van Lawick, 1971. *In the Shadow of Man*. London (Collins).

Haldane, J. B. S., 1924. *Daedalus or Science and the Future*. London (Kegan Paul).

Jones, R., 1973. Emerging picture of Pleistocene Australians. *Nature* (N.B.) **246,** 277–81.

Leakey, R. E. F., 1973. *Australopithecines and Homines* (E. Africa). London (Academic Press).

Morris, D., 1969. *The Naked Ape*. London (Hutchinson).

Mulvaney, D. J., 1975. *Prehistory of Australia*. London, Sydney (Penguin).

Newman, R. W., 1970. Why man is such a sweaty and thirsty naked animal. *Hum. Biol*. **42**: 12–27.

Pilbeam, D., 1972. *The Ascent of Man* (Java, Australia). New York (Macmillan).

II *Sex*

Darlington, C. D., 1971. The evolution of polymorphic systems. In: *Ecological Genetics and Evolution*. R. Creed (ed.), Oxford (Blackwell).

Darlington, C. D., 1973. Gender differences (Review). *J. Biosoc. Sci.* **5**: 410–2.

Goodman, M. and Moore, G. W., 1975. Darwinian evolution in the genealogy of haemoglobin. *Nature* **253**: 603–8.

Harris, G. W., 1970. Hormonal differentiation of the developing central nervous system etc. *Phil. Trans. R.S. Lond. B.* **259**: 165–77.

Jost, A., 1970. Hormonal factors in the sex differentiation of the mammalian foetus (Y chromosome). *Phil. Trans. R.S. Lond. B.* **259**: 119–30.

Ounsted, C. and Taylor, D. C. (ed.), 1972. *Gender Differences*. Edinburgh (Churchill).

III *Breeding*

Bertram, B. C. R., 1975. The social system of lions. *Sci. Am.* **232** (5): 54–65.

Darlington, C. D., 1960. Cousin marriage and the evolution of the breeding system in man. *Heredity* **14**: 297–332.

Day, M. M., 1965. *Guide to Fossil Man* (diversity in all samples). London (Cassell).

Packer, C., 1975. Male transfer in olive baboons. *Nature* **255**: 219–20.

IV *Brain*

Holloway, R. L., 1974. The casts of fossil hominid brains. *Sci. Am.* **231** (1): 106–15.

Jerison, H. J., 1973. *Evolution of the Brain and Intelligence*. New York (Academic Press).

Magoun, H. W., 1960. Evolutionary concepts of brain function following Darwin and Spencer (Figs. 1 and 5) *Evolution of Man,* Sol Tax (ed). Chicago (University Press).

Rensch, B., 1972. *Homo sapiens: From Man to Demigod*. London (Methuen).

Sherrington, C. S., 1907 (1947). *The Integrative Action of the Nervous System*. Cambridge (University Press).

Sherrington, C. S., 1929. Article: Brain. *Encyclopedia Britannica*. 14th edn.

Tobias, P. V., 1971. *The Brain in Hominid Evolution*. New York (Columbia University Press).

V *Feedback*

Bielicki, T., 1965. The intensity of feedbacks between physical and cultural evolution. *Inter. Social Sci. J.* **17**: 97–9.

Brues, A., 1959. The spearman and the archer: an essay on selection in body build (selective effect of invention). *Am. Anthrop.* **61**: 457–69.

Darlington, C. D., 1959. *Darwin's Place in History* (Blyth and stabilising selection). Oxford (Blackwell).

Huxley, J. S., 1953. *Evolution in Action* (Orthogenesis, Eugenics, Psychosocial selection). London (Chatto).

Maruyama, M., 1963. The second cybernetics: deviation-amplifying mutual causal processes. *Sci. Am.* **51**: 164–79.

Muller, H. J., 1963. Genetic progress by voluntarily conducted germinal choice. In: *Man and his Future*, G. Wostenholme (ed.). London (Churchill).

Szarski, H., 1971. The importance of deviation-amplifying circuits in evolution, etc. *Acta Biotheoretica* **20**: 168–70.

Wallace, A. R., 1858. On the tendency of varieties to depart indefinitely from the original type. *J. Linn. Soc. Zool.* **3**: 54–62.

VI *Origin*

Chiarelli, A. B. and Capanna, E., 1973. *Cytotaxonomy and Vertebrate Evolution* (Primate chromosomes). London and New York (Academic Press).

Napier, J. R. and P. H., 1967. *Handbook of Living Primates* (Monkeys, Systematics and Chromosomes). London and New York (Academic Press).

CHAPTER 2. SOCIETY

I *Paleo Climax*

Bueler, L. E., 1974. *Wild Dogs of the World* (domestication). London (Constable).

Lévy-Bruhl, L., 1910. *Les Fonctions Mentales dans les Sociétés Inférieures*. Paris (Alcan).

Lévy-Bruhl, L., 1928. *The Soul of the Primitive* (trans.). London (George Allen & Unwin).

Mangelsdorf, P. C., 1952. *Plants and Human Affairs* (Drugs, Maize). Notre Dame University Press.

Scott, J. P. and Fuller, J. L., 1965. *Genetics and the Social Behavior of the Dog*. Chicago (University Press).

Worsely, P., 1959. Cargo cults (Melanesia *et al.*). *Sci. Am.* **200:** 5.

II *Root Growers*

Chang, K. C., 1970. The beginnings of agriculture in the Far East. *Antiquity* **44:** 175–85.

Clark, R. M. and Renfrew, C., 1973. Tree-ring calibration of radio carbon dating and the chronology of Ancient Egypt. *Nature* **243:** 266–70.

Columbus, C., 1969. *Four Voyages* (1492–1504). J. M. Cohen (ed., trans.). London (Penguin).

Driver, H. E. (ed.), 1964. *The Americas on the Eve of Discovery* (Nootka, Eskimo, Tupinamba). New Jersey (Prentice-Hall).

Kidder, J. E., 1968. *Jomon Pottery* (11,000 BP). Tokyo (Kodansha).

Libby, W. F., 1970. Radiocarbon dating, *Phil. Trans. R.S. London. A.* **269:** 1–10.

Sauer, C. O., 1952. *Agricultural Origins and Dispersals, Am. Geog. Soc.* New York.

Solheim, W. G., 1972. An earlier agricultural revolution, *Sci. Am.* **226** (4): 34–41.

III *Grain Growers*

Beadle, G. W., 1975. *The Origin of Zea Mays*, see below C. A. Reed, 1975.

Harlan, J. R. and Zohary, D., 1966. Distribution of wild wheats and barley (Maps). *Science* **153:** 1074–80.

Harris, D. R., 1967. New light on plant domestications and the origins of agriculture (Rev.) *Geog. Rev.* **57:** 90–107.

Helbaek, H. *et al.*, 1970. Origins of farming. *Nature* **228:** 808–9.

Helbaek, H., 1972. Samarran irrigation agriculture at Choga Mami in Iraq. *IRAQ* **34:** 35–48.

Helbaek, H., 1974. A geographical and chronological study of rye. *Nord. Fortidsminder* B (2), Copenhagen.

Hopf, M., 1969. Plant remains and early farming in Jericho. In: Ucko and Dimbleby: 355–9.

Kihara, H. and Lilienfeld, F., 1949. A new synthesised 6x-wheat. *Proc. 8 Int. Cong. Genet.* (Stockholm): 307–19.

Reed, C. A. (ed.), 1975. *The Origins of Agriculture*. Hague (Mouton).

Riley, R. *et al.*, 1967. Chromosomal interchanges and the phylogeny of wheat (Chinese 6x). *Heredity* **22:** 233–48.

Steensberg, A., 1975. The husbandry of food production (Neolithic). *Phil. Trans. Roy. Soc. B.* **266.**

Ucko, P. J. and Dimbleby, G. W. (ed.), 1969. *The Domestication and Exploitation of Plants and Animals.* London (Duckworth).

Watson, W., 1973. *The Genius of China.* London (Times).

Wendorf, F. *et al.*, 1970. Egyptian prehistory: some new concepts. *Science* **169:** 1161–71.

Wright, H. E., 1970. Environmental changes and the origin of agriculture in the Near East. *Bio Science* **20:** 210–12.

Zeest, W. van, 1976. On macroscopic traces of food plants in south western Asia (Neolithic). *Phil. Trans. Roy. Soc.* B. **266.**

Zimmerman, C. C., 1966. The people and changing culture of the North American plains (Mennonites). *Rev. Int. Soc.* II. **2**(3): 153–202.

Zohary, D., 1973. The origin of cultivated cereals and pulses in the Near East (Maps). *Chrs. Today* **4:** 307–20.

Zohary, D. and Spiegel-Roy, P., 1975. Beginnings of fruit growing in the Old World. *Science* **187:** 319–27.

IV *A City*

Dixon, J. E. *et al.*, 1968. Obsidian and the origins of trade. *Sci. Am.* **218** (3): 38–46.

Mellaart, J., 1967. *Çatal Hüyük.* London (Thames & Hudson).

V *Society*

Benveniste, E., 1970. *Le Vocabulaire des Institutions Indo-européennes*, 2 vols. ed. Minuit, Paris.

Thomas, H., 1974. *The Linguistic Geography of Wales* (Rev.), *J. Biosoc. Sci.* **6:** 393–6.

VI *Feedback*

Darlington, C. D., 1973. *Chromosome Botany and the Origin of Cultivated Plants.* London (George Allen & Unwin). 3rd edn.

Simmonds, N. W. (ed.), 1976. *Evolution of Crop Plants.* London (Longman).

VII *Metals*

Gimbutas, M., 1973a. Old Europe *c.* 7000–3500 B.C. *J. Indo-Eur. St.* **1:** 1–20.

VIII *S.E. Asia*

Bibby, G., 1970. *Looking for Dilmun* (Bahrein). London (Collins).

O'Brien, P. J., 1972. The sweet potato: its origin and dispersal. *Am. Anthrop.* **74:** 342–65.

Price, D. J. de S. and Posposil, L., 1966. A survival of Babylonian arithmetic in New Guinea. *Ind. J. Hist. Sci.* **1:** 30–3.

IX *Europe*

Anati, E., 1960. La Civilisation du Val Camonica. B. Arthaud, Paris (trans. Knopf. N.Y. 1961: Cape, London 1964).

Gimbutas, M., 1973b. The beginning of the Bronze Age in Europe and the Indo-Europeans: 3500–2500 B.C. *J. Indo-Eur. St.* **1:** 163–214.

Jankovich, M., 1970. *They Rode into Europe* (Horse: trans.). London (Harrap).
Piggott, S., 1965. *Ancient Europe*. Edinburgh (University Press).
Renfrew, C., 1972. *Before Civilization.* London (Cape).
Thom, A., 1967. *Megalithic Sites in Britain.* Oxford (University Press).

CHAPTER 3. HEREDITY AND GENETICS

I–III *Principles*

Darlington, C. D., 1964. *Genetics and Man.* (Lamarck, Spencer, Wells, and Mendel). London (George Allen & Unwin).
Darlington, C. D., 1971. Axiom and process in genetics. *Nature* **234:** 521–5.
Olby, R. C., 1966. *Origins of Mendelism.* New York (Schocken).
Wanscher, J. H., 1975. An analysis of Wilhelm Johannsen's genetical term 'genotype': 1909–26. *Hereditas* **79:** 1–4.

IV–VIII *People*

Blacker, C. P., 1952. *Eugenics: Galton and After.* London (Duckworth).
Bloomfield, P., 1957. *Uncommon People: a Study of England's Elite.* London (H. Hamilton).
Bol, L. J., 1960. *The Bosschaert Dynasty* (Painters). Leigh-on-Sea (Lewis).
Darlington, C. D., 1976. The Chromosomes, Meiosis and Man. *Chrs. Today* **5:** 1–20.
Darlington, C. D. and Mather, K., 1949. *The Elements of Genetics.* London (George Allen & Unwin).
Fisher, R. A., 1918. The correlation between relatives on the supposition of mendelian inheritance. *Trans. R. S. Edin.* **52:** 399–434.
Fisher, R. A., 1919. The causes of human variability. *Eug. Rev.* **10:** 213–20.
Fisher, R. A., 1930. The Genetical Theory of Natural Selection. Oxford (University Press).
Galton, F., 1869. *Hereditary Genius.* London (Macmillan). (Collins, Fontana: 1962).
Karp, L. *et al.*, 1975. Gonadal dysgenesis in association with monozygotic twinning (XY-XO). *J. Med. Gen.* **12:** 70–8.
Mather, K., 1975. *Genetical Structure of Populations.* London (Chapman & Hall).
Miller, L. H. *et al.*, 1975. Erythrocyte receptors for malaria: Duffy blood group determinants (Negroes). *Science* **189:** 561–3.
Selmanoff, M. K. *et al.*, 1975. A Y chromosomal contribution to an aggressive phenotype in inbred mice. *Nature* **253:** 529–30.
Yule, G. U., 1906. On the theory of inheritance of quantitative compound characters on the basis of Mendel's laws. *Rep. 3 Int. Conf. Genetics, London* 140–42.

IX *Chemistry*

Allison, A. C., 1954. Protection by sickle-cell trait against subtertian malaria. *B. Med. J.* **4857:** 298.
Allison, A. C., 1961. Abnormal haemoglobins and erythrocyte enzyme-deficiency traits. See G. A. Harrison below.
Bloch, M. R., 1963. The social influence of salt. *Sci. Am.* **209**(1): 88–98.
Bruce-Chwatt, L. J., and Zulueta, J. de, 1976. *The Rise and Fall of Malaria in Europe.* Geneva (World Health Organization).
Burnet, F. M. and White, D. O., 1972. *Natural History of Infectious Disease.* Cambridge (University Press). 4th edn.

Flatz, G. and Rotthauwe, H. W., 1973. Lactase and calcium absorption. *Lancet* ii. 85.
Ford, E. B., 1975. *Ecological Genetics*. London (Chapman). 4th edn.
Harris, H., 1974. Genetic heterogeneity in inherited disease. *J. Clin. Path.* **27,** Suppl. (R. C. Path.) **8:** 32–7.
Harrison, G. A., (ed.), 1961. *Genetical Variation in Human Populations* (Symposium). Oxford (Pergamon).
Kretchmer, N., 1972. Lactose and Lactase. *Sci. Am.* **227**(4): 71–8. (and *Biol. Anthrop.* 1975).
Lambrecht, F. L., *c.* 1967. Trypanosomiasis in prehistoric and later human populations (sleeping sickness). *Diseases in Antiquity*. Springfield, Ill. (Thomas).
Murdoch, G. P., 1959. *Africa, its Peoples and their Culture History*. New York (McGraw-Hill).
Perring, R. P. *et al.*, 1972. Benign sickle-cell anaemia. *Lancet* ii. 1163–7.
Schneider, R. G., 1956. Abnormalities of hemoglobin in 1550 Negro hospital patients (H_s, 8–10%). *Amer. J. Clin. Path.* **26:** 1270.
Simoons, F. J., 1961. *Eat not this Flesh*. Wisconsin (University Press).
Weatherall, D. J., 1971. The molecular basis of Thalassaemia. In: *Ecological Genetics and Evolution*. E.R. Creed (ed.). Oxford (Blackwell).
Zulueta, J. de, 1973a. Malaria and Mediterranean history. *Parassit.* **15.**
Zulueta, J. de, 1973b. Malaria eradication in Europe. *J. Trop. Med. Hyg.* **76:** 279–82.

CHAPTER 4. BRAIN AND INTELLIGENCE

II *Evolution*

Altman, J., 1970. Postnatal growth and differentiation of the mammalian brain etc. *Neurosciences* **1:** 723. New York (Rock. University Press).
Eccles, J. C., 1973. *The Understanding of the Brain*. New York (McGraw-Hill).
Ewert, J.-P., 1974. The neural basis of visually guided behavior. *Sci. Am.* **230**(3): 34–42.
Gray, J., 1974. *The Psychology of Fear and Stress* (Brain, Sex). London (Weidenfeld).
Llinas, R. R., 1975. The Cortex of the cerebellum. *Sci. Am.* **232**(1): 56–71.
MacLean, P. D., 1971. The triune brain, emotion and scientific bias. *Neurosciences* **2.** New York (Rock. University Press).
Magoun, H. W., 1960. (See ref. under Ch. 1, IV Brain).
Walter, W. G., 1953. *The Living Brain*. London (Duckworth).
Woollard, H. H., 1929. The Australian Aborigine brain. *J. Anat.*, **63:** 207–23.

III–IV *Instinct*

Ardrey, R., 1969. *The Territorial Imperative*. London (Collins).
Ardrey, R., 1970. *The Social Contract*. London (Collins).
Buffery, A. W. H. and Gray, J. A., 1972. Sex differences in the development of spatial and linguistic skills. In: *Gender Differences*. Edinburgh (Churchill).
Czapek, K. and J., 1923. *The Insect Play*. London (Playhouse, 1938) (BBC, 1977).
Darwin, C., 1871. *The Descent of Man*. London (Murray).
Darwin, C., 1873. *The Expression of the Emotions in Man and Animals*. London (Murray).
Fuller, J. L. and Thompson, W. R., 1960. *Behavior Genetics*. New York (Wiley).
Harlow, H. F., McGaugh, J. L., and Thompson, R. F., 1971. *Psychology*. San Francisco (Albion).
Hinde, R. A. and Tinbergen, N., 1958. The comparative study of species—specific

behavior. In: *Behavior and Evolution.* A. Roe and G. Simpson (eds.). Yale (University Press).

Huxley, J., 1966. Ritualisation of behaviour in animals and man. *Phil. Trans. R.S.* (*London*) B. **251**: 249–71.

Kropotkin, P., 1904. *Mutual Aid.* (evolution of morals). London.

Lorenz, K., 1970. *Studies in Animal and Human Behavior* (2 vols. trans. R. Martin). Cambridge, Mass. (Harvard University Press).

Lorenz, K., 1973. *Civilized Man's Eight Deadly Sins.* New York (Jovanovich).

Lorenz, K., 1974. Analogy as a source of knowledge (of human and animal behaviour). *Science* **185**: 229–34.

Morgan, C. T., 1947. The hoarding instinct. *Psych. Rev.* **54**: 335–41.

Ratcliffe, F., 1938 (1947). *Flying Fox and Drifting Sand.* Sydney (Angus); London (Chatto).

Thorpe, W. H., 1961. *Bird Song.* Cambridge (University Press).

Tinbergen, N., 1951. *The Study of Instinct.* Oxford (University Press).

Tinbergen, N., 1972. Functional ethology and the human sciences. *Proc. R.S.* (*London*) B **182**: 385–410.

Trotter, W., 1916 (1919). *Instincts of the Herd in War and Peace.* London (George Allen & Unwin).

Williams, J. H., 1956. *Elephant Bill* (Instinct and Intelligence). London (Penguin).

V *Genetics*

Barlow, P., 1973. The influence of inactive chromosomes on human development. *Human gen.* **17**: 105–36.

Brady, R. O., 1973. Hereditary fat-metabolism diseases. *Sci. Am.* **229** (2): 88–97.

Crome, L. and Stern, J., 1972. *The Pathology of Mental Retardation.* London (Churchill). 2nd edn.

Darlington, C. D., 1973. The Effects of Heredity and Environment in the Development of Human Intelligence. In: *Brain and Intelligence.* F. Richardson (ed.), Hyattsville Md. (Nat. Educ. Press).

Gajdusek, D. C., 1968. Variation in the brain of man. *Proc. 8 Cong. Anthrop. Ethn. Sc.* 247–8.

Geschwind, N., 1972. Language and the Brain. *Sci. Am.* (Biol. Anthrop. 1975).

Langmaid, H. and Laurence, K. M., 1974. Deletion of long arm of Y chromosome with normal male development and intelligence. *J. Med. Gen.* **11**: 208–11.

Lashley, K. S., 1947. Structural variation in the nervous system in relation to behavior. *Psych. Rev.* **54**: 325–34.

McFie, K., 1972. Factors of the Brain. *Bull. Br. Psych. Soc.* **25**: 11–14.

Marshall, J., 1864. On the brain of a Bushwoman; and on the brains of two idiots of European descent. *Phil. Trans. Roy. Soc.* **154**: 501–58.

Money, J., 1973. Turner's syndrome and parietal lobe functions. *Cortex* **9**: 387–93.

Moor, L., 1967. Niveau intellectuel et polygonosomie (excès de chromosomes X ou Y). *Rev. Neuropsych. infantile* **15**: 325–48.

Polani, P. E., 1967. Chromosome anomalies and the brain. *Guy's Hosp. Rep.* **116**: 365–96.

Pratt, R. T. C., 1967. *The Genetics of Neurological Disorders.* Oxford (University Press).

Price, W. H. and Whatmore, P. B., 1967. Criminal behaviour and the XYY male. *Nature* **213**: 815.

Price, W. H. and Jacobs, P., 1970. The 47 XYY male with special reference to behaviour. *Sem. Psych.* **2**: 30–9.

Quain, J., 1867. *Elements of Descriptive and Practical Anatomy*. London (University College).

Richardson, F. (ed.), 1973. *Brain and Intelligence*. Hyattsville, Md. (Nat. Educ. Press).

Terman, L. M. and Miles, C. C., 1936. *Sex and Personality*. New York (McGraw-Hill).

Van Valen, L., 1974. Brain size and I.Q. (correlation and selection). *Am. J. Phys. Anthrop.* N.S. **40**: 417–23.

Wahrman, J. *et al.*, 1966. The oral-facial-digital syndrome in a boy (47/XXY). *Pediatrics* **37**: 812–21.

Walker, E., 1966. Internal structure of the thalamus. In: *The Thalamus*. Purpura *et al.* (eds.), New York (Columbia University Press).

Willis, T., 1681. *The Anatomy of the Brain*. W. Feindel (ed.) (1965), Montreal (McGill University Press).

VI–VII *I.Q.*

Baker, J. R., 1974. *Race* (I.Q.). Oxford (University Press).

Burks, B. S., 1928. The relative influence of nature and nurture upon mental development (true and foster parents). *Nat. Soc. St. Educ. Yr. Bk.* **27**: 221–310.

Burt, C., 1921. *Mental and Scholastic Tests*. London (Staples). 4th edn. 1962.

Burt, C., 1924. The principles of vocational guidance. *Brit. J. Psychol.* **14**: 336–52.

Burt, C., 1947. Family size, intelligence and social class. *Population Studies* **1**: 177–86.

Burt, C., 1955. The evidence for the concept of intelligence. *Brit. J. Educ. Psychol.* **25**: 158–77.

Burt, C., 1961. Intelligence and social mobility. *Br. J. Stat. Psych.* **14**: 3–24.

Burt, C., 1975. *The Gifted Child*. London (Hodder).

Butcher, H. J., 1970. *Human Intelligence*. London (Methuen).

Conway, J., 1958. The inheritance of intelligence and its social implications. *Brit. J. Stat. Psychol.* **11**: 171–90.

Darlington, C. D., 1959. *Darwin's Place in History*. Oxford (Blackwell).

Erlenmeyer-Kimling, L. *et al.*, 1963. Genetics and intelligence: a review. *Science* **142**: 1477–9.

Eysenck, H. J. (ed.), 1973. *The Measurement of Intelligence*. Lancaster (Med. Tech. Pub.).

Herrnstein, R., 1973. *I.Q. in the Meritocracy*. Boston (Little B.), London (Lane).

Jensen, A. R., 1974. Kinship correlations reported by Sir Cyril Burt. *Behav. Gen.* **4**: 1–28.

Kamin, L. J., 1974. *The Science and Politics of I.Q.* New York (Wiley).

Martin, N. G., 1975. Inheritance of scholastic abilities in a sample of twins. *Ann. Hum. Gen. London* **39**: 219–29.

Munsinger, H., 1975. The adopted child's I.Q.: a critical review. *Psych. Bull.* **82**: 623–59.

Piaget, Jean, 1973. The Development of Intelligence in the Child: Heredity, Environment and Self-organisation. In: *Brain and Intelligence*. F. Richardson (ed.), Hyattsville Md. (Nat. Educ. Press).

Roberts, J. A. F., 1940. Studies on a child population V: the resemblance in intelligence between sibs. *Ann. Eug.* **10**: 293–312.

Sorokin, P. A., 1928 (1956). *Contemporary Sociological Theories*. New York (Harper).

Terman, L. M., and Oden, M. H., 1959. *Genetic Studies of Genius* V, Stanford (University Press).

Vernon, P. E., 1969. *Intelligence and Cultural Environment*. London (Methuen).

VIII *Twins*

Annett, M., 1973. Handedness in families (maternal influence). *Ann. Hum. Gen.* **37**: 93–105.

Bulmer, M. G., 1970. *The Biology of Twinning in Man.* Oxford (University Press).

Darlington, C. D., 1953, 1964. *The Facts of Life* (twins). London (George Allen and Unwin).

Darlington, C. D., 1954. Heredity and environment (twins). *Caryologia* **6**: 370–81. (Proc. of Int. Gen. Congress).

Darlington, C. D., 1970. Twin biology. *Heredity* **25**: 655–7.

Edwards, J. H. *et al.*, 1966. Monozygotic twins of different sex. *J. Med. Gen.* **3**: 117–23.

Galton, F., 1883 (1951). *Inquiries into Human Faculty and its Development.* London (Dent).

Hunter, K., 1964. *Duet for a Lifetime: 1811–1874* (Siamese twins). London (Joseph).

Newman, H. H. *et al.*, 1937. *Twins: a Study of Heredity and Environment.* Chicago (University Press).

Roberts, J. A. F., 1947. Mental deficiency and differential fertility. *J. Mental Sci.* **93**: 289–302.

Shields, J., 1962. *Monozygotic Twins Brought Up Apart and Together.* Oxford (University Press).

Sutton, H. E. *et al.*, 1962. The hereditary abilities study: selection of twins, etc. *Am. J. Hum. Gen.* **14**: 52–63.

IX. *Mental Defect*

Bajema, C. J., 1963. Natural selection in relation to human intelligence etc. *Eug. Quart.* **10**: 175–87.

Blacker, C. P., 1952. *Eugenics, Galton and After.* London (Duckworth).

Brock, L. G., 1934. Report of the departmental committee on sterilisation (England and Wales). *Sessional Papers*, G.B. **15**: 1–137.

Carter, C. O., Roberts, D. F., Edwards, J. H., Gould, D., Baxter, M., Huntingford, P. J. *et al.*, 1975/6. *Equalities and Inequalities in Health* (*Heredity and Medicine*). *Symp. Eug. Soc.* (London).

Dugdale, R. L., 1874. (1910). *The Jukes: a Study in Crime, Pauperism, Disease and Heredity.* New York (Putnam).

Estabrook, A. H., 1915. *The Jukes in 1915.* Washington (Carn. Inst.).

Falek, A., 1971. Differential fertility and intelligence. *Soc. Biol.* **18**: 550–9.

Friedmann, T., 1971. Prenatal diagnosis of genetic disease (amniocentesis). *Sci. Am.* (*Biol. Anthrop.* 1975).

Goddard, H. H., 1912. *The Kallikak Family.* New York (Macmillan).

Hans, M. B., 1964. A study in family pathology, *Genet. Psych. Monog.* **69**: 421–49.

Harris, H., 1975. *Prenatal Diagnosis and Selective Abortion.* London (Nuffield Prov. Hosp. Trust).

Higgins, J. V., Reed, E. W., and S. C., 1962. Intelligence and family size: a paradox resolved. *Eugenics Q.* **9**: 84–90.

Hofsten, N. von, 1949. Sterilisation in Sweden. *J. Heredity* **40**: 243–7.

Hofsten, N. von, 1963. Sterilisation in Sweden: 1941–1953. *Soc. med. Tidskr* (Uppsala): **28**

Mednick, S. V. *et al.* (eds.), 1974. *Genetics, Environment and Psychopathology.* Elsevier, N. Holland.

Mohr, J., 1967. Genetic Counseling (in Denmark). *P.3. Int. C. Hum. Gen.* (Baltimore) 37–43.

Morton, N. E. *et al.*, 1977. Colchester revisited: a genetic study of mental defect. *J. Med. Gen.* **14:** 1–9.

Patrick, J., 1972. *The Glasgow Gangs*. London (Eyre Methuen).

Reed, E. W. and S. C., 1965. *Mental Retardation: a Family Study*, Philadelphia (Saunders).

Reed, N., 1976. What is the Hippocratic Oath? (Pythagorean abortion rule). *New Hum.* **91:** 291.

Reed, S. C., 1965. The evolution of human intelligence . . . a continuing process. *Am. Scientist* **53:** 317–26.

Roberts, J. A. F., 1952. The genetics of mental deficiency. *Eug. Rev.* **44:** 71–83.

Shields, J., 1975. Polygenic influences on abnormal behaviour (Crime, Stuttering). *Eug. Soc. Bull.* **7:** 39–43.

Speed, R. M., Johnston, A. W., and Evans, H. J., 1976. Chromosome survey of total population of mentally subnormal in N.E. Scotland (10 per cent abnormal). *J. Med. Genet.* **13:** 285–306.

Williams, G., 1958. *The Sanctity of Life and the Criminal Law*. London (Faber).

Wyatt, P. R., 1975. Eugenics in the Oneida Community, New York, 1869–1879. *Eug. Soc. Bull.* **7:** 35–8.

CHAPTER 5. CULTURE

I–III *Origins*

Darlington, C. D., 1958. The control of evolution in man. *Eugenics Rev.* **50:** 169–78.

Darlington C. D., 1961. Instincts and morals. *Rat. Ann.*, 23–34.

Hughes, P., 1952. *Witchcraft*. London (Longman).

Jones, M. A., 1976. *Destination America* (Immigration, Race, and Culture). London (Weidenfeld).

Marett, R. R., 1911. *Anthropology* (Spencer and Gillen). Oxford (University Press).

Mason, O. T., 1895 (1968). *The Origins of Invention: a study of industry among primitive peoples*. Cambridge, Mass. (M.I.T.).

Mossiker, F., 1969. *The Affair of the Poisons* (Louis XIV). New York (Knopf).

Scholes, P. A., 1967. *The Oxford Companion to Music*. Oxford (University Press). 9th edn.

Tylor, E. B., 1871. *Primitive Culture*. London (Macmillan).

Tylor, E. B., 1881. *Anthropology*. London (Macmillan).

IV *Divisions*

Blythe, R., 1969. *Akenfield: Portrait of an English Village* (Suffolk). London (Allen Lane).

Hamdun, S. and King, N. (trans.), 1975. *Ibn Battuta in Black Africa*. London (Collins).

Huxley, Aldous, 1934. *Beyond the Mexique Bay* (Guatemala). London (Chatto).

Opie, I. and P., 1969. *Children's Games in Street and Playground*. Oxford (University Press).

Sorenson, E. R. and Gajdusek, D. C., 1966. Child behavior and development in primitive cultures. *Pediatrics* **37:** Suppl.

V *Genetic Environment*

Bakker, R., 1975. Dinosaur renaissance (origins of warm-blooded animals). *Sci. Am.* **232**(4): 58–78.

Bernard, C., 1856. *Introduction à l'étude de la médecine experimentale*, Paris (var. eds.).
Darlington, C. D., 1971. Axiom and process in genetics. *Nature* **234**: 521–5.
Desmond, A. J., 1975. *The Hot-blooded Dinosaurs*. London (Blond & Briggs).
Uexküll, J. von, 1921. *Umwelt and Innenwelt der Tiere*. Berlin (Springer).

VI *The Fallacy*

Darlington, C. D., 1959. *Darwin's Place in History* (also Lamarck and Lysenko). Oxford (Blackwell).
Huxley, Julian, 1941. *Evolution: the Modern Synthesis*. London (George Allen & Unwin) 3rd edn. 1974.
Wilson, E. O., 1975. *Sociobiology: the New Synthesis*. Chicago (University Press).

CHAPTER 6. EDUCATION

I *Origins*

Cobban, A. B., 1975. *The Mediaeval Universities*. London (Methuen).
Gadd, C. J., 1956. Teachers and students in the oldest schools (Sumer). *Sch. Orient. Afr. St.* (U. London).
Harlow, H. F., 1958. The evolution of learning. In: *Behaviour and Evolution*. A. Roe and G. Simpson (eds.), Yale (University Press).

II *Equality*

Arnold, H., 1975. *Randgruppen Zigeunervolkes* (Gipsy Hybrids: Professions, Pedigrees). Neustadt (Pfälz Verlag).
Clébert, J.-P., 1961 (1963). *The Gypsies* (trans.) London (Vista).
Haining, P., 1975. *The Penny Dreadful*. London (Gollancz).
Lawson, J., 1967. *Mediaeval Education and the Reformation*. London (R.K.P.).
Mandeville, B., 1714–24. *The Fable of the Bees or Private Vices, Publick Benefits*. (Parents more important than schools). (Penguin, 1970).
Puxon, G., 1973. *Rom: Europe's Gypsies*. London (Min. Rights Group: Craven Str.).
Russell, D., 1975. *The Tamarisk Tree* (Experiment). London (Elek-Pemberton).
Sandford, J., 1973. *Gypsies*. London (Secker).
Stone, L., 1969. Literacy and education in England, 1640–1900. *Past and Present* **42**: 69–139.
Willis, T., 1907. *Whatever happened to Tom Mix?* (Failure of Education). London (Cassell).

III *Privilege*

Cross, C., 1976. Workers' sons stay down. *Observer* 19 Sept. (*Aberdeen Univ. Scot. Mobility Study*).
Figueroa, J. J., 1963. Selection and differentiation in Soviet Schools. *Communist Education*. E. J. King, (ed.), London (Methuen).
Meade, J. E. and Parkes, A. S., 1966. *Genetic and Environmental Factors in Human Ability*. Edinburgh (Oliver & Boyd).
Smith, H., 1976. *The Russians* (Party, Privilege, Women, Education, Religion, Dissent). Times, N.Y. & London.
Squibbs, G. D., 1973. *Founder's Kin* (Oxford Colleges). Oxford (University Press).
Young, M. and Gibson, J. B., 1965. Social mobility and fertility (and I.Q.). In: *Genetic and Environmental Factors in Human Ability*. J. E. Meade and A. S. Parkes (eds.), Edinburgh (Oliver & Boyd).

V *Integration*

Burt, C., 1975. *The Gifted Child* (History). London (Hodder).

Coleman, J. S. *et al.*, 1966. (4 July) *Equality of Educational Opportunity.* U.S. Office Ed., Washington, D.C.

Cox, C. B., and Boyson, R. (eds.), 1975. *Black Paper* (on Education). London (Dent).

Eysenck, H. J., 1971. *Race, Intelligence and Education.* London (Temple Smith).

Goodman, P., 1964. *Compulsory Miseducation.* New York (Knopf).

Jensen, A. R., 1972. *Genetics and Education.* London (Methuen).

Jensen, A. R., 1973. *Educability and Group Differences.* London (Methuen).

Martin, B., 1971. Progressive education versus the working classes. *Critical Q.* **13**(4).

Shuey, A. M., 1966. *The Testing of Negro Intelligence.* (2nd edn.), Soc. Sci. P. N.Y.

VI *Knowledge*

Darlington, C. D., 1948. *The Conflict of Science and Society.* London (Watts).

Snow, C. P., 1959. *The Two Cultures and the Scientific Revolution.* Cambridge (University Press).

VII *Evolution*

Davenport, H. W., 1970. Teaching versus research (1/20,000 creative). *Bioscience* **20:** 228–30.

Gilbert, M., 1969. *Jewish History Atlas.* London (Weidenfeld).

Hardy, K. R., 1974. Social (and religious) origins of American scientists and scholars (Jewish rise). *Science* **185:** 497–506.

Herrnstein, R. J., 1973. *IQ in the Meritocracy.* London (Allen Lane).

Scott, F. D. (ed.), 1968. *World Migration in Modern Times.* New Jersey (Prentice-Hall).

Sorokin, P. A., 1928 (1956). *Contemporary Sociological Theories.* New York (Harper).

Stark, F., 1960. *The Razor's Edge.* London (Murray).

Vasari, G., 1550. *The Lives of the Artists* (trans. G. Bull 1965). London (Penguin).

CHAPTER 7. ASIA

II–V *India*

Agwani, M. S., 1973. India and the Arab World. *Ind. Horizons* **22**(2) : 46–63.

Bonarjee, N. B., 1970. *Under Two Masters* (Religion, Government and Superstition). Bombay (Oxford University Press).

Cannon, G., 1975. Sir William Jones, Sir Joseph Banks, and the Royal Society. *Notes Rec. RS,* **29:** 205–30.

Chaudhuri, N. C., 1976a. *Clive of India.* London (Thames).

Chaudhuri, N. C., 1976b. How and why Indira rules (upper class restored). *Encounter* **47**(5) : 84–93.

Collis, M., 1956. *First and Last in Burma.* London (Faber).

Corps, E. V., 1965. Assam (Tea). *Geog. Mag.,* **37:** 666–81.

Das, S., 1971. Caste and politics in India. *N. Humanist* **87:** 16–19.

Das, S., 1972. India: pressures for change. *N. Humanist* **88:** 99–101.

Edwardes, M., 1971. *Nehru* (1889–1964). London (Allen Lane).

Gardner, B., 1972. *The East India Company.* London (Hart-Davis).

Hodson, T. C., 1937. *India. Census Ethnography: 1901–1931.* Gov. India P: New Delhi.

Kripalani, K., 1974. Rammohun Roy and Mahatma Gandhi (anti-Westernism). *Indian Hor.* **23**(2) : 32–7.

La Guerre, J., 1974. *Calcutta to Caroni: the East Indians of Trinidad.* London (Longman).
Lunt, J. (ed.), 1970. *From Sepoy to Subedar* (Sita Ram, 1873). London (R.K.P.).
Masani, Z., 1975. *Indira Gandhi* (Nehru). London (H. Hamilton).
Mitra, R., Hoernle, A. F. R., and Bose, P. N., 1885. *Centenary Review of the Asiatic Soc. of Bengal: 1, History. 2, Archaeology. 3, Nat. Sci.* Calcutta (Thacker, Spink).
Morris, J., 1968. *Pax Britannica: the Climax of an Empire* (to 1897). London (Faber).
Naipaul, V. S., 1964. *An Area of Darkness* (India). London (Deutsch).
Nehru, J., 1948. Address to U.N. General Assembly (Nov.). cit. M.S. Agwani.
Palmer, L., 1975. Corruption in India. *New Society* **32**: 577–9.
Raj, K. N., 1974. Some myths and realities of Indian economic development (cattle). *Ind. Horizons* **23**: 5–18.
Stein, A., 1900–1916. *On Central Asian Tracks* (introd. J. Mirsky, 1975). Chicago (University Press).
Tinker, H., 1966. *South Asia: a Short History* (India, Burma, Ceylon). London (Pall Mall).
Woodruff (Mason), P., 1953. *The Men who ruled India. I. The Founders. II. The Guardians.* London (Cape).

VI–VIII *U.S.S.R.*

Botting, D., 1973. *Humboldt and the Cosmos* (Siberia). London (Sphere).
Charques, R., 1958. *The Twilight of Imperial Russia.* Oxford (University Press).
Conquest, R., 1970. *The Nation Killers* (USSR). London (Macmillan).
Cowles, V., 1969. *The Russian Dagger* (Communist antecedents). London (Collins).
Dmitriev-Mamonov, A. I. *et al.* (eds.), 1900 (1971). *Guide to the Great Siberian Railway.* Devon (David & Charles Reprint).
Dostoevsky, F. M., 1871. *The Devils* (or *The Possessed:* Nechaev Conspiracy). London (Penguin).
Farson, N., 1935. *The Way of a Transgressor* (Russia 1914–17, 1928, India 1930). London (Gollancz).
Hingley, R., 1970. *The Russian Secret Police* (Okhrana-KGB, 1815–1945). London (Hutchinson).
Intourist, 1932. *A Pocket Guide to the Soviet Union* (Census, 1926). Moscow (Vneshtorgisdat).
Kaiser, R. G., 1976. *Russia: the People and the Power* (abortion). London (Secker).
Kropotkin, P., 1899. *Memoirs of a Revolutionist* (Introd. Nicolas Walter). New York (Dover Reprint, 1971).
Lias, G., 1956. *Kazak Exodus.* London (Evans).
Maclean, F., 1974. *To the Back of Beyond* (Central Asia). London (Cape).
Reddaway, P., 1975. Church of Soviet Georgia (KGB). *Times,* 16 Aug.
Rich, V., 1976. Environmental protection under state socialism (Baikal: pollution). *Nature* **259**: 438–9.
Semyonov, Y., 1937 (1944). *The Conquest of Siberia.* London (Routledge).
Seton-Watson, H., 1961. *The New Imperialism* (Soviet). London (Bodley).
Sheehy, A., 1972. The Crimean Tatars and the Volga Germans. In: *The Fourth World.* B. Whitaker (ed.), London (Sidgwick).
Smith, H., 1976. *The Russians.* Times, N.Y. and London.
Solzhenitsyn, A., 1974. *The Gulag Archipelago: 1918–1956.* London (Collins).
Stevens, E., 1975. Life hangs on the internal passport. *Times,* 24 July, London.
Tolstoy, L. N., 1905. A great iniquity. *Essays.* Oxford (University Press).

Tutaev, D. (ed.), 1968. *The Alliluyev Memoirs* (1946). London (Michael Joseph).
Whitaker, B. (ed.), 1972. *The Fourth World* (Soviet Empire). London (Sidgwick).

IX *China*

Bao, P. and Chelminski, R., 1975. *Prisoner of Mao* (1957–64). London (Deutsch).
Collis, M., 1941. *The Great Within* (Ming and Manchu). London (Faber).
Collis, M., 1946. *Foreign Mud* (Opium War, 1840). London (Faber).
Fitzgerald, C. P., 1964a. *The Birth of Communist China*. London (Penguin).
Fitzgerald, C. P., 1964b. *The Chinese View of their Place in the World*. Oxford (University Press).
Fitzgerald, C. P., 1966. *A Concise History of East Asia*. Australia (Heinemann).
Morris, J., 1976. *Travels* (Indo-China, India, etc.). London (Faber).
Needham, J., 1971. *Clerks and Craftsmen in China and the West*. Cambridge (University Press).
Waley, A., 1952. *The Real Tripitaka* (Buddhism). London (George Allen & Unwin).
Wang, W. S-Y., 1973. The Chinese language (spread of Mandarin). *Sci. Am.* **228**(2): 51–60.
Warner, M., 1972. *The Dragon Empress* (China, 1835–1908). London (Weidenfeld).

X–XI *S.E. Asia*

Brittain, V., 1975. General Vo Nguyen Giap. *Times*, 2 June 1975.
Collis, M., 1936. *Siamese White* (1650–1689). London (Faber).
Fitzgerald, F., 1973. *Fire in the Lake* (Vietnam). London (Macmillan).
Goullart, P., 1965. *River of the White Lily: 1953–61* (Sarawak). London (Murray).
Hall, D. G. E., 1968. *A History of South East Asia* (3rd edn.). London (Macmillan).
Hudson, G., 1965. Fifteen years after—the Chinese State. *China Quarterly* **21**: 71–73.
Minority Rights Group, 1972. *The Chinese in Indonesia, the Philippines and Malaysia*, M.R.G., London WC2.
Moore, W. R., 1960. Angkor, jewel of the jungle. *Nat. Geog. Mag.* **117**: 517–69.
Parkinson, C. N., 1963. *East and West*. London (Murray).
Schmidt, P., 1973. Of race, class and I.Q. (in Kuala Lumpur). *Encounter* **41**(2): 55–8.
Theroux, P., 1975. *The Great Railway Bazaar: by Train thro' Asia*. London (H. Hamilton).
Tinker, J., 1974. Java: birth control battlefields. *New Sci.* **61**: 483–6.

XII *Japan*

Barr, P., 1965. *The Coming of the Barbarians* (to Japan, 1853–70). London (Macmillan).
Barr, P., 1968. *The Deer Cry Pavilion* (1868–1905). London (Macmillan).
Chamberlain, B. H., 1905 (1971). *Things Japanese*. Tokyo (Tuttle).
Hall, J. W., 1968. *Japan: from Prehistory to Modern Times*. London (Weidenfeld).
Keene, D., 1969. *The Japanese Discovery of Europe*. Stanford (University Press).
Smith, T. C., 1973. Pre-modern economic growth: Japan and the West. *Past and Present* **60**: 127–60.

CHAPTER 8. AFRICA

I *Evolution*

Clegg, E. J. *et al.*, 1976. Human adaptability in Ethiopia (race, culture, history and disease). *Proc. R.S.* (*B*) **194**: 1–98.

Franklyn, J., 1971. *Death by Enchantment* (Witchcraft). London (H. Hamilton).
Idriess, I. L., 1965. *Our Stone Age Mystery* (Sorcery). Sydney (Angus & R.).
Lambrecht, F. L., 1968. The evolution of communicable disease in man. *S. Afr. J. Sci.* **64**(2): 64–71.
Oliver, R. (ed.), 1961. *The Dawn of African History*. Oxford (University Press).
Oliver, R. and Fage, J. D., 1962. *A Short History of Africa*. London (Penguin).
Wostenholme, G. (ed.), 1965. *Man and Africa* (disease). London (Churchill).

II *Slavery*

Briggs, L. C., 1960. *Tribes of the Sahara*. Harvard (University Press).
Burton, R. F., 1864. A Mission to Gelele, King of Dahome. *W. African Explorers*. Oxford (University Press).
Fage, J. D., 1969. The slave trade. *Listener*, 5 June.
Miner, H., 1953. *The Primitive City of Timbuctoo* (Muslim Slavery). Princeton (University Press).

III *America*

Benoist, A. de, 1976. La population américaine (U.S. immigration) *Nouvelle Ecole* **27–28**: 97–105.
Cole, H., 1967. *Christophe, King of Haiti*. London (Eyre).
Trollope, A., 1862. *North America*. London (Penguin, 1962).
Washington, B. T., 1901 (1945). *Up from Slavery*. Oxford (University Press).
West, R., 1970. *Back to Africa* (Liberia). London (Cape).
Weyl, N. and M. W., 1971. *American Statesmen on Slavery and the Negro*. New Rochelle (Arlington).

IV *Free Negro*

Chaudhuri, J. P., 1970. Liberia. *Times* (Suppl.), 19 March.
Cohen, J. M., 1976. *La revolucíon cubana* (Rev.). *Times Lit. Suppl.* 3882: 982–3.
Cole, P., 1975. *Elites in Lagos* (ex-slaves in Nigeria). Cambridge (University Press).
Comer, J. P., 1967. The social power of the Negro (USA). *Sci. Am.* **216**(4): 21–7.
Gillman, P., 1975. Banana Republic (Panama). *Observer* (Suppl.), 31 Aug.
Haley, A., 1964. *Autobiography of Malcolm X* (Harlem). New York (Grove P.).
Headley, J. T., 1873. *The Great Riots of New York* (1712–1873). New York (Dover, 1971).
Lewis, O., 1966. The culture of poverty (Puerto Ricans). *Sci. Am.* **215**(4): 19–25.
Montejo, E., 1968. *The Autobiography of a Runaway Slave* (Cuba). London (Bodley).
Naipaul, V. S., 1962. *The Middle Passage: the Caribbean Revisited*. London (Deutsch).
Niedergang, M., 1971. *The Twenty Latin Americas*, 2 vols. London (Penguin).
Osofsky, G., 1963. *Harlem: The Making of a Ghetto* (Negro New York: 1890–1930). New York (Harper).
Robertson, W., 1972. *The Dispossessed Majority* (U.S.A.). Canaveral, Fla. (Allen).
Wigg, R., 1970. Dr Castro's utopian hopes that failed (Cuba). *Times*, 29 July.

V *Serf or Slave*

Genovese, E. D., 1974. *Roll, Jordan Roll: the World the Slaves made* (U.S.A.). New York (Pantheon).
Kropotkin, P., 1899. *Memoirs of a Revolutionist*. New York (Dover, 1971).

VI *Struggle*

Barry, J., 1975. Kenya on the brink (Kenyatta). *Sunday Times*: 10, 17, 24 Aug. London.

Greenland, J., 1973. African blood-bath ignored (Ruanda). *Times*, 4 Jan.

Gwynn, S., 1932 (1940). *The Life of Mary Kingsley* (W. Africa: 1893–1895). London (Penguin).

Hall, R., 1974. *Stanley: An Adventurer Explored*. London (Collins).

Hunter, F., 1969. A continent on the move (a million refugees in Africa). *Christ. Sci. Mon.*, Boston, 14 May.

Huxley, Elspeth, 1954. *The Four Guineas* (Gambia, Sierra Leone, Gold Coast, Nigeria: colonial and precolonial history; references). London (Chatto).

Huxley, E., 1959. *The Flame Trees of Thika* (Kenya: 1913). London (Chatto).

Huxley, E., 1964. *Forks and Hope* (East Africa). London (Chatto).

Huxley, E., 1971. *The Challenge of Africa* (Exploration). London (Chatto).

Jacobson, P., 1975. Papa Boc (Pres. Bokassa, Rép. Centrafricaine). *Sunday Times Mag.*, 22 June.

Jesman, C., 1963. *The Ethiopian Paradox*. Oxford (University Press).

Johnston, H. H., 1891. *Livingstone and the Exploration of Central Africa*. London (Philip).

Kalous, M., 1975. *Cannibals and Tongo Players of Sierra Leone*. London (Kegan Paul).

Listowel, J., 1974. *The Other Livingstone* (Lászlo Magyar). Lewes (Friedmann).

Lloyd, A., 1964. *The Drums of Kumasi* (Ashanti Wars, 1697–1957). London (Penguin).

Meinertzhagen, R., 1957. *Kenya Diary: 1902–1906*. Edinburgh (Oliver & Boyd).

Moorehead, A., 1959. *No Room in the Ark* (E. Africa). London (Hamilton).

Naipaul, V. S., 1975. A new King (Mobuto) for the Congo (Zaïre). *N.Y. Rev. Books* **22**: 19–25.

Pearson, J. D. *et al.* (ed.), 1976. *Encyclopaedia of Africa*. London (Macdonald).

Turnbull, C. M., 1973. *The Mountain People* (Uganda, population control) London (Cape).

Wolfers, M., 1975. An assessment of Amin (murder in Uganda). *I.L.N.* **263,** Nov. 33–6.

VII *South Africa*

Botha, M. C., 1972. Blood group gene frequencies (races in Cape Town). *S. Afr. Med. Jour. Suppl.* (1 April).

Klerk, W. A. de, 1976. *The Puritans in Africa* (Afrikaners). London (Collins).

Meintjes, J., 1975. *President Paul Kruger* (1825–1904). London (Cassell).

Times Correspondent, 1960. *Anatomy of Apartheid*. *Times*: 8 Jan.–11 March (Pamphlet).

Tinker, H., 1974. *A New System of Slavery: The Export of Indian Labour Overseas: 1830–1920*. Oxford (University Press).

VIII *Colonization Reversed*

Bell, R. M., 1973. Rates of immigration (fraudulent official figures). *Times*, 10 April 1973.

Cameron, J. *et al.*, 1974. How Jamaica came to England. *Listener* **92:** 165–6.

Castles, S. and Kosack, G., 1973. *Immigrant Workers and Class Structure in Western Europe*. Oxford (University Press).

Evans, P., 1971–4. Race relations in Britain. *Times*, 24 Feb. 71; 15 Oct. 71; 16 Mar. 74; 17 July 74.

More, T., 1516. *Utopia* (trans. Paul Turner). London (Penguin, 1965).

Power, J., 1974. The new proletariat (migration to Europe). *Encounter* **43**(3): 8–22.

CHAPTER 9. ECONOMICS IN EVOLUTION

I–IV *Population*

Brown, L. R., 1970. Human food production as a process in the biosphere. *Sci. Am.* (*Biol. Anthrop.* 1975).

Burton, R., 1976. *The Mating Game* (Breeding systems—animals and man). Oxford (Elsevier).

Carr-Saunders, A., 1932. *The Population Problem: a Study in Human Evolution.* Oxford (University Press).

Coale, A. J., 1974. The history of the human population. *Sci. Am.* (*Biol. Anthrop.* 1975).

Coleman, T., 1965. *The Railway Navvies.* London (Hutchinson).

Durrell, G., 1976. *The Stationary Ark* (Mammalian Breeding Restraints). London (Collins).

Engels, F., 1844. The condition of the working class in England in 1844. *Selected Writings.* Penguin 1967.

Flinn, M. W., 1969. *British Population Growth: 1700–1850.* London (Macmillan).

Hagberg, K., 1952. *Carl Linnaeus* (trans. Blair). London (Cape).

Hammond, J. L. and I. B., 1911. *The Village Labourer* (England: 1795–1830). London (Longman).

Malthus, T. R., (1766–1834). *Dictionary of National Biography.*

Malthus, T. R., 1798. *An Essay on the Principle of Population as it Affects the Future Improvement of Society* etc. (Dent, London, 7th edn. 1870: Penguin, 1st edn. 1970).

Quennell, P., 1956. *Mayhew's London* (1851). London (Spring).

Short, R. V., 1976. The evolution of human reproduction (population control). *Proc. Roy. Soc. B.* **195**: 1–24.

Wynne-Edwards, V. C., 1962. *Animal Dispersion in Relation to Social Behaviour* (Family Planning). Edinburgh (Oliver & Boyd).

V–VIII *Economics*

Barnett, C., 1975. The German miracle (and Marshall Aid to U.K.). *Times*, 15 Feb.

Bauer, P. T., 1973. *Dissent on Development.* Harvard (University Press).

Bauer, P. T., 1974. Foreign aid forever? Critical reflections on a myth of our time. *Encounter* **42**(3): 15–28.

Bauer, P. T., 1975. Economic differences and inequalities. *Modern Age* **19**: 295–306.

Briggs, H. W., 1952. *The Law of Nations*, 2nd edn. (U.N. Charter). New York (Appleton).

Dumont, R., 1974. *Socialism and Development.* London (Deutsch).

Friedman, M., 1976a. Inflation (the tax not passed by Parliament). *Times*, 13 Sept.

Friedman, M., 1976b. The line we dare not cross (Government Welfare). *Encounter* **47**(5): 8–14.

Hartley, H., 1974. (on Keynes, cit. Duke of Edinburgh). *Notes and Records R.S.* (London) **29**: 16.

Hayek, F. A., 1967. *Studies in Philosophy, Politics and Economics.* Chicago (University Press).

Hayek, F. A., 1975. *Full Employment at any Price?* Inst. Econ. Aff. O.P.45, London.
Hildyard, N., 1976. How an ideal city works (Siena). *Ecologist*, **6**: 320–6.
Johnson, P., 1972. *The Offshore Islanders* (U.K. History). London (Weidenfeld).
Johnson, P., 1976. Towards the parasite state (closed shop trade unionism). *N. Statesman* **92**: 299–304.
Keynes, J. M., 1919. *The Economic Consequences of the Peace*. Lab. Res. Dept. London.
Keynes, J. M., 1933. (1972) *Essays in Biography* (Malthus, Jevons, Villiers). London (Macmillan).
Keynes, J. M., 1937. *The General Theory of Employment, Interest and Money*. New York (Harcourt).
Leach, G., 1975. The Energy Costs of Food Production. In: *The Man/Food Equation*. Steele and Bourne (eds.), London (Academic Press).
Mishan, E. J., 1974. The new inflation: its theory and practice. *Encounter* **42**(5): 12–24.
Moller, D., 1976. Ill fares the Welfare State (Europe). *Encounter* **47**(3): 58–64.
Papandreou, A. C., 1974. *Paternalistic Capitalism*. Minn. (University Press).
Payer, C., 1974. *The Debt Trap* (Foreign Aid). London (Penguin).
Parkinson, C. N., 1958. *Parkinson's Law or the Pursuit of Progress*. London (Murray).
Rees-Mogg, W., 1976. Monetarism (Thornton, Jevons, Friedman). *Times*, 23 Aug.
Revelle, R., 1974. Food and population (and foreign aid). *Sci. Am.* **231**(3): 161–8.
Ruehl, L., 1976. International arms sales take off. *Europa* (Times) 6 April.
Sampson, A., 1975. *The Seven Sisters: the Great Oil Companies and the World they Made*. London (Hodder).
Schumacher, E. F., 1973. *Small is Beautiful: a Study of Economics as if People Mattered*. London (Blond & Briggs).
Simes, D. K., 1975. The Soviet parallel market. *Survey: E-W Studies* **21**(3)9: 42–52.
Szulc, T., 1975. *The Energy Crisis*. London (Watts).
Terkel, L. (Studs.), 1975. *Working* (and not enjoying it). London (Wildwood).
Whitaker, R. W., 1976. *A Plague on Both your Houses* (Welfare Establishments in U.S.A.) New York (R. B. Luce).
Wolynski, A., 1976. *Western Economic Aid to the USSR*. Inst. Study of Conflict, London.

IX *Environment*

Bates, M. *et al.*, 1969. *Resources and Man: Com. Nat. Ac. Sci.* San Francisco (Freeman).
Benthall, J. (ed.), 1973. *Ecology in Theory and Practice*. New York (Viking).
Clarke, R. (ed.), 1976. *Notes for the Future* (Kropotkin, Borgstrom, Commoner, Ehrlich, Roszak, Meadows *et al.*,) London (Thames).
Cole, H. A. and Smith, J. E., 1975. Organic pollutants in the sea (discussion). *Proc. R.S. (B)* **189**: 277–483.
Cole, J. P., 1974. *Geography of World Affairs* (population, economics). 4th edn. London (Penguin).
Darlington, C. D., 1973. The Impact of Man on Nature. In: *Ecology in Theory and Practice*. J. Benthall (ed.), New York (Viking).
Hicks, C. S., 1974. *Man and Natural Resources*. London (Croom Helm).
Jope, E. M., 1965. Man's use of natural resources (historical). *Adv. Sci.* **22**: 455–64.
Kellog, C. E. and Orvedal, A. C., 1969. Potentially arable soils of the world and critical measures for their use. *Adv. Agron.* **21**: 109–70.
Martin, P. S., 1970. Pleistocene niches for alien animals (fauna destroyed). *Bio Science* **20**: 218–21.

Richards, P. W., 1973. The tropical rain forest. *Sci. Am.* **229**(6): 58–68.
Thomas, W. L. (ed.), 1956. *Man's Role in Changing the Face of the Earth* (N.B. F. Fraser Darling, C. J. Glecken). Chicago (University Press).

CHAPTER 10. THE PROBLEM AND THE CHOICE

Bateson, W., 1925. Science in Russia. *Nature* **116:** 681.
Lorenz, K., 1973. *Die Rückseite des Spiegels*. München (Piper).

Index